National Key Scheme Guide 2013

Accessible Toilets for Disabled People

Compiled by John Stanford
15th Edition © Disability Rights UK

National Key Scheme Guide 2013
Accessible Toilets for Disabled People

ISBN 978-1-903335-61-1
15th edition © Disability Rights UK 2013
Published by Disability Rights UK
Registered Charity No. 1138585

Design: © Anderson Fraser Partnership, London
Printed & bound by: Stephens & George Print Group, Merthyr Tydfil

Disability Rights UK
12 City Forum, 250 City Road
London EC1V 8AF

Tel: 020 7250 3222
Fax: 020 7247 8765
www.disabilityrightsuk.org

Disability Rights UK was formed through the merger of Disability Alliance, Radar and National Centre for Independent Living.

Local authorities and other providers of public toilets supply most of the information and this is supported by information and feedback from individuals, local access guides and other sources. I would like to thank everyone involved for their assistance and our advertisers for their support.

All information is provided in good faith but Disability Rights UK cannot be held responsible for any omissions or inaccuracies. We have tried to get information from all organisations who may provide NKS toilets but this has not always been forthcoming. We would therefore, be pleased to hear of any additions or amendments that we can use to update our records and include in future editions.

We welcome feedback on this and all our publications. Please email feedback@disabilityrightsuk.org with any comments.

John Stanford, Editor
February 2013

CONTENTS

PREFACE

Disability Rights UK is now one year old – following our merger (of Radar, Disability Alliance and the National Centre for Independent Living) and already over half a million people have used the information on our website, with over 5000 people getting involved in our events and campaigns. We are disabled people leading change and we work always for the freedom to live independently and the opportunity to live free of poverty.

Disability Rights UK continues all the work to provide Radar keys to accessible toilets and to let you know where you can find those accessible toilets around the country – and that is the subject of this guide.

Disability Rights UK is the largest UK organisation that is both pan-disability (we serve people whatever type of impairment or health condition they experience) and led by people with personal experience of disability. We have hundreds of organisations in our membership – and you can also join as an individual, which brings many benefits, from discounts on publications to regular bulletins and updates.

We campaign for rights in practice. This year we have campaigned on welfare reform. We influenced Government to delay implementing the new personal independence payment meaning less change all at once for us as disabled people, and on the future of social care.

We support disabled leaders – because we believe that the more disabled people there are in positions of influence, the more likely it is that accessibility and equal chances for disabled people will be considered across society.

I hope you find this guide useful. We believe that having the confidence to go out knowing that public toilets will be available to meet your needs is really important – it is one of the keys to living independently.

Liz Sayce OBE
Chief Executive, Disability Rights UK

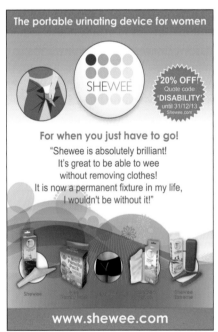

NATIONAL KEY SCHEME GUIDE 2013

About Disability Rights UK

Disability Rights UK is the largest, national pan-disability organisation in the UK led by disabled people. Our vision is a society where everyone with lived experience of disability or health conditions can participate equally as full citizens.

Our objectives are:
* To mobilise disabled people's leadership and control – in our own lives, our organisations and society;
* To achieve independent living in practice;
* To break the link between disability and poverty;
* To put disability equality and human rights into practice across society.

We provide unrivalled information on our website on benefits and opportunities for disabled people in education, apprenticeships and independent living.

It has never been more important to have a strong organisation that stands up for disabled people's rights and supports disabled people's organisations nationally. We bring proposals and solutions to help assert the rights of disabled people and encourage social change. We campaign on policy issues with full participation of disabled people and provide expert advice and resources for disabled people and the organisations that support you.

To find out more about who we are and what we do, contact us at:

Disability Rights UK
12 City Forum, 250 City Road, London EC1V 8AF
Telephone: 020 7250 3222
Email: enquiries@disabilityrightsuk.org
Website: www.disabilityrightsuk.org

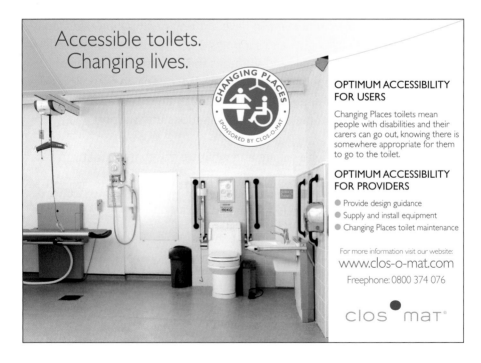

THE NATIONAL KEY SCHEME

The availability of appropriately designed lavatories in public places is essential if disabled people are to be able to engage in their communities and take part in everyday activities.

Radar would have liked public toilets for disabled people to be kept unlocked and in a usable condition at all times, but even a low level of damage or lack of maintenance can make toilets unusable. In many situations providers have found it necessary to restrict entry to purpose-designed toilets in order to prevent damage caused by wilful or casual misuse.

So, over 30 years ago, Radar recognised that two elements of its policy had become irreconcilable. We initiated discussions with disability organisations and local authorities and the National Key Scheme for Toilets for Disabled People was established.

We have also been involved with the development of automatic, vandal resistant 'superloos' that can be used by disabled people, and the 'Changing Places Campaign', which calls for toilets with the additional facilities required by people with severe impairments to be installed in all major public places in addition to standard accessible toilets.

Changing Places toilets
Changing Places toilets have more space and extra features:
- An adjustable height adult changing table
- A tracking or mobile hoist
- Space both sides of the WC for assistants

For further information:
Telephone 020 7696 6019 (England);
01382 385154 (Scotland) or
visit www.changing-places.org

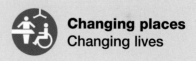

Changing places
Changing lives

The design of toilets for disabled people

Design recommendations for unisex public toilets have focussed on features for wheelchair-users and people who can walk only a short distance:

- The approach must be level or ramped, the doorway level and of an adequate width, and the space large enough for wheelchair manoeuvre to allow for different directions of transfer to the WC;
- As some disabled people will need assistance from a companion, this necessitates adequate space within a unisex cubicle;
- The recommended layout of fittings aims to cater for the maximum possible range of requirements.

It has become clear that people with a far wider range of experiences of disability or health conditions need specially designed toilets with specific features, and a means of entry:

- For many, it is the fact that the facilities are unisex that is valuable. For example, some people with Alzheimer's might need their clothing to be checked or adjusted before leaving the toilet;
- Some blind people welcome being able to avoid the threatening atmosphere of some public conveniences and need space for their guide dog;
- Speedy access to a toilet can be necessary for some with bladder or bowel conditions;
- People with a range of conditions need a washbasin close to the WC and the more hygienic conditions they can expect to find in a toilet fitted with the NKS lock.

The provision of well-designed public unisex toilets suitable for disabled people does not eliminate the need to pay attention to the design and maintenance of other toilets. Many people would be helped by simple fittings such as a handrail in at least one WC cubicle and beside a urinal. Some trends such as reducing the size of cubicles and the height of WCs are making modern public toilets more difficult or even impossible for many people to use.

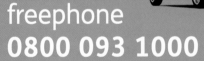

How the National Key Scheme works

The NKS toilet lock and key

Within the National Key Scheme (NKS), a standard NKS toilet door lock is fitted if the facility provider, in discussion with disabled people, considers it necessary to keep their disabled toilets locked. Local authorities adopting the Scheme should arrange for disabled people in their area to obtain a key and wherever possible, one is made available nearby. Keys are also available directly from Disability Rights UK, who keep an up-to-date listing of NKS toilet locations.

The Scheme started with local authorities and now almost all of those that have public conveniences participate. A wide range of commercial and community organisations have also adopted the Scheme and toilets fitted with the NKS lock can now be found in shopping centres, pubs, cafes, department stores, transport undertakings, educational establishments and many other locations as well as public conveniences in most parts of the country.

Many disabled people value the Key Scheme highly for the increased independence it provides, both by reducing damage and misuse and by cutting out the need to find a member of staff to unlock a disabled toilet.

Other applications of the scheme

Owners of a range of other types of premises soon realised that the Scheme could be useful in other situations.

- An accessible entrance to a building may not be permanently open for security reasons;
- On gates in rural areas, it may be necessary to prevent stock straying or horses and motorcycles from damaging footpaths;
- The National Trust and other similar bodies have properties where only cars with disabled people may go to certain areas.

The use of the NKS lock in these situations, either in its regular form or as a padlock, makes access possible for disabled people.

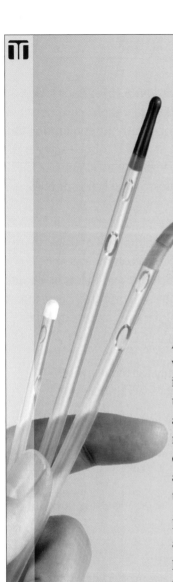

HOW TO USE THIS GUIDE

The 2013 edition of this guide includes over 9,000 NKS toilets across the country. While some councils have closed some or all of their public conveniences for disabled people or transferred them to other providers, increased provision by other organisations means that the number of NKS toilets continues to grow.

Toilets listed are those we have been told are fitted with the NKS lock. It is not a list of all public toilets designed for disabled people.

Order of entries
Toilets locations are listed by:
- Region of the country
- District or borough council area (in alphabetical order)
- Locality (towns and villages)

Finding an NKS toilet
Within local authority districts or borough council areas, localities (towns and villages) are listed first, in alphabetical order. Locations of toilets provided by the relevant council are then shown (alphabetically), followed by locations of toilets provided by other organisations.

An index of localities is provided at the back of this book. It includes all towns and villages in the main listings, but not all the localities within large towns and cities. For example Edinburgh is listed in the index but not the 13 individual areas of the city.

Information in entries

Opening times

Many toilets listed are available to NKS keyholders at all times. You can assume that most of the non-council toilets are not available on a 24-hour basis. Where possible, we indicate opening times, for example:

- (08.00-20.00), (Summer) or (Park hrs)

Some entries are for new toilets, planned but not yet open or those due to close at some point in the future. These are indicated by, for example:

- [Summer 13], [Under review], or [To be replaced]

Gender

The majority of toilets are unisex. Those which are not, are indicated by:

- (M only), (F only), (M+F)

Number of NKS toilets available

At some locations, there is more than one NKS toilet.

- This is indicated by a number in brackets after the location.

Rural areas

In some rural areas specific details of locations are not available. It should be assumed that in those localities the location of the toilet will be obvious.

- These are indicated by: [Location details not available]

Changing Places toilets

- **CP** indicates NKS key required
- CP indicates NKS key not required

Toilet providers

Most toilets fitted with the NKS lock are run by the district or borough council in whose area they are located. Other providers include public authorities such as parish and county councils, commercial bodies including shopping centres, public houses, rail companies and a wide variety of other public and voluntary organisations.

An indication of the ownership of the non-district council toilets is given at the end of the entry, for example:
- *(National Trust)*, *(ScotRail)* or *(Nandos)*
- In other instances *(Private)* has been used

Some of the provider names have been abbreviated, for example:
J D Wetherspoon pubs (JDW); Transport for Greater Manchester (TfGM); Mitchells & Butlers (M&B) and Transport for London (TfL).

Although some of these toilets can be considered ordinary public conveniences, in most cases they are provided for the customers/users of the premises and are not available, as a right, to the public. They will also only usually be available when the premises are open.

REGION

District

Locality	CP Location (10:00-16:00) (M+F)
	Location (3) *(Private)*
	'Pub or Restaurant', Location *(JDW)*
Locality	[Location details not available]
Locality	CP Location (1) *(Private)*
	Shopping Centre, Location *(Shopping Centre)*
	Toilet Provider (8) *(Private)*

Examples
Above: an illustration of the abbreviations, terms and colour coding used in the listing and explained on these pages. See pages 18 and 19 for details of the areas included in each region.

Regions and the areas they include

● **Greater London**
The London boroughs of Greater London and a Central London area, (roughly that within the Congestion Charge area) including the City of London and parts of Camden, Islington, Lambeth, Southwark and Westminster.

● **South East England**
East Sussex, Kent, Surrey and West Sussex.

● **Southern England**
Berkshire, Buckinghamshire, Hampshire, the Isle of Wight and Oxfordshire.

● **West Country**
Gloucestershire, Somerset, Wiltshire, Dorset and the area around Bristol.

● **Devon & Cornwall**

● **Eastern England**
Bedfordshire, Cambridgeshire, Essex, Hertfordshire, Norfolk and Suffolk.

● **East Midlands**
Derbyshire, Leicestershire, Lincolnshire, Northamptonshire and Nottinghamshire and the southern part of the area that used to form Humberside.

● **West Midlands**
Herefordshire, Shropshire, Staffordshire, Warwickshire, West Midlands and Worcestershire.

● **North West England**
Cheshire, Cumbria, Greater Manchester, Lancashire and Merseyside.

● **Yorkshire**
North, South and West Yorkshire and the East Riding of Yorkshire and Kingston-upon-Hull districts.

● **North East England**
Durham, Northumberland and Tyne & Wear and the Tees Valley.

● **South East Scotland**
Edinburgh, Falkirk, the Lothians and the Scottish Borders.

● **South West Scotland**
Ayrshire, Dumfries & Galloway, Dunbartonshire, Lanarkshire, Renfrewshire and Glasgow.

● **East Scotland**
Aberdeenshire, Angus, Clackmannan, Fife, Perth & Kinross and Stirling.

● **Highlands & Islands of Scotland**
Argyle & Bute, Highlands, Moray, Orkney, Shetland and the Western Isles.

● **North Wales**
Anglesey, Conwy, Denbighshire, Flintshire and Gwynedd.

● **Mid & West Wales**
Carmarthenshire, Ceredigion, Pembrokeshire and Powys.

● **South Wales**
The area that formed the counties of Glamorgan and Gwent including Cardiff and Swansea.

● **Northern Ireland**

● **Channel Islands**

● **Isle of Man**

The National Key Scheme regions cover the areas of Great Britain and Northern Ireland, the Channel Islands and the Isle of Man. They do not necessarily correspond to official administrative areas but have been devised for the convenience of keyholders.

DISABILITY RIGHTS HANDBOOK

38th Edition
April 2013 - April 2014

A guide to benefits and services for all disabled people, their families, carers and advisers

Disability Rights UK

NEW EDITION

As comprehensive as ever

- How the benefit system works and how to make a claim
- Benefits for people with an illness, injury or disability
- Benefits for carers, young people and children and those looking for work, or in retirement
- Benefits for people injured at work or serving in the Armed Forces
- Challenging benefit decisions
- Getting and paying for care services

New in 2013

For people aged 16-64
- Personal Independence Payment: how to claim, what to do if you are turned down and what happens to people on Disability Living Allowance
- Extra information on Access to Work
- The new sanctions rules for Jobseeker's Allowance and Employment and Support Allowance
- The benefit cap: who will be affected and how it works

For families with disabled children
- Expanded guidance on Disability Living Allowance for children

For people 65 and over:
- Additional information on claiming Attendance Allowance

Personal Independence Payment is coming ...

From April 2013, Disability Living Allowance for people aged 16-64 will start to be replaced by a new benefit, the Personal Independence Payment. Over 2 million people will be affected.

The next two years will also see the biggest changes to the benefits system since the introduction of the welfare state. In this period of unprecedented change and benefits cuts, keeping up with the new rules is crucial.

Information and advice you can trust

The new edition of our Disability Rights Handbook, fully updated for 2013, provides in-depth information on the entire benefits system and comprehensive guidance on these critical changes.

The must-buy edition – out May 2013

Disability Rights Handbook 2013-2014 (38th Edition)
£29.99 inc P&P (£15.00 for people claiming benefits)

Order online at www.disabilityrightsuk.org

Stay informed – know your rights

This year's Handbook explains Personal Independence Payment and includes new additional guidance on Disability Living Allowance for children and Attendance Allowance (for people 65 and over) with tactics and tools to help make a successful claim.

It introduces Universal Credit which will replace several income-related benefits and tax credits and is planned to be phased in from April 2013.

All benefits explained in one book

Written in plain English by benefits specialists and legally referenced, it's the only user-friendly benefits guide designed specifically for both claimants and their advisers. It has the answers you need to help ensure the quality of your advice or to claim what you are entitled to.

Keep your Handbook up to date all year

Become a member of Disability Rights UK and we'll keep you up-to-date throughout the year with 'Disability and Welfare Rights Updates' our bi-monthly PDF magazine. 20+ pages of news and page-by-page Handbook updates. Download a free sample copy from our website.

If only I'd known that ...

Our companion guide, 'If only I'd known that a year ago' provides practical advice on accessing the help, services and equipment available for disabled people of all ages. See overleaf for more information.

Order your copy now at www.disabilityrightsuk.org

Central London

E1	Old Spitalfields Market (2) *(Private)*
	'Nandos', 114 Commercial Street *(Nandos)*
	'Nandos', Middlesex Street *(Nandos)*
	'Shooting Star', Middlesex Street *(Fullers)*
	'Slug & Lettuce', Stoney Lane *(Private)*
EC1	City Road/Central Street *(Islington)*
	Clerkenwell Road/Leather Lane *(Camden)*
	Long Lane, Aldersgate Street *(City of London)*
	Old Street Station Underpass (Mon-Sat daytime) *(Islington)*
	West Smithfield *(City of London)*
	'Butchers Hook & Cleaver', West Smithfield *(Fullers)*
	'Lord Raglan', St Martin-le-Grand *(Spirit)*
	'Printworks', Farringdon Road *(JDW)*
	'Sir John Oldcastle', Farringdon Road *(JDW)*
	'Three Compasses', Cowcross Street *(Private)*
	Finsbury Leisure Centre *(Private)*
EC2	Liverpool Street Station, Platform 10 *(Network Rail)*
	'All Bar One', Finsbury Pavement *(M&B)*
	'Bluu Moorgate', Moorgate *(Marstons)*
	'Green Man', Poultry *(JDW)*
	'Hamilton Hall', Liverpool Street Station *(JDW)*
	'Rack & Tenter', Moorfields *(Private)*
	Bishopsgate Institute *(Private)*
	Guildhall School of Music *(Private)*
EC3	Monument Pavilion *(City of London)*
	Tower Hill *(City of London)*
	Tower Place *(City of London)*
	Fenchurch Street Station, Lower Level *(C2C)*
	'All Bar One', Houndsditch *(M&B)*
	'Bar 38', St Clare House, Minories *(Spirit)*
	'Caffe Nero', London Street *(Caffe Nero)*
	'Caffe Nero', London Wall *(Caffe Nero)*
	'Crosse Keys', Gracechurch Street *(JDW)*
	'Fine Line', Monument Street *(Fullers)*
	'Liberty Bounds', Trinity Square *(JDW)*

	'Revolution', 140 Leadenhall Street *(Private)*
	'Revolution', America Square *(Private)*
	'Slug & Lettuce', St Mary Axe *(Private)*
EC4	Paternoster Square (Daytime) *(City of London)*
	Watermark Place, All Hallows Lane *(City of London)*
	Cannon Street Station, Main Concourse *(Network Rail)*
	'Alibi', Shoe Lane *(Private)*
	'All Bar One', Ludgate Hill *(M&B)*
	'Costa Coffee', New Bridge Street *(Costa)*
	'Fine Line', Bow Churchyard *(Fullers)*
	'Hog's Head', Fetter Lane *(Private)*
	'Leon', Ludgate Circus *(Private)*
	'Nandos', One New Change *(Nando)*
	'Slug & Lettuce', Fetter Lane *(Private)*
	'The Banker', Cousin Lane *(Fullers)*
	'The Paternoster', Paternoster Square *(Private)*
N1	'Nandos', 12-16 York Way *(Nando)*
NW1	Marylebone Road, opp Tussauds (7.30-23.00) *(Westminster)*
	Regents Park (4) *(Royal Parks)*
	London Euston Station, Concourse *(Network Rail)*
	Marylebone Station, Concourse *(Chiltern Trains)*
	'Globe', Marylebone Road *(Spirit)*
	'Metropolitan', Station Approach, Marylebone Road *(JDW)*
	35 Marylebone Road (2) *(Westminster Univ)*
	Fitness Centre, Taunton Centre *(London Business School)*

SE1		London Bridge Station, Forecourt *(Network Rail)*
		London Bridge Station, Platform 5/6 *(Network Rail)*
		Waterloo East Station, Platform B/C *(SouthEastern)*
		Waterloo Station, Concourse *(Network Rail)*
		Waterloo Station, Forecourt *(Network Rail)*
		Gabriels Wharf *(Private)*
		'All Bar One', London Bridge Street *(M&B)*
		'Founders Arms', Hopton Street *(Youngs)*
		'Market Porter', Stoney Street *(Private)*
		'Nandos', 225 Clink Street *(Nandos)*
		'Slug & Lettuce', 32 Borough High Street *(Private)*
		Boland House, Guy's Campus (2) *(Kings College)*
	CP	City Hall *(GLA)*
	CP	Tate Modern *(Tate)*

SW1
Bressenden Place/Victoria Street *(Westminster)*
Kensington Road, opp. Palace Gate (10.00-18.00, longer in summer) *(Westminster)*
Orange Square *(Westminster)*
Regency Place *(Westminster)*
Tachbrook Street (Mon-Sat 7.30-20.00, Sunday 10.00-18.00) *(Westminster)*
St James's Park, Marlborough Gate *(Royal Parks)*
Victoria Coach Station, Arrivals Area & Help Point *(TfL)*
Victoria Station, Concourse *(Network Rail)*
Victoria Place Shopping Centre *(Private)*
'All Bar One', Cardinal Walk *(M&B)*
'Lord Moon of the Mall', Whitehall *(JDW)*
'Nandos', 107 Wilton Road *(Nandos)*
'Nandos', 17 Cardinal Walk *(Nandos)*
'Shakespeare', Buckingham Palace Road *(Spirit)*
'Slug & Lettuce', Artillery Row *(Private)*
'Travellers Tavern', Elizabeth Street *(Spirit)*
'Willow Walk', Wilton Road *(JDW)*
Churchill War Rooms *(Private)*

W1
Balderton Road, off Oxford Street *(Westminster)*
Broadwick Street, Soho *(Westminster)*
Mayfair Place, Shepherd Market *(Westminster)*
Paddington Street Gardens (10.00-18.00, later in summer) *(Westminster)*
Piccadilly Circus Station (steps on approach) (Station hrs) *(Westminster)*

Princes Street/Regent Street *(Westminster)*
Whitcombe Street *(Westminster)*
Plaza Centre, Oxford Street *(Private)*
'Duke of Wellington', Wardour Street *(Private)*
'Nandos' Great Portland Street *(Nando)*
'Nandos', 113 Baker Street *(Nandos)*
'Nandos', 57/9 Googe Street *(Nandos)*
'O'Neills', Great Marlborough Street *(M&B)*
'O'Neills', Wardour Street *(M&B)*
'Revolution', St Annes Court *(Private)*
'Rising Sun', 46 Tottenham Court Road *(Private)*
'Slug & Lettuce', 19/20 Hanover Street *(Private)*
'Tyburn', Edgware Road *(JDW)*
115 New Cavendish Street *(Westminster Univ)*
2-12 Little Titchfield Street *(Westminster Univ)*
309 Regent Street, 1st Floor *(Westminster Univ)*
32-38 Wells Street (2) *(Westminster Univ)*

W2

Bishops Bridge Road *(Westminster)*
Hyde Park, Bandstand *(Royal Parks)*
Hyde Park, Reservoir *(Royal Parks)*
CP Paddington Station, Platforms 1 & 14 *(Network Rail)*
Whiteleys Shopping Centre, Queensway *(Private)*
'Garfunkles', Praed Street *(Private)*
'McDonalds', 178 Edgware Road *(McDonalds)*
'Nandos', 63 Westbourne Grove *(Nandos)*
'Shish', Bishops Bridge Road *(Private)*
Grosvenor Victoria Casino, Edgware Rd *(Private)*

WC1

Russell Square, opp. Bernard Street *(Camden)*
'All Bar One', New Oxford Street *(M&B)*
'Marquis Cornwallis', Russell Square *(M&B)*
'Nandos', The Brunswick Centre *(Nandos)*
'Pendrells Oak', High Holborn *(JDW)*
CP Great Ormond Street Hospital *(Hospital)*

WC2

High Holborn, opp. Proctor Street *(Camden)*
Jubilee Hall, Covent Garden (7.30-23.00) *(Westminster)*
Shaftesbury Avenue, off Piccadilly Circus *(Westminster)*
Strand/Arundel Street *(Westminster)*
Charing Cross Station, Concourse *(Network Rail)*
'All Bar One', Cambridge Circus *(M&B)*
'All Bar One', Kingsway *(M&B)*

'All Bar One', Villiers Street *(M&B)*
'Brewmaster', Cranbourne Street *(Private)*
'Chiquito', Leicester Square *(Private)*
'Columbia Bar', Aldwych *(Private)*
'Knights Templar', Chancery Lane *(JDW)*
'Montagu Pyke', Charing Cross Road *(JDW)*
'Moon Under Water', Leicester Square *(JDW)*
'Nandos', 66-8 Chandos Place *(Nandos)*
'Shakespeare's Head', Kingsway *(JDW)*
'Walkabout', Henrietta Street *(Private)*
'Walkabout', Temple Place *(Private)*
'Yates's Bar', Leicester Square *(Private)*
Macadam Building, Surrey Street *(Kings College)*
Odeon Leicester Square *(Odeon)*
Odeon West End, Leicester Square *(Odeon)*
Peacock Theatre, Portugal Street *(Private)*

Barking & Dagenham

Barking	Barking Park, Tennis Courts (8.00-17.00)
	Beacontree Heath (8.00-17.00)
	Clockhouse Avenue, Town Centre
	Faircross
	Fanshaw Avenue (Mon-Sat, daytime)
	Greatfields Park (Park hrs)
	Housing Advice Centre, Bevan Avenue (Office hrs)
	North Street (Mon-Sat, daytime)
	Rippleside Cemetery (Mon-Sat, daytime)
	Thames View (8.00-17.00)
	Barking Station, Overbridge *(C2C)*
	Vicarage Field Shopping Centre *(Private)*
	'Nandos', Long Bridge Road *(Nandos)*
	'The Barking Dog', 61 Station Parade *(JDW)*
Chadwell Heath	Chadwell Heath Cemetery (Mon-Sat, daytime)
	Robert Jeyes Library, High Road (Library hrs)
	St Chads Park (Park hrs)
	'Coopers Arms', High Road *(Spirit)*
Collier Row	City Pavilion, Collier Row Road *(Private)*
Dagenham	Central Park, Pavilion (Park hrs)
	Eastbrookend Cemetery (Mon-Sat, daytime)
	Hedgemans Road/Heathway

		Lodge Avenue
		Marks Gate Library, Rose Lane (Library hrs)
		Stamford Road (8.00-17.00)
		Wellgate Children Training Centre (Centre hrs)
		Marks Gate Community Centre, Rose Lane *(Private)*
		Dagenham Dock Station, Platform 2 *(C2C)*
		Morrisons Store, Wood Lane *(Morrisons)*
		'Beacon Tree', Green Lane *(Private)*
		'KFC', Merrielands Crescent *(KFC)*
		'Lord Denman', 270 Heathway *(JDW)*
		'McDonalds', Whalebone Lanes *(McDonalds)*
		Dagenham & Redbridge Stadium *(Dagenham & Redbridge FC)*
	CP	Becontree Heath Leisure Centre *(Private)*
Rush Green		Barking & Dagenham College (6) *(College)*

Barnet

Childs Hill	Childs Hill Park, Nant Road
Colindale	'Moon Under Water', Varley Parade *(JDW)*
East Barnet	Oakhill Park, Parkside Gardens
	Victoria Recreation Ground, Glyn Road (Park hrs)
Edgware	Edgwarebury Park, Edgwarebury Lane
	'Nandos', Station Road *(Nandos)*
Finchley	Victoria Park, Ballards Lane (Park hrs)
Friern Barnet	Friary Park, Friern Barnet Road (Park hrs)
Golders Green	Golders Hill, by Café *(City of London)*
	Bus Station, Golders Green Road *(TfL)*
Hendon	Hendon Park, Queens Road (Park hrs)
	'Nandos', Brent Park *(Nando)*
High Barnet	Old Court Recreation Ground (Café hrs)
Mill Hill	Mill Hill Park, Daws Lane
New Barnet	'Railway Bell', East Barnet Road *(JDW)*
North Finchley	Sainsbury's Store, 836 High Road *(Sainsbury)*
	'Nandos', Great North Leisure Park *(Nandos)*
	'The Tally Ho', 749 High Road *(JDW)*
Whetstone	Swan Lane Open Space, café (Café hrs)

Bexley

Abbey Wood	Lesnes Abbey (Park hrs)
	Abbey Wood Station, Station Front *(SouthEastern)*
	Abbey Wood Caravan Club Site *(Caravan Club)*
Albany Park	Albany Park Station, Booking Hall *(SouthEastern)*
Belvedere	Belvedere Recreation Ground, Heron Hill (Park hrs)
	Tower Block, Tower Road Campus (3) *(Bexley College)*
	Works Block, Tower Road Campus *(Bexley College)*
Bexley	High Street
	Bexley Station, Platform 2 *(SouthEastern)*
Bexleyheath	Danson Park (Park hrs)
	Danson Park Mansion (Summer) (Park hrs)
	Friswell Place
	Broadway Shopping Centre (2) *(Private)*
	'Earl Haig', Little Heath Road *(Private)*
	'Nandos', Market Place *(Nando)*
	'Wrong 'Un', 234 The Broadway *(JDW)*
	'Yates's Bar', Mayplace Road West *(Private)*
	Bexley Adult Education College *(College)*
	Gala Bingo, Broadway *(Gala)*
Blackfen	Blackfen Library (Library hrs)

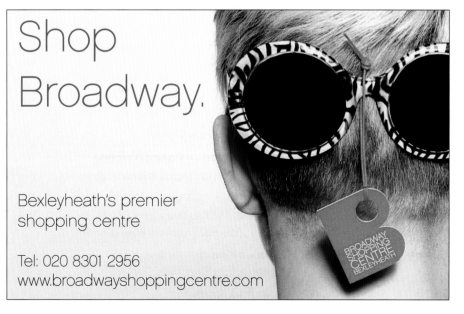

Crayford	Waterside, Crayford Way
	Crayford Station, Platform 1 *(SouthEastern)*
	'Nandos', Tower Retail Park *(Nandos)*
Erith	Town Centre
Sidcup	St John's Road
	Sidcup Station, Platform 1 *(SouthEastern)*
	'George Stables', Blackfen Road *(Private)*
	'Tailor's Chalk', 47-49 High Street *(JDW)*
	'The Portrait', 7-8 Elm Parade *(Private)*
	'Woodman', Blackfen Road *(Spirit)*
	Sidcup Leisure Centre, changing area *(Private)*
Welling	Hillview Cemetery (Cemetery hrs)
	Welling Library, Bellgrove Road (Library hrs)
	Welling Station, Platform 1 *(SouthEastern)*
	'Jolly Fenman', 49 Halfway Street *(Private)*
	'Lord Kitchener', 21 Wrotham Road *(Private)*
	'New Cross Turnpike', Bellegrove Road *(JDW)*

Brent

Alperton	Douglas Avenue, by Ealing Road
Brent Cross	Brent Cross Shopping Centre *(Private)*
Harlesden	Harlesden Library, Craven Park Road (Library hrs)
	Roundwood Park (Park hrs)
	Tavistock Road Car Park
	Willesden Junction Station, Low Level *(London Overground)*
	'Misty Moon', Manor Park Road *(JDW)*
Kensal Rise	Chamberlayne Road/Station Terrace
Kilburn	Victoria Road/Kilburn High Street
	'Caffe Nero', 102 Kilburn High Road *(Caffe Nero)*
	'Nandos', Kilburn High Road *(Nandos)*
	Mecca Bingo, Kilburn High Road *(Mecca)*
	Tricycle Theatre & Cinema, Kilburn High Road (2) *(Private)*
Kingsbury	Kingsbury Road, Car Park
	'J J Moons', 553 Kingsbury Road *(JDW)*
	'Nandos', 658-660 Kingsbury Road *(Nandos)*
Queens Park	Car Park, by Station
	Queens Park, by Playground (Park hrs)
Sudbury	Barham Park, Car Park

Wembley	Mahatma Gandhi House, Wembley Hill Road (Office hrs)
	Oakington Manor Drive/Harrow Road (9.00-19.00)
	St Johns Road Car Park
	St Johns Road/Elm Road
	Church of the Ascension, The Avenue *(Private)*
	Paddy Power Bookmaker, 389 High Road *(Private)*
	'Black Horse', Harrow Road *(Private)*
	'Fusilier', 652 Harrow Road *(Private)*
	'J J Moons', 397 High Road *(JDW)*
	'KFC', 434/6 High Road *(KFC)*
	'McDonalds', 482 High Road *(McDonalds)*
	'Nandos', 420 High Road *(Nandos)*
	'The Preston', Preston Road *(Private)*
	Wembley Arena (7) *(Private)*
	Wembley Stadium (147) *(Private)*
Willesden	High Road, off Richmond Avenue
	Quality House, Willesden Lane (Office hrs)

Bromley

| Beckenham | High Street/Kelsey Park Road |
| | Beckenham Junction Station, Platform 2 *(SouthEastern)* |

	Clock House Station, Concourse *(SouthEastern)*
	'Slug & Lettuce', 150 High Street *(Private)*
Bromley	Library Gardens, off High Street
	Stockwell House 2, Civic Centre (Office hrs)
	Glades Centre MSCP *(Private)*
	Bromley North Station, Booking Hall *(SouthEastern)*
	Bromley South Station, Platform 3/4 *(SouthEastern)*
	'Ivory Lounge', Ringers Road *(Private)*
	'Nandos', 9 Widmore Road *(Nandos)*
	'Partridge', High Street *(Fullers)*
	'Richmal Crompton', Westmoreland Place *(JDW)*
	'Slug & Lettuce', 3-5 High Street *(Private)*
	'Walkabout', 190 High Street *(Private)*
	Widmore Centre, Nightingale Lane *(College)*
	Bromley Campus, Rookery Lane (13) *(College)*
	Churchill Theatre, High Street *(Private)*
	Empire Cinema, High Street *(Private)*
Chislehurst	High Street, Car Park [Currently closed]
Coney Hall	Kingsway
Crystal Palace	Crystal Palace Park, by Information Office (Park hrs)
	Crystal Palace Caravan Club Site *(Caravan Club)*
Leaves Green	Ashmore Lane, car park [Currently closed]
Locksbottom	Pallant Way, off Crofton Road [Currently closed]
Orpington	The Walnuts Shopping Centre, off High Street
	Orpington Station, Platform 3/4 *(SouthEastern)*
	'Harvest Moon', High Street *(JDW)*
	'Nandos', Nugent Shopping Park *(Nandos)*
	Orpington Campus, The Walnuts (7) *(Bromley College)*
	Walnuts Leisure Centre, Fitness Suite *(Private)*
Penge	High Street
	'McDonalds', 130 High Street *(McDonalds)*
	'Moon & Stars', High Street *(JDW)*
Petts Wood	'Daylight Inn', Station Square *(M&B)*
	'Sovereign of the Seas', Queensway *(JDW)*
West Wickham	Glebe Way, by Library
	West Wickham Station, Platform 1 *(SouthEastern)*
	'Railway Hotel', Red Lodge Road *(Private)*

Camden (see also Central London)

Camden Town	Camden Lock Market *(Private)*
	'Edward's', Camden High Street *(M&B)*
	'Ice Wharf', Suffolk Wharf *(JDW)*
	'Jongleurs', East Yard, Camden Lock *(Private)*
	'The Crescent', Camden High Street *(Private)*
Cricklewood	'Beaten Docket', Cricklewood Broadway *(JDW)*
Hampstead	Nassington Road, Athletics Track *(City of London)*
	Vale of Health, East Heath Road *(City of London)*
Highgate	Pond Square, South Grove
	Millfield Lane, Highgate West Hill *(City of London)*
	Parliament Hill Fields *(City of London)*
Kentish Town CP	Camden Society, Holmes Road *(Private)*
Kilburn	West End Lane/Fortune Green Road
Swiss Cottage	Queens Crescent/Malden Road
West Hampstead	'Walkabout', O2 Centre, Finchley Road *(Private)*
	'Wetherspoons', O2 Centre, Finchley Road *(JDW)*

The City of London (see Central London)

Croydon

Addiscombe	Ashburton Park
Coulsdon	Coulsdon Memorial Ground (Park hrs)
	Farthing Downs *(City of London)*
Croydon	Croydon Clocktower (Library hrs)
	Lunar House, Wellesley Road
	West Croydon Bus Station *(TfL)*
	East Croydon Station, Platform 3/4 *(Southern)*
	'All Bar One', Park Lane *(M&B)*
	'Builders Arms', Leslie Park Road *(Fullers)*
	'Escapade', High Street *(Private)*
	'Goose on the Market', Surrey Street *(M&B)*
	'Milan Bar', High Street *(JDW)*
	'Nandos', 26 High Street *(Nandos)*
	'Nandos', 4 Valley Leisure Park *(Nandos)*
	'Porter & Sorter', Station Road *(Marstons)*
	'Ship of Fools', 9 London Road *(JDW)*

'Spread Eagle', Katherine Street *(Fullers)*
'The George', George Street *(JDW)*
'The Skylark', Southend *(JDW)*
'Tiger Tiger', High Street *(Private)*
'Yates's Bar', High Street *(Private)*

Crystal Palace	'Postal Order', 33 Westow Street *(JDW)* Gala Bingo, Church Road *(Gala)*
Norbury	'Moon Under Water', 1327 London Road *(JDW)*
Purley	'Foxley Hatch', Russell Hill Park *(JDW)* Purley Bowl, Brighton Road *(AMF)*
Selsdon	Selsdon Library (Library hrs) 'Sir Julian Huxley', 152 Addington Road *(JDW)*
South Croydon	Lloyd Park Monks Hill Sports Centre *(Private)*
South Norwood	'William Stanley', High Street *(JDW)*
Thornton Heath	'Flora Sandes', Brigstock Road *(JDW)*
Upper Norwood	Biggin Woods (Park hrs)

Ealing

Acton		'Goldsmiths Arms', East Acton Lane *(Private)* 'Red Lion & Pineapple', Acton High Street *(JDW)*
	CP	Carlton Road Day Centre
	CP	Ealing, Hammersmith & West London College *(College)*
Ealing		Pitshanger Park Walpole Park (April-September) Ealing Broadway Station *(Gt Western)* Broadway Shopping Centre *(Private)* 'Fox & Goose', Hanger Lane *(Fullers)* 'Nandos', Bond Street *(Nandos)* 'Rose & Crown', St Marys Road *(Fullers)* 'Sir Michael Balcon', The Mall *(JDW)* 'The Green', The Green *(Private)*
Greenford		'Hare & Hounds', 229 Ruislip Road *(Marstons)*
Hanwell		Brent Lodge Park
Park Royal		'Nandos', Royal Leisure Park *(Nandos)*

Southall	Southall Park, Southall High Street
	Ealing Hospital, Uxbridge Road *(Health Trust)*
West Ealing	'Drayton Court', The Avenue *(Fullers)*
	'Duke of Kent', Scotch Common *(Fullers)*

Enfield

Edmonton	Craig Park (Park hrs)
	Jubilee Park (Park hrs)
	Edmonton Green Shopping Centre *(Private)*
	'Stag & Hounds', Bury Street West *(Private)*
Enfield	Albany Park, Hertford Road (Centre hrs)
	Civic Centre (M+F) (Office hrs)
	Enfield Playing Field (Park hrs)
	Forty Hall, Forty Hill (Park hrs)
	Town Park
	Enfield Town Station *(Greater Anglia)*
	Palace Gardens Shopping Centre (2) *(Private)*
	'Moon Under Water', Chase Side *(JDW)*
	'Robin Hood', 240 The Ridgeway *(Private)*
	'Rose & Crown', 185 Clay Hill *(Private)*
Enfield Highway	Durants Park, Hertford Road (2)
	Turkey Street/Hertford Road
New Southgate	Arnos Park (Park hrs)
Palmers Green	Broomfield Park (2) (Park hrs)
	'Alfred Herring', Green Lanes *(JDW)*
	'McDonalds', 286 Green Lane *(McDonalds)*
Ponders End	Recreation Ground, High Street (2)
	'Picture Palace', High Street *(JDW)*
Southgate	Boundary Playing Fields
	Grovelands Park (Park hrs)
	Tatem Park (Park hrs)
	'New Crown', Chase Side *(JDW)*
	'White Hart', 290 Chase Road *(Private)*
Upper Edmonton	Pymmes Park, Victoria Road (Park hrs)
	'Gilpins Bell', Fore Street *(JDW)*

Greenwich

Abbey Wood		Bostall Gardens (Dawn-dusk)
Blackheath		Batley Park
		Blackheath Station, Platform 1 *(SouthEastern)*
		Westcombe Park Station, Platform 1 *(SouthEastern)*
		'Royal Standard', Vanbrugh Park *(Private)*
Charlton		Charlton House (Daytime)
Eltham		Avery Hill Park, Bexley Road (Dawn-dusk)
		Crematorium, behind office (Crematorium hrs)
	CP	Eltham Centre, Archery Road (Centre hrs)
		Eltham Park South
		Well Hall Pleasaunce (Park hrs)
		Eltham Station, Booking Hall *(SouthEastern)*
		New Eltham Station, Platform 1 *(SouthEastern)*
		'Bankers Draft', High Street *(JDW)*
Greenwich		Cutty Sark Gardens
		East Greenwich Library, Woolwich Road (Library hrs)
		Rodmere Street
		Tourist Information Centre (10.00-17.00)
		Greenwich Park, Blackheath Gate *(Royal Parks)*
		Greenwich Park, by Play Area *(Royal Parks)*
		Greenwich Station, Booking Hall *(SouthEastern)*
		Maze Hill Station, Booking Hall *(SouthEastern)*
		'Auctioneer', 217 Greenwich High Road *(M&B)*
		'Gate Clock', Creek Road *(JDW)*
		'The Yacht', Crane Street *(Spirit)*
		Greenwich Picturehouse, Greenwich High Street *(Private)*
Mottingham		Mottingham Station, Platform 1 *(SouthEastern)*
North Greenwich		'Las Iguanas', Peninsula Square *(Private)*
		'Nandos', O2, Millennium Way *(Nandos)*
		'Nandos', UCI, Bugsbys Way *(Nandos)*
		'Slug & Lettuce', Prninsula Square *(Private)*
Shooters Hill		'Fox Under the Hill', 286 Shooters Hill Road *(Private)*
		'Latin Touch Café', Oxleas Wood *(Private)*
Thamesmead		'Princess Alice', Battery Road *(Private)*
Woolwich		Beresford Square
		Herbert Road
		The Ferry

Vincent Road
Woolwich Arsenal Station, Platform 1 *(SouthEastern)*
'Earl of Chatham', Thames Street *(Private)*
'Great Harry', 7-9 Wellington Street *(JDW)*
'McDonalds', Powis Street *(McDonalds)*
'Nandos', 50 Powis Street *(Nandos)*
Gala Bingo, Powis Street *(Gala)*
CP Woolwich Centre, Wellington Road

Hackney

Dalston		Birkbeck Road, Ridley Road Market
		Kingsland Passage, Dalston Junction
		Kingsland Waste
		Kingsland Shopping Centre Car Park *(Private)*
		'Nandos', Kingsland High Street *(Nandos)*
Hackney		Narrow Way, Mare Street
		Wilton Way, by Town Hall
		St John at Hackney Gardens *(Private)*
		'Baxters Court', Mare Street *(JDW)*
Hommerton	CP	Hackney Marshes Centre (2) *(Private)*
Hoxton		Stanway Street, Hoxton Market
Stamford Hill		Stamford Hill Broadway
Stoke Newington		Clissold Park (Park hrs)
		'Nandos', Church Street *(Nandos)*
		'Rochester Castle', Stoke Newington High Street *(JDW)*

Hammersmith & Fulham

Fulham	'Crabtree', Rainville Road *(Private)*
	'Durell', 704 Fulham Road *(Private)*
	'Nandos', 20 Fulham Broadway *(Nandos)*
	'Oyster Rooms', Fulham Broadway *(JDW)*
	Craven Cottage Stadium *(Fulham FC)*
Hammersmith	Hammersmith Broadway Centre (2)
	Ravenscourt Park, Café (9.30-17.30)
	Social Services Office, King Street (Office hrs)
	Kings Mall Shopping Centre *(Private)*
	'Hop Poles', King Street *(Private)*
	'Plough & Harrow', King Street *(JDW)*
	'Rutland Arms', Lower Mall *(Spirit)*

	'The Trout', Broadway *(Private)*
	'William Morris', Swan Island, King Street *(JDW)*
	Hammersmith Apollo *(Private)*
Shepherds Bush	Shepherds Bush Green, by Post Office
	White City Bus Station *(TfL)*
	'Central Bar', West 12 Shopping Centre *(JDW)*
	'Nandos', 284 Uxbridge Road *(Nandos)*
	'Nandos', Westfield Shopping Centre *(Nandos)*
	'Walkabout', Shepherds Bush Green *(Private)*
	Vue Cinema, Shepherds Bush Green *(Vue)*

Haringey

Crouch End	Hatherley Gardens/Haringey Park
	'Devonshire House', The Broadway *(JDW)*
Finsbury Park	Finsbury Park entrance, Seven Sisters Rd
Highgate	Highgate Wood *(City of London)*
	'The Gatehouse', North Road *(JDW)*
Hornsey	'The Tollgate'. Turnpike Lane *(JDW)*
Muswell Hill	Summerland Gardens Car Park
South Tottenham	Apex Corner, Seven Sisters Road
	St Ann's Road, Chestnut Recreation Ground
Tottenham	Tottenham Hale Station *(Greater Anglia)*
Wood Green	High Road/Alexandra Road
	The Mall Wood Green *(Private)*
	'The Gate', Buckingham Road *(Private)*
	'Wetherspoons', Spouters Corner *(JDW)*
	'Yates's Bar', Metroplex Complex *(Private)*

Harrow

Edgware	Bob Lawrence Library (Library hrs)
	Whitchurch Lane/Buckingham Road
	Broadwalk Shopping Centre *(Private)*
	'Zan Zi Bar', 113 High Street *(Private)*
Harrow	Gayton Library, 5 St Johns Road (Library hrs)
	Greenhill Way, nr. Havelock Place
	Harrow Leisure Centre (Centre hrs)
	Harrow Bus Station *(TfL)*
	St Anns Shopping Centre *(Private)*

St George's Shopping Centre *(Private)*
'Castle', West Street *(Fullers)*
'Junction', 9 Gaydon Way *(Private)*
'Moon on the Hill', 373 Station Road *(JDW)*
'Mumbai Junction', 231 Watford Road *(Private)*
'O'Neills', Station Road *(M&B)*
'Royal Oak', St Anns Road *(Spirit)*
'Yates's Bar', 269 Station Road *(Private)*

Harrow Weald		High Road
		'Duck in Pond', Kenton Lane *(Private)*
		'Leefe Robinson VC', Uxbridge Road *(Private)*
		'Vue Point Bar', Old Redding *(Private)*
	CP	Harrow Weald Campus, Newton Building *(Harrow College)*
Hatch End		'Moon & Sixpence', 250 Uxbridge Road *(JDW)*
Kenton		Belmont Circle, Kenton Lane
		'The New Moon', Kenton Park Parade *(JDW)*
North Harrow		Pinner Road
Northwick Park		A Block, Harrow Campus *(Westminster Univ)*
		J Block, Harrow Campus *(Westminster Univ)*
		M Block, Harrow Campus *(Westminster Univ)*
		The Street, Harrow Campus *(Westminster Univ)*
Pinner		Chapel Lane
		'Caffe Nero', Love Lane *(Caffe Nero)*
		'Village Inn', 402 Rayners Lane *(JDW)*
Rayners Lane		Rayners Lane/Alexandra Avenue
South Harrow		Northolt Road
		'Nandos', 309 Northolt Road *(Nandos)*
Stanmore		Stanmore Recreation Ground
		'Crazy Horse', Church Road *(Private)*
		'Man in the Moon', Buckingham Parade *(JDW)*
Sudbury Hill		'Rising Sun', Greenford Road *(Private)*
Wealdstone		Gladstone Way MSCP
		Harrow & Wealdstone Station *(London Overground)*
		'Goodwill to All', Headstone Drive *(Private)*
		'Miller & Carter', Brockhurst Corner *(Private)*
		'Stone Rose', High Street *(Private)*

Havering

Collier Row		Collier Row Road
		'Aspen Tree', Gobions Avenue *(Greene King)*
		'Bell & Gate', Collier Row Lane *(Private)*
		'Colley Rowe Inn', 54 Collier Row *(JDW)*
Corbetts Tay		'Huntsman & Hounds', Ockendon Road *(Private)*
Cranham		'Golden Crane', Avon Road *(Private)*
Elm Park		Station Parade
Gidea Park		Station Road
Harold Hill		Hilldene Avenue
Harold Wood	CP	Harold Wood Polyclinic, The Drive *(NHS)*
Havering-atte-Bower		'Orange Tree', Orange Tree Hill *(Private)*
Hornchurch		Appleton Way
		'Ardleigh & Dragon', Ardleigh Green Road *(Private)*
		'Harrow', Hornchurch Road *(Private)*
		'Hogs Head', Station Lane *(Private)*
		'J.J.Moons', 46 High Street *(JDW)*
		'Nandos', 111 High Street *(Nandos)*
		'Railway', Station Lane *(Private)*
Rainham		Cherry Tree Lane
		'Albion', Rainham Road *(Private)*
Romford		South Street
		Romford Station, Platform 4 *(Greater Anglia)*
		Liberty Shopping Centre *(Private)*
		The Mall Romford, Mercury Gardens *(Private)*
		Debenhams Store, Market Place *(Debenhams)*
		'Custom House', South Street *(Private)*
		'Edwards', South Street *(M&B)*
		'Moon & Stars', 99 South Street *(JDW)*
		'Nandos', The Brewery *(Nandos)*
		'Squire', North Street *(Private)*
		'Worlds Inn', South Street *(JDW)*
		'Yates's Bar', South Street *(Private)*
		Rush Green Campus (6) *(Barking & Dagenham College)*
Upminster		Upminster Bridge, Upminster Road
		Upminster Station, Lower Ticket Office *(C2C)*
		'Optimist', Hacton Lane *(Private)*

Hillingdon

Cowley	Station Road
Devonshire Lodge	Car Park
Eastcote	'The Manor', Field End Road *(Private)*
Harefield	Park Lane, by Library
Hatton Cross	by Underground Station
Hayes	Barra Hall Park (Events only)
	Botwell Lane (Mon-Sat, 8.00-18.00)
	Coldharbour Lane
	Connaught Recreation Ground
	St Anselms Road, Town Centre
	Hayes *&* Harlington Station *(Gt Western)*
	'Botwell Inn', Coldharbour Lane *(JDW)*
Hillingdon	'Red Lion', Royal Lane *(Fullers)*
Ickenham	Community Close
	'Titchenham Inn', Swakeleys Road *(JDW)*
Northwood	Joel Street
	Oaklands Gate
	'William Jolle', Broadway, Joel Street *(JDW)*
Ruislip	High Street
	Manor Farm (Mon-Sat, 8.00-18.00)
	'J J Moons', Victoria Road *(JDW)*
Ruislip Manor	Linden Avenue

ARJOWIGGINS

Supported by
Arjo Wiggins
Fine Papers
Limited

**Hillingdon Council
is happy to support
Disability Rights UK
and is committed to
providing accessible
public buildings**

HILLINGDON
LONDON

Uxbridge	Fairfield Road
	The Mall Pavilions *(Private)*
	Debenhams Store, The Chimes *(Debenhams)*
	'Good Yarn', 132 High Street *(JDW)*
	'Nandos', The Chimes *(Nandos)*
	'Slug & Lettuce', 219 High Street *(Private)*
	'White House', Stockley Park *(JDW)*

Hounslow

Bedfont	Bedfont Library, 639 Staines Road (Library hrs)
Brentford	Half Acre, Brentford High Street
	Brentford Station, Waiting Room *(SW Trains)*
	Syon Park, Garden Centre *(Private)*
	Kew Bridge Steam Museum, Green Dragon Lane *(Private)*
Chiswick	'Hogs Head', Chiswick High Road *(Private)*
	'Nandos', 187-9 Chiswick High Road *(Nandos)*
	'Packhorse & Talbot', 145 Chiswich High Street *(Spirit)*
	'Paragon', Chiswick High Road *(Private)*
	'Revolution', 18 Chiswick High Road *(Private)*
	'Roebuck', 122 Chiswick High Road *(Private)*
	Quintin Hogg Memorial Sports Ground *(Westminster Univ)*
Cranford	'Jolly Waggoner', 618 Bath Road *(Spirit)*
Feltham	Feltham Library, The Centre (Library hrs)
	Feltham Station *(SW Trains)*
	'Moon on the Square', The Centre *(JDW)*
	'Nandos', Longford Shopping Centre *(Nandos)*
	Gala Bingo, Airpark Way *(Gala)*
	Hounslow Urban Farm, Fagg's Road *(Private)*
Gunnersbury	Gunnersbury Park, by Café (Park hrs)
Heston	'Rose & Crown', 220 Heston Road *(Private)*
Heston M4	Heston Services East, J2/3 *(Moto)*
	Heston Services West, J2/3 *(Moto)*
Hounslow	Hounslow Station *(SW Trains)*
	Treaty Shopping Centre (2) *(Private)*
	'Bullstrode', Lampton Road *(Private)*
	'KFC', 183 High Street *(KFC)*
	'Moon Under Water', 84 Staines Road *(JDW)*
	'Nandos', High Street *(Nandos)*

	'TJB's Café', Treaty Centre *(Private)*
	'Yates's Bar', Bath Road *(Private)*
	Gala Bingo, Staines Road *(Gala)*
	Lampton Sports Centre, Lampton Avenue *(Private)*
Isleworth	'London Apprentice', Church Street *(Private)*
Osterley	'Hare & Hounds', Windmill Lane, Wyke Green *(Private)*

Islington (see also Central London)

Archway	Archway Leisure Centre (Centre hrs) *(Private)*
Barnsbury	'Albion', Thornhill Road *(Private)*
Cannonbury	Newington Green
	'The House', Canonbury Road *(Private)*
Finsbury Park	N4 Library, Blackstock Road (Library hrs)
	Seven Sisters Road, by Rainbow Theatre
	Centre for Lifelong Learning, Blackstock Road *(City & Islington College)*
Highbury	Highbury Fields, Tennis Court end
	Emirates Stadium *(Arsenal FC)*
Holloway	Holloway Road/Camden Road
	Sobell Leisure Centre (Centre hrs) *(Private)*
	James Selby Ltd, Holloway Road *(Private)*
	Morrisons Store, Holloway Road *(Morrisons)*
	'The Coronet', Holloway Road *(JDW)*
	London Met University, Holloway Road *(University)*
Islington	Council Offices, Upper Street (Office hrs)
	Islington Green, Essex Road
	White Conduit Street, Chapel Market
	N1 Centre, Islington High Street *(Private)*
	'Glass Works', N1 Centre *(JDW)*
	'Steam Passage', Upper Street *(Private)*
	'The Angel', Islington High Street *(JDW)*
Stroud Green	'White Lion of Mortimer', Stroud Green Road *(JDW)*

Kensington & Chelsea

| **Chelsea** | St Lukes Gardens (7.30-dusk) |
| | 'Beaufort House', 354 Kings Road *(Private)* |

Earls Court	Earls Court Underground Station 'McDonalds', 208 Earls Court Road *(McDonalds)*
Kensington	Holland Park, Ilchester Place (8.00-dusk) Kensington Church Street Kensington High Street, by Cinema Kensington Town Hall Car Park (Daytime)
North Kensington	Emslie Hornimans Pleasance, Bosworth Road (7.30-dusk) Little Wormwood Scrubs (7.30-dusk)
Notting Hill	Kensington Memorial Park, St Marks Road (7.30-dusk) Notting Hill Gate, opp. Cinema Portobello Road/Lonsdale Road Tavistock Piazza. Portobello Road Westbourne Grove/Colville Road (Fri & Sat, daytime) 'Bar 128', 128 Notting Hill Gate *(Private)* 'Castle', 225 Portobello Road *(Private)* 'Duke of Wellington', 179 Portobello Road *(Youngs)* 'Nandos', 58 Notting Hill Gate *(Nandos)* 'The Mitre', 40 Holland Park Avenue *(Private)*
South Kensington	Courtfield Road Mount Gate (M+F) *(Royal Parks)* 'Black Widow', Gloucester Road *(Spirit)* 'Nandos', 117 Gloucester Road *(Nandos)*

West Brompton	Westfield Park
West Kensington	'Kensington', Russell Gardens *(Spirit)*

Kingston-upon-Thames

Chessington	'Chessington Oak', 116 Moore Lane *(M&B)*
	'North Star', 271 Hook Road *(M&B)*
Hook	Hook & Chessington Library, Hook Road (Library hrs)
Kingston	Barnfield Youth & Community Centre (Centre hrs)
	Bittoms Car Park (Mon-Sat, 7.45-19.00)
	Eden Walk Car Park, by Shopmobility
	Guildhall 1, Foyer (Office hrs)
	Guildhall 2, Ground Floor (Office hrs)
	Kingsmeadow Fitness Centre (Centre hrs)
	Kingston Crematorium (Crematorium hrs)
	Market Hall, Market Place
	The Rose Car Park, Kingston Hall Road
	Cromwell Street Bus Station *(TfL)*
	Kingston Station, Platforms 2 & 4 *(SW Trains)*
	Bentalls Centre, 2nd floor (3) *(Private)*
	'All Bar One', Charter Quay *(Private)*
	'British Oak', Richmond Road *(Private)*
	'Frangos', 9 The Rotunda *(Private)*
	'Gazebo', Riverside Walk *(Private)*
	'Kings Tun', 153 Clarence Street (2) *(JDW)*
	'Kingston Mill', 58 High Street *(M&B)*
	'Litten Tree', Castle Street *(Private)*
	'McDonalds', 90 Eden Street *(McDonalds)*
	'Oceana', Clarence Street *(Private)*
	'O'Neill's', 3 Eden Street *(M&B)*
	'Slug & Lettuce', 6 Charter Quay *(Private)*
	Kingston College, Richmond Road *(Kingston College)*
	Gala Bingo, Richmond Road *(Private)*
	Hawker Leisure Centre *(YMCA)*
New Malden	Blagdon Road Car Park
CP	Crescent Resource Centre, Cocks Crescent (Centre hrs)
	New Malden Library, Kingston Road (Library hrs)
	'Bar Malden', St Georges Square *(Marstons)*
	'The Fountain', Malden Road *(Private)*
	'Watchman', 134 High Street *(JDW)*

Norbiton	'Kingston Gate', 204 London Road (Private)
Surbiton	Victoria Recreation Ground, St Marys Road
	Surbiton Station, Platforms 1/2 & 3/4 (SW Trains)
	'Cap in Hand', 174 Hook Rise (JDW)
	'Coronation Hall', St Mark's Hill (JDW)
	'Elm Tree', Victoria Road (Private)
	'Rat & Parrot', St Marks Hill (Spirit)
	'Surbiton Flyer', Victoria Road (Fullers)
Tolworth	Alexandra Recreation Ground, Bloomfield Road
	'Broadway Café Bar', The Broadway (Marstons)
	Tolworth Recreation Centre (DC Leisure)

Lambeth (see also Central London)

Brixton	Popes Road
	'The Beehive', 407 Brixton Road (JDW)
Clapham	'Revolution', Clapham High Street (Private)
Herne Hill	Herne Hill Station, Platform 3 (SouthEastern)
Streatham	The Rookery, Streatham Common
	'Crown & Sceptre', Streatham Hill (JDW)
	'Holland Tringham', Streatham High Road (JDW)
	'Nandos', 6 High Parade (Nandos)
Vauxhall	Vauxhall Bus Station (TfL)
West Norwood	Norwood High Street, by Library

Lewisham

Blackheath	Blackheath Grove
	'The Railway', 16 Blackheath Village (Private)
Brockley	'Brockley Barge', 184 Brockley Road (JDW)
Catford	Catford Broadway/Catford Grove
	Catford Bridge Station, Platform 2 (SouthEastern)
	'London & Rye', 109 Rushey Green (JDW)
	'Nandos', 74 Rushey Green (Nandos)
Deptford	Brookhill Park (Park hrs)
CP	Deptford Lounge, Giffin Street
Downham	Downham Way/Old Bromley Road
Forest Hill	By Forest Hill Station
	'The Capitol', 11-12 London Road (JDW)

Grove Park	Grove Park Station, Platform 2/3 *(SouthEastern)*
Kidbrooke	Kidbrooke Station, Platform 1 *(SouthEastern)*
Lee	Lee Station, Platform 1 *(SouthEastern)*
	Sainsburys Store, Burnt Ash Road *(Sainsbury)*
	'The Crown', 117 Burnt Ash Hill *(Youngs)*
Lewisham	Lewisham High Street
	Lewisham Library (Library hrs)
	Lewisham Station, Platforms 2/3 *(SouthEastern)*
	Lewisham Shopping Centre *(Private)*
	Market Tavern', High Street *(Marstons)*
	'Nandos', Lee High Road *(Nandos)*
	'One'. 1 Lee High Road *(Private)*
	'Watch House', 198 High Street *(JDW)*
	'Yates' Bar', Lee High Road *(Private)*
New Cross	New Cross Station, Platform A/B *(SouthEastern)*
	'Hobgobblin', New Cross Road *(Private)*
	Hoggart Building, Goldsmiths *(College)*
	Library, Goldsmiths *(College)*
	Pimlott Building, Goldsmiths *(College)*
	Student Union, Goldsmiths *(College)*
Sydenham	Home Park (Park hrs)
	'Two Halfs', 198 Sydenham Road *(Private)*

Merton

Colliers Wood	Colliers Wood Recreation Ground (Park hrs)
	'Nandos', 12 Tandem Centre *(Nandos)*
Merton Park	John Innes Park, Church Path (Park hrs)
Mitcham	Canons Recreation Ground, Madeira Road (Park hrs)
	Rowan Road Recreation Ground (Park hrs)
	Tamworth Farm Recreation Ground (Park hrs)
	'White Lion of Mortimer', 223 London Road *(JDW)*
Morden	Joseph Hood Recreation Ground, Martin Way (Park hrs)
	King George's Playing Field, Tudor Drive (Park hrs)
	Merton Civic Centre, London Road (Office hrs)
	Morden Park, London Road (Park hrs)
	North East Surrey Crematorium *(Private)*
	Merton Campus, Morden Park (7) *(S Thames College)*
	Mecca Bingo Rosehill, Bishopsford Road *(Mecca)*

Motspur Park	Sir Joseph Hood Playing Fields (Park hrs)
Raynes Park	Cottenham Park Recreation Ground (Park hrs)
	'Edward Rayne', Coombe Lane *(JDW)*
	'Raynes Park Tavern', 32 Combe Lane *(Private)*
Roehampton	Commons Extension, Robin Hood Lane (Park hrs)
West Wimbledon	Holland Gardens (Park hrs)
Wimbledon	Cannizaro Park, West Side (Park hrs)
	Dundonald Recreation Ground (Park hrs)
	Haydons Road Recreation Ground (Park hrs)
	South Park Gardens, Dudley Road (Park hrs)
	The Broadway/Queens Road (Daytime)
	Wimbledon Library, Wimbledon Hill Road (Library hrs)
	Wimbledon Park, Home Park Road (Park hrs)
	South Wimbledon Community Association *(Private)*
	Wimbledon Station, Platforms 1 & 8 *(SW Trains)*
	Centre Court Shopping Centre, Food Court *(Private)*
	Debenhams Store, Centre Court *(Debenhams)*
	Morrisons Supermarket, The Broadway *(Morrisons)*
	'Edwards', 18 Hartfield Road *(Private)*
	'Nandos', Russell Road *(Nandos)*
	'O'Neill's', The Broadway *(M&B)*
	'Wibbas Down Inn', Gladstone Road *(JDW)*
	'Wingfield Café', Wimbledon Tennis Club *(AETC)*
	'Yates' Bar', Hartfield Road *(Private)*

Newham

Beckton	Beckton District Park North (Park hrs)
	St John's Road Car Park
	'Nandos', Gallions Reach Shopping Park *(Nandos)*
Canning Town	Rathbone Market, Barking Road
	Docklands Campus *(University of East London)*
Custon House	ExCeL, Western Gateway *(Private)*
East Ham	Central Park, Café (Café hrs)
	Clements Road/High Street North
	Gooseley Recreation Ground (Park hrs)
	Plashet Park (7.00-16.00)
	Town Hall (Office hrs)
	'Miller's Well', 419 Barking Road *(JDW)*

East Ham Campus, High Street South *(Newham College)*
Gala Bingo, Barking Road *(Gala)*
CP East Ham Leisure Centre, Barking Road

Forest Gate
Romford Road/Woodgrange Road
Shaftesbury Road Car Park
'Hudson Bay', 1-5 Upton Lane *(JDW)*

Manor Park
Romford Road/Herbert Road
City of London Cemetery (2) (Cemetery hrs) *(City of London)*

Plaistow
Greengate Street/Barking Road
Hamara Ghar Square
Queens Market
Boleyn Ground, Upton Park *(West Ham Utd)*
CP Community Centre, Balaam Street

Royal Victoria
Royal Victoria Gardens, Pier Road (Park hrs)

Stratford
Stratford Station, Jubilee Line Concourse *(TfL)*
In Shops, Stratford Shopping Centre *(Private)*
Stratford Shopping Centre *(Private)*
'Golden Grove', 146 The Grove *(JDW)*
'Goose on the Broadway', The Broadway *(M&B)*
'Nandos', 1 Romford Road *(Nandos)*
'Swan', The Broadway *(Private)*
'Yates' Bar', The Broadway *(Private)*
Stratford Campus, Welfare Road *(Newham College)*
Gala Bingo, High Street *(Gala)*
CP Westfield Stratford City, Grd & 1st fls *(Private)*

West Ham
Memorial Avenue
West Ham Lane/Whalebone Lane
West Ham Park *(City of London)*

Redbridge

Barkingside
Cranbrook Road, by Recreation Ground
Fulwell Cross Library (Library hrs)
'New Fairlop Oak', Fencepiece Road *(JDW)*
Gala Bingo, Fairlop Road *(Gala)*

Chadwell Heath
Wangey Road (7.30-21.00)
'Eva Hart', 1128 High Road *(JDW)*

Clayhall
Clayhall Park, Longwood Gardens

Gants Hill	Clarence Avenue (7.30-21.00)
Goodmayes	Barley Lane, Recreation Ground (Mon-Sat, 7.30-18.30)
Hainault	Hainault Recreation Ground, Changing Rooms (Park hrs)
	Manford Way (Mon-Sat, 7.30-18.30)
Ilford	Chapel Road/Roden Street
	Ilford Central Library (Library hrs)
	Ilford High Road, Griggs Approach (Mon-Sat, 7.30-21.00)
	Ley Street MSCP
	Valentines Park Café (Park hrs)
	Clements Road MSCP *(Private)*
	Ilford Station, Overbridge *(Greater Anglia)*
	The Exchange Ilford (3) *(Private)*
	'Great Spoon of Ilford', 114 Cranbrook Road *(JDW)*
	'Nandos', Clements Road *(Nandos)*
Seven Kings	High Road, nr Station Car Park (Mon-Sat, 7.30-18.30)
	South Park Road, off Green Lane (7.30-18.30)
Wanstead	Christchurch Green, of High Street (M+F) (7.30-21.00)
	Wanstead Park *(City of London)*
	'Cuckfield', High Street *(Private)*
	'The George', High Street *(JDW)*
Woodford Green	Hillside Avenue
	Johnson Road/Broomhill Road

Richmond-upon-Thames

Barnes		'Red Lion', Castelnau *(Fullers)*
Hampton		Bushy Park, by Playground *(Royal Parks)*
		'Tiltyard Café', Hampton Court Palace *(Private)*
Kew	**CP**	Kew Gardens *(Private)*
Richmond		Buccleuch Gardens, off Petersham Road
		Old Town Hall, Whitaker Avenue
		Princes Street, behind Waitrose
		Victoria Place
		Richmond Station. Lower Concourse *(SW Trains)*
		Sainsburys Store, Lower Richmond Road *(Sainsbury)*
		'Bull', 1 Kew Road *(Private)*
		'Edwards', Kew Road *(M&B)*
		'New Inn', Petersham Road *(Private)*

	'O'Neills', The Quadrant *(M&B)*
	'Orange Tree', 45 Kew Road *(Youngs)*
	'Revolution', Whittaker Avenue *(Private)*
	'The Lot', Duke Street *(Private)*
Teddington	'The Lion', 27 Wick Road *(Private)*
Twickenham	Twickenham Station, Platform 3 *(SW Trains)*
	'George', 32 King Street *(Spirit)*
	'Hook Line & Sinker', York Street *(Fullers)*
	'St Margaret', 107 St Margarets Road *(Private)*
	'William Webb Ellis', 24 London Road *(JDW)*
	Twickenham Rugby Stadium *(RFU)*
Whitton	Whitton Library Car Park
	Whitton Sports & Fitness Centre (Centre hrs)

Southwark (see also Central London)

Bermondsey	'All Bar One', Butlers Wharf *(M&B)*
	'Pommelers Rest', Tower Bridge Road *(JDW)*
CP	Southwark College, Keetton's Road *(College)*
Camberwell	'Fox on the Hill', Denmark Hill *(JDW)*
	Gala Bingo, Camberwell Road *(Gala)*
Dulwich	Dulwich Park, Pavilion Café
East Dulwich	Sainsbury's Store, Dog Kennel Hill *(Sainsbury)*
Elephant & Castle	'Rockingham Arms', Metro Central Heights *(JDW)*
Peckham	'Kentish Drovers', Peckham High Street *(JDW)*
Rotherhithe	Southwark Park Café (Café hrs)
	Surrey Quays Shopping Centre (2) *(Private)*
	'Quebec Curve', Redriff Road *(Marstons)*
	'Surrey Docks', 185 Lower Road *(JDW)*
	Gala Bingo, Surrey Quays *(Gala)*

Sutton

Carshalton	Grove Park, by Café
	Oaks Park
Cheam	Cheam Park, Cheam Park Way
	Nonsuch Park, by Mansion Café *(Epsom & Ewell Council)*
North Cheam	'Nonsuch Inn', 552 London Road *(JDW)*
	'Woodstock', Stonecot Hill *(Spirit)*

Sutton	CP	SCILL, Robin Hood Lane *(Private)*
		St Nicholas Centre, Ground & 3rd floors *(Private)*
		Morrisons Store, High Street *(Morrisons)*
		'Caffe Nero', Carshalton Rd/High Street *(Caffe Nero)*
		'Cock & Bull', High Street *(Fullers)*
		'Moon on the Hill', Hill Road *(JDW)*
		'Revolution', 1-3 High Street *(Private)*
		'The Grapes', High Street *(JDW)*
		'Treasury', 59 High Street *(Marstons)*
	CP	Sutton Station, Platform 2/3 *(Southern)*
Wallington		Beddington Park, Church Road
		Mellows Park
		'Whispering Moon', Woodcote Road *(JDW)*

Tower Hamlets

Bethnal Green	'Nandos', 366 Bethnal Green Road *(Nandos)*
Bow	Armagh Road Housing Office (Office hrs)
	Heylyn Square Housing Office (Office hrs)
	'Jongleurs', Bow Wharf *(Private)*
	'Morgan Arms', Morgan Street *(Private)*
	'The Match Maker', 580 Roman Road *(JDW)*
	Thames Magistrates Court *(Courts Service)*
Canary Wharf	Jubilee Place Mall *(Private)*
	'All Bar One', South Colonnade *(M&B)*
	'Café Rouge', Mackenzie Walk *(Private)*
	'Cat & Canary', Fishermans Walk *(Fullers)*
	'Fine Line', Fishermans Walk *(Fullers)*
	'Nandos', 25-26 Jubilee Place *(Nandos)*
	'Nandos', West Cabot Place *(Nando)*
	'Pizza Express', Cabot Place East *(Private)*
	'Slug & Lettuce', South Colonnade *(Private)*
	'Wagamama', Jubilee Place *(Private)*
Limehouse	'Oporto', West India Dock Road *(Private)*
Mile End	'Half Moon', 213 Mile End Road *(JDW)*
	'Hayfield', Mile End Road *(Private)*
	'Nandos', 552 Mile End Road *(Nando)*
	'Nandos', 9 Mile End Road *(Nandos)*
Poplar	East India Dock Rd/Burdett Road

	Market Square Housing Office (Office hrs)
	'Gun', Coldharbour *(Private)*
Wapping	'Prospect of Whitby', Wapping Wall *(Private)*
West India Quay	'Bar 38', Hertsmere Road *(Spirit)*
	'The Ledger Building', Hertsmere Road *(JDW)*
Whitechapel	Idea Store, 321 Whitechapel Road (Library hrs)
	Whitechapel Market
	'Goodman's Fields', Mansell Street *(JDW)*

Waltham Forest

Chingford	Ridgeway Park (Park hrs)
	Royal Hunting Lodge *(City of London)*
	Chingford Station, off Platform 2 *(Greater Anglia)*
	Sainsbury's Store, Walthamstow Avenue *(Sainsbury)*
	'KFC', Albert Crescent *(KFC)*
	'Kings Head', Kings Head Hill *(Private)*
	'Obelisk', Old Church Road *(Barracuda)*
	'Queen Elizabeth', Forest Side *(Private)*
	'Station House', Station Road *(Marstons)*
	'The King's Ford', 250 Chingford Mount Road *(JDW)*
Leyton	Tesco Store, Bakers Arms *(Tesco)*
	'Burger King', Leyton Mills *(Private)*
	'KFC', Leyton Mills *(KFC)*
	'The Drum', 557 Lea Bridge Road *(JDW)*
	Gala Bingo, 366 Lea Bridge Road *(Gala)*
Leytonstone	Leytonstone Bus Station, Church Road *(TfL)*
	Tesco Store, Gainsborough Road *(Tesco)*
	'Heathcote Arms', 344 Grove Green Road *(Private)*
	'O'Neills', 762 High Road *(M&B)*
	'Walnut Tree', 857 High Road *(JDW)*
Walthamstow	Walthamstow Bus Station, Selborne Road *(TfL)*
	The Mall Walthamstow *(Private)*
	'The Goose', 264 Hoe Street *(Private)*
	Waltham Cricket, Squash and Tennis Club *(Private)*

Wandsworth

| **Balham** | 'Clarence', 90 Balham High Road *(Private)* |
| | 'Jackdaw & Rook', 100 Balham High Road *(Fullers)* |

Battersea	Station Approach, Clapham Junction
	Clapham Junction Station, Overbridge *(SW Trains)*
	'Asparagus', 1-13 Falcon Road *(JDW)*
	'Bank', 31 Northcote Road *(Fullers)*
	'Duck', Battersea Rise *(Spirit)*
	'Falcon', St Johns Hill *(Private)*
	'Nandos', 1 Northcote Road *(Nandos)*
	'Northcote', Northcote Road *(Spirit)*
	'Prince Albert', Albert Bridge Road *(Spirit)*
	'Revolution', 276 Lavender Hill *(Private)*
	'Walkabout', Lavender Gardens *(Private)*
Earlsfield	Earlsfield Library, Magdalen Road (Library hrs)
	Earlsfield Station *(SW Trains)*
	'Leather Bottle', 538 Garratt Lane *(Youngs)*
Putney	Putney Bridge Road/Putney High Street
	Putney Vale Cemetery (Cemetery hrs)
	Exchange Shopping Centre *(Private)*
	'Boathouse', Brewhouse Way *(Youngs)*
	'Cedar Tree', Putney Bridge Road *(Spirit)*
	'Dukes Head', 8 Lower Richmond Road *(Youngs)*
	'Half Moon', 93 Lower Richmond Road *(Private)*
	'Old Spotted Horse', Putney High Street *(Youngs)*

'Real Greek Souvlaki', Putney High Street *(Private)*
'The Railway', 202 Upper Richmond Road *(JDW)*
'Wagamama', 50-54 Putney High Street *(Wagamama)*
'Windmill Tea Rooms', Wimbledon Common *(Private)*

Southfields	'Grid Inn', 22 Replingham Road *(JDW)* 'Old Garage', 20 Replingham Road *(Greene King)*
Tooting	Tooting Bec Common, by Dr Johnson Avenue Tooting Bec Lido (Pool hrs) Tooting Broadway, by Garratt Lane 'A Bar 2 Far', 44 Mitcham Road *(Private)* 'J J Moons', Tooting High Street *(JDW)* 'Kings Head', Upper Tooting Road *(Spirit)* 'McDonalds', 42 Mitcham Road *(McDonalds)* 'Mitre Hotel', 130 Mitcham Road *(Private)* 'Nandos', 224 Upper Tooting Road *(Nandos)* 'Tramshed', Mitcham Road *(Private)*
Wandsworth	Garratt Lane/Magdalen Road Wandsworth High Street, by Southside Centre 'Alma', 499 Old York Road *(Youngs)* 'Nandos', Southside Centre *(Nandos)* 'Queen Adelaide', Putney Bridge Road *(Private)* 'Rose & Crown', 134 Wandsworth High Street *(JDW)* 'Windmill Tea Rooms', Windmill Road *(Private)*

Westminster

Maida Vale	'Elgin Bar & Grill', Elgin Avenue *(Private)*
Paddington	Walterton Road/Prince of Wales Junction
St Johns Wood	Salisbury Street, by Church Street (7.30-18.00) Wellington Place, by Lords Cricket Ground (10.00-18.00) Lords Cricket Ground (6) *(MCC)*

SOUTH EAST ENGLAND

Adur

Lancing
Beach Green
Shopsdam Road, Lancing Beach
Widewater, Lancing Beach
Yew Tree Close, South Street

Shoreham
Adur Recreation Ground, Brighton Road
Beach Green, Beach Road
Buckingham Park
Civic Centre, Ham Road [To be redeveloped] (Office hrs)
Fort Haven, Shoreham Beach
Middle Street

Southwick
Southwick Beach, Basin Road (F only)
Southwick Square (Monday-Saturday)

Arun

Aldingbourne
Aldingbourne Country Centre, Blackmill Lane *(Private)*

Aldwick
West Park

Angmering
Haskins Roundstone Garden Centre *(Private)*

Arundel
Crown Yard
Mill Road

Bognor Regis
Bedford Street
East Promenade Foreshore Office
Hotham Park, High Street
London Road Car Park (8.00-20.00)
Regis Centre (Centre hrs)
Bognor Regis Station *(Southern)*
'Hatter's Inn', Queensway *(JDW)*
Rowan Park Caravan Site *(Caravan Club)*

Felpham
Blakes Road (8.00-20.00)
'Southdowns', Felpham Way *(M&B)*

Littlehampton
Arun Civic Centre (Office hrs)
Coastguard Toilets
Mewsbrook Park
Norfolk Gardens
St Martins Car Park

	West Beach, by Visitor Centre
	Littlehampton Station, Ticket Office *(Southern)*
	'George Inn', Surrey Street *(JDW)*
Middleton-on-Sea	Shrubbs Field (8.00-20.00)
Pagham	Sandy Road (8.00-20.00)
Rustington	Broadmark Avenue *(Parish Council)*
	Churchill Parade Car Park *(Parish Council)*
	The Street, by Church *(Parish Council)*
	Woodlands Centre, Recreation Ground *(Parish Council)*

Ashford

Ashford	Forge Lane, New Rents
	St Johns Lane
	Ashford Int. Station, Platforms 1/2 & 5/6 *(SouthEastern)*
	County Square Shopping Centre *(Private)*
	Sainsbury's Store, Bybrook *(Sainsbury)*
	'County Hotel', High Street *(JDW)*
	Ashford Campus, B, C & E Blocks *(K College)*
CP	Ashford Gateway, Church Street *(County Council)*
Chilham	Taylors Hill Car Park
Tenterden	Recreation Ground
	Station Road
CP	Tenterden Gateway, High Street (Office hrs)
Woodchurch	Front Road Car Park

Brighton & Hove

Aldrington	Recreation Ground, Saxon Road (Daytime)
Brighton & Hove Seafront	Black Rock
	Kings Esplanade, by King Alfred Leisure Centre (8.00-20.00, later in summer)
	Kings Esplanade, opp. First Avenue (8.00-20.00, later in summer)
	Lagoon, Kingsway (8.00-17.00, later in summer)
	Lower Prom at West Street (8.00-18.00, later in summer)
	Lower Prom, E of Brighton Pier (Summer) (8.00-20.00)
	Lower Prom, West Pier Play Area (Summer) (8.00-17.00)
CP	Madeira Drive, Colonnade (8.00-18.00, later in summer)
	Madeira Drive, Play Area (10.00-17.00, later in summer)

	Western Esplanade, Kingsway (8.00-17.00, later in summer)
	Brighton Pier, by Café *(Private)*
	'Concord 2', Madeira Hall *(Private)*
	'Terraces Bar', Madeira Drive *(Private)*
Brighton Marina	Mermaid Walk *(Private)*
	'Karmer', Waterfront *(Private)*
	'West Quay', Brighton Marina Village *(JDW)*
	BowlPlex *(BowlPlex)*
Brighton Town Centre	Black Lion Street, The Lanes (8.00-20.00, later in summer)
	Brighton History Centre, Church Street (Centre hrs)
	Brighton Museum & Art Gallery (Museum hrs)
	Dyke Road Park (10.00-16.00, later in summer)
	Jubilee Library, Church Street (Library hrs)
	Old Steine (8.00-20.00, later in summer)
	Prince Regent Swimming Complex (Centre hrs)
	Queens Park, West Drive (10.00-20.00, later in summer)
	Royal Pavilion (Pavilion hrs)
	Royal Pavilion Gardens (8.00-20.00, later in summer)
	'All Bar One', Pavilion Buildings *(Private)*
	'Bright Helm', West Street *(JDW)*
	'Browns Restaurant', Duke Street *(Private)*
	'Browns', Ship Street *(M&B)*
	'Caffe Nero', Prince Albert Street *(Caffe Nero)*
	'Curve Bar', Gardner Street *(Private)*
	'Nandos', 34 Duke Street *(Nandos)*
	'Pitcher & Piano', Kings Road *(Marstons)*

NATIONAL KEY SCHEME GUIDE 2013

'Post & Telegraph', 155 North Street *(JDW)*
'Revolution', 77 West Street *(Private)*
'Standard', West Street *(Private)*
'Varsity', East Street *(Barracuda)*
'Yates's Bar', West Street *(Private)*
Brighton Law Courts *(Courts Service)*
Duke of Yorks Cinema, Preston Circus *(Private)*

East Brighton	Hollingbury Park (Summer & weekends) (10.10-18.00) Stanley Deeson Leisure Centre (Centre hrs) Withdean Sports Centre (Centre hrs) Sheepcote Valley Caravan Park *(Caravan Club)*
Five Ways	Blakers Park, Cleveland Road (8.00-18.00)
Hangleton	Grenadier Shopping Parade (8.00-20.00, later in summer) Hangleton Library, West Way (Library hrs)
Hove	Goldstone Villas/Eaton Villas (8.00-20.00, later in summer) Hove Library (Library hrs) Hove Museum & Art Gallery (Museum hrs) Hove Park (8.00-18.00, later in summer) Hove Rugby Club (Daytime) Norton Road (Weekends & Bank Holidays 8.00-20.00) St Ann's Well Gardens (8.00-16.00, later in summer) West Blatchington Windmill (Business hrs) Hove Station, Platform *(Southern)* 'Slug & Lettuce', George Street *(Private)* 'Station', Goldstone Villas *(Spirit)*
Kemp Town	Gala Bingo, Freshfield, Business Park *(Gala)*
Mile Oak	Mile Oak Library (Library hrs)
Moulscombe	Moulscombe Community Centre (Centre hrs) Wild Park (Summer & weekends) (10.00-18.00)
Ovingdean	Undercliff (10.00-16.00, later in summer)
Patcham	Patcham Library (Library hrs)
Portslade	Easthill Park (10.00-16.00, longer in summer) Portslade Library (Library hrs) Station Road, S. of railway (8.00-20.00, later in summer) Victoria Recreation Ground (8.00-16.00, later in summer)
Preston Park	Chalet (8.00-16.00, later in summer)

	Rotunda (8.00-16.00, later in summer)
Rottingdean	Recreation Ground (8.00-17.00, later in summer)
	Undercliff (8.00-16.00, later in summer)
Saltdean	Undercliff Walk (8.00-17.00, later in summer)
Stanmer	Stanmer Village (8.00-18.00, later in summer)
Whitehawk	Whitehawk Library & Community Centre (Centre hrs)

Canterbury

Canterbury		Best Lane
		Canterbury Lane
		Longport
		Pound Lane
		Toddlers Cove (April-early October)
		Tower Lane
		Worthgate
	CP	Northgate Ward Community Centre *(Private)*
		Canterbury East Station, Platform 2 *(SouthEastern)*
		Canterbury West Station, Platform 1 *(SouthEastern)*
		BHS Store, Marlowe Arcade *(BHS)*
		Debenhams Store, Guildhall Square *(Debenhams)*
		Sainsbury's Store, Kingsmead Road *(Sainsbury)*
		'All Bar One', St Margarets Street *(Private)*
		'Nandos', 46 St Peters Street *(Nandos)*
		'Thomas Ingoldsby', Burgate *(JDW)*
		'West Gate Inn', North Lane *(JDW)*
		Sidney Cooper Gallery, St Peters Street *(University)*
Fordwich		'George & Dragon', King Street *(Private)*
Herne Bay		Bandstand (2)
		Beltinge
		Hampton Pier
		Hampton Pleasure Gardens (Easter-September)
		Herne Bay Cemetery (Cemetery hrs)
		Herne Village, Cherry Orchard
		Kings Hall
		Reculver Country Park
		St Georges
		William Street
		Herne Bay Station, Platform 2 *(SouthEastern)*
		'Saxon Shore', Central Parade *(JDW)*

Upstreet	Grove Ferry Picnic Site *(Kent CC)*
Whitstable	Faversham Road (Easter-early October)
	Harbour Street
	Horse Bridge
	Priest and Sow
	Skinners Alley
	St Annes
	St Johns
	Tankerton Beach
	Whitstable Cemetery
	Whitstable Station, Platform 1 *(SouthEastern)*
	Whitstable Bowl, Tower Parade *(AMF)*

Chichester

Bosham	Bosham Lane Car Park (Daytime)
Bracklesham Bay	Bracklesham Beach Car Park
	'Lively Lady', Stocks Lane *(Private)*
Chichester	Avenue de Chartres MSCP (Daytime)
	Cathedral Way (Daytime)
	Little London Car Park (Daytime)

Children First

A guide for everyone involved in the care and support of disabled children. It covers a wide range of topics including health, play, children's services, school and benefits.

Available to order from our online shop
www.disabilityrightsuk.org

Chichester District Council

For information on toilet facilities and access to local attractions, please visit our website
www.chichester.gov.uk
before you travel.

Alternatively please telephone
01243 785166

	Market Road Car Park (Daytime)
	Northgate Car Park (Daytime)
	Portfield Cemetery (F only) (Cemetery hrs)
	Priory Park (7.30-Dusk)
	Tower Street (Daytime)
	Chichester Cathedral *(Cathedral)*
	Chichester Station, Platform 1 *(Southern)*
	'Chicago Rock Café', Chichester Gate *(Private)*
	'Dolphin & Anchor', West Street *(JDW)*
	'Gatehouse', Chichester Gate *(JDW)*
	'Globe Inn', Southgate *(Private)*
	'Nandos', Chichester Gate *(Nandos)*
	'Slug & Lettuce', Southgate *(Private)*
	'The Vestry', Southgate *(Private)*
Cobnor	Footpath Car Park *(Harbour Conservancy)*
Dell Quay	by Education Centre *(Harbour Conservancy)*
East Wittering	Bracklesham Lane Car Park (Daytime)
	Kingfisher Parade (Daytime)
Fishbourne	Roman Palace Car Park *(Private)*
	'Bulls Head', Fishbourne Road *(Fullers)*
Goodwood	Goodwood Racecourse (4) *(Private)*
Midhurst	North Street Car Park (Daytime)
	'The Wheatsheaf', Wool Lane *(Private)*
Petworth	Town Centre Car Park (Daytime)
Selsey	East Beach Amenity Area (Daytime)
	Hillfield Road (Daytime)
	Lifeboat Station, Kingsway (Daytime)
Sidlesham	Pagham Nature Reserve *(W Sussex CC)*
West Itchenor	The Street (F only)
West Wittering	Marine Drive Car Park (March-October) (Daytime)
	Pound Road (Daytime)
	Pavilion Restaurant, Car Park *(Private)*

Crawley

Bewbush	Dorsten Square
Broadfield	Broadfield Barton Car Park
	Buchan Country Park *(W Sussex CC)*

Crawley Town Centre	Bus Station, Friary Way (Under review)
	Ifield Road
	The Boulevard Car Park
	Crawley Station *(Southern)*
	County Mall Shopping Centre *(Private)*
	'Bar Med', 100 High Street *(Private)*
	'Coffee Republic', 14 Queensway *(Private)*
	'Jubilee Oak', Grand Parade, High Street *(JDW)*
	'Liquid Envy', Station Way *(Private)*
	'McDonalds', 24 Haslett Avenue *(McDonalds)*
	'Nandos', Crawley Leisure Park *(Nandos)*
	'Rat & Parrot', High Street *(Spirit)*
	Don Munro Block *(Central Sussex College)*
	Longley Building *(Central Sussex College)*
Furnace Green	Weald Drive Parade
Gatwick	Gatwick Airport Station, Platform 2 *(Network Rail)*
CP	Gatwick Airport, North Terminal Airside *(Airport)*
CP	Gatwick Airport, South Terminal Airside *(Airport)*
Gossops Green	Capel Lane Parade
Ifield	Ifield Parade

	'Pelham Buckle', 216 Ifield Drive *(Private)*
Langley Green	Langley Drive Parade
Lowfield Heath	Amberley Fields Caravan Club Site *(Caravan Club)*
Maidenbower	Maidenbower Square
Northgate	Woodfield Road Parade
Pease Pottage	K2 Leisure Centre, Brighton Road (Centre hrs)
	Pease Pottage Services A23 *(Moto)*
	'Black Swan', Old Brighton Road *(Private)*
Pound Hill	Worth Road Parade
Three Bridges	Gales Drive, Gales Place
Tilgate	Ashdown Drive Parade
	Tilgate Park, Car Park
	'The Tilgate', Ashdown Drive *(Spirit)*
West Green	Snell Hatch Cemetery (Cemetery hrs)
	West Green Drive/Ewhurst Road

Dartford

Bluewater	House of Fraser Store *(Private)*
	'Nandos', The Wintergarden *(Nandos)*
CP	Bluewater Centre *(Private)*
Dartford	Central Park (Park hrs)
	Dartford Civic Centre (Office hrs)
	Hesketh Park (Park hrs)
	Market Street, nr. Library (8.15-18.00)
	Tree Community Centre, Cedar Road (Centre hrs)
	Dartford Station, Booking Hall *(SouthEastern)*
	Orchards Shopping Centre *(Private)*
	Priory Centre, Car Park *(Private)*
	'Clipper', High Street *(Private)*
	'Crush', Spital Street *(Private)*
	'Flying Boat', Spital Street *(JDW)*
	'Paper Moon', High Street *(JDW)*
	'Royal Victoria & Bull', High Street *(Private)*
	Gala Bingo, Spital Street *(Gala)*
Greenhithe	Greenhithe Station, Platform 2 *(SouthEastern)*
Longfield	Waitrose Car Park *(Private)*

Dover

Ash	Village Car Park, The Street
Deal	Deal Pier
	King Street
	Kingsdown Road/Granville Road
	Town Hall (Weekdays, 8.00-17.00, later in summer) *(Town Council)*
	Deal Station, Waiting Room *(SouthEastern)*
Dover	**CP** Dover Gateway, Castle Street (Office hrs)
	East Cliff
	Kearsney Abbey
	Maison Dieu Gardens
	Stembrook Car Park
	White Cliffs Visitor Centre *(National Trust)*
	Dover Priory Station, Waiting Room *(SouthEastern)*
	Charlton Shopping Centre *(Private)*
	'Eight Bells', Cannon Street *(JDW)*
	Dover Campus, Burgundy Building *(K College)*
	Dover Campus, Provence Building *(K College)*
	Gala Bingo, Biggin Street *(Gala)*
Sandwich	The Quay *(Town Council)*
	Pegwell Bay Country Park *(Kent CC)*
St Margarets-at-Cliffe	St Margarets Bay
Wingham	Village Car Park

Eastbourne

Beachy Head	Beachy Head Car Park
Eastbourne	Archery, Channel View Road
	Bandstand, Lower Promenade
	Bandstand, Upper Promenade (M+F) (Easter-Oct) (8.00-20.00)
	Fisherman's Green
	Helen Gardens, by Pavilion
	Holywell, Lower Promenade
	Hyde Gardens, by Tourist Information Centre
	Junction Road, Coach Park
	Pier, Lower Promenade

Prince William Parade
Princes Park, by Café
Redoubt, by Bowls Pavilion
Eastbourne Station, Concourse *(Southern)*
Arndale Shopping Centre (3) *(Private)*
Enterprise Shopping Centre Car Park *(Private)*
'London & County', Terminus Road *(JDW)*
'Terminus Hotel', Terminus Road *(Harveys)*
'The Lamb', Old Town *(Harveys)*
'Wetherspoons', Cornfield Road *(JDW)*
Aldro Building, Darley Road *(Univ of Brighton)*
Queenswood, Darley Road *(Univ of Brighton)*
Stokers, Carlisle Road *(Univ of Brighton)*

Hampden Park	Brassey Parade Hampden Park, near Café
Langney	Langney Shopping Centre Car Park *(Private)*
South Harbour	The Waterfront, pedestrian entrance

Elmbridge

Claygate	Recreation Ground, Church Road (Daytime)
Cobham	Hollyhedge Road Car Park
East Molesey	Molesey Lock, Hurst Road Walton Road Car Park Hampton Court Station *(SW Trains)* 'Prince of Wales', Bridge Road *(Greene King)*
Esher	High Street 'Marquis of Granby', Portsmouth Road *(Private)* Sandown Park Racecource *(Private)*
Hersham	Hersham Green Shopping Centre *(Private)*
Walton-on-Thames	Cowey Sale, Walton Bridge Walton Library, The Heart (Library hrs) *(Surrey CC)* 'Ashley Park', Ashley Park Road *(Private)* 'Nandos', 7 The Heart *(Nandos)* 'The Regent', Church Street *(JDW)* 'Wagamama', The Heart *(Private)*
West Molesey	Recreation Ground, Walton Road
Weybridge	Churchfield Road (Daytime) High Street, behind shops

Weybridge Station *(SW Trains)*
'Slug & Lettuce', 29 High Street *(Private)*
Brooklands Museum, Club House *(Private)*

Epsom & Ewell

Epsom	Alexandra Recreation Ground (Daytime)
	Epsom Town Hall (Office hrs)
	Horton Country Park, Horton Lane (Daytime)
	Ashley Shopping Centre *(Private)*
	'Assembley Rooms', High Street *(JDW)*
	'Nandos', The Oaks Square *(Nandos)*
	'Slug & Lettuce', The Derby Square *(Private)*
	'Yates's Bar', Derby Square *(Private)*
Epsom Downs	Tattenham Corner
West Ewell	Poole Road Recreation Ground (Daytime)

Gravesham

Gravesend	Borough Market, Queen Street
	Clive Road
	Gordon Promenade
	CP Gravesham Gateway, Windmill Street (Office hrs)
	St George's Centre (Shopping hrs)
	Visitor Centre, St Georges Square (Centre hrs)
	Woodlands Park, Dashwood Road [Closed at present]
	Gravesend Station, Platform 1 *(SouthEastern)*
	Debenhams Store, New Road *(Debenhams)*
	'Pembroke', King Street *(Barracuda)*

		'Robert Pocock', Windmill Street *(JDW)*
	CP	Cyclopark, Wrotham Road *(Private)*
Higham		School Lane
Meopham		Camer Park, Camer Park Road
		Wrotham Road/Pitfield Drive

Guildford

Ash Common	Recreation Ground *(Parish Council)*
Burpham	Sutherland Memorial Park (Park hrs)
Guildford	Allen House, by York Road MSCP
	Bedford Road Car Park
	Farnham Road MSCP
	Shalford Park, Shalford Road
	Stoke Park, by Challenger Centre
	Stoke Park, by Nurseries
	Stoke Park, Tennis Courts
	Tunsgate, Guildford High Street (7.00-19.00)
	Ward Street (7.00-20.00)
	Woodbridge Road (7.00-19.00)
	Guildford Station, Platform 2 *(SW Trains)*
	Debenhams Store, Millbrook *(Debenhams)*
	'All Bar One', North Street *(Private)*
	'George Abbot', High Street/Riverside *(Greene King)*
	'Nandos', 11-12 Friary Street *(Nandos)*
	'Old Orleans', Wayside Square *(Private)*
	'Rodboro Buildings', Bridge Street *(JDW)*
	'Slug & Lettuce', North Street *(Private)*
	'Stoke', Stoke Road *(Spirit)*
Ripley	High Street
Shere	Middle Street *(Parish Council)*

Hastings

Hastings	Alexandra Park, Tennis Pavilion
	Harold Place
	Hastings Country Park, Coastguard Lane
	Hastings Country Park, Helipad
	Rock-a-Nore Road
	Hastings Station, Booking Hall *(SouthEastern)*
	Priory Meadow Shopping Centre, 1st Floor *(Private)*

		Morrisons Store, Queens Road *(Morrisons)*
		'John Logie Baird', Havelock Road *(JDW)*
		'KFC', 5 York Buildings *(KFC)*
		'McDonalds', 8-9 Wellington Place *(McDonalds)*
		'Yates's Bar', 53 Robertson Street *(Private)*
	CP	The Stade
Ore		Ore Village, Fairlight Road
	CP	Friary Gardeners, Ore Place Farm *(Private)*
St Leonards		Marina, Lower Promenade
		Warrior Square
		St Leonards Warrior Square Station *(SouthEastern)*
		'Royal Hotel', St Johns Road *(Private)*

Horsham

Amberley		Chalk Pits (Daytime)
		Houghton Bridge Tea Garden (Daytime)
Billingshurst		Mill Lane Car Park
Bramber		The Street Car Park
Broadbridge Heath	CP	Broadbridge Heath Leisure Centre *(Private)*
Dial Post		Honeybridge Caravan Park *(Private)*
Henfield		High Street Car Park
Horsham		North Parade Boxing Club (Club hrs)
		Piries Place Car Park
		The Forum, Lower Tandridge Way (Daytime)
		Swan Walk Shopping Centre *(Private)*
		'Lynd Cross', Springfield Road *(JDW)*
		'Olive Tree', Bishopric *(Private)*
Southwater		Southwater Country Park
		Southwater Library (Library hrs) *(W Sussex CC)*
Steyning		High Street Car Park
		Steyning Centre
Washington		Village Hall

Lewes

Ditchling		Village Hall Car Park
Glynde		Recreation Ground

Lewes	Greyfriars Court Road
	Market Lane
	Southover Grange Gardens (8.00-Dusk)
	Western Road
	'The Dorset', 22 Malling Street *(Harveys)*
Newhaven	Fort Road
	Lower Place
	Newhaven Fort
Peacehaven	Meridian Centre (9.00-17.00)
	Peacehaven Leisure Centre
	Roderick Avenue
Ringmer	Village Hall
Seaford	Martello Tower
	Place Lane
	Salts Recreation Ground
	The Buckle

Maidstone

Allington	Mid Kent Shopping Centre
Aylesford	Cobtree Manor Park, Ranger Station
Headcorn	Headcorn Station, Platform 2 *(SouthEastern)*
Maidstone	Brenchley Gardens (M+F) (Daytime)
	Clare Park, Tonbridge Road (Park hrs)
	Fairmeadow (Easter-August)
	Lockmeadow Market Centre (7.00-16.30)
	Mote Park (2) (Park hrs)
	Penenden Heath Road
	South Park (7.00-18.00)
	Maidstone East Station, Platform 1 *(SouthEastern)*
	Fremlin Walk, Earl Street *(Private)*
	Royal Star Arcade *(Private)*
	The Mall Maidstone, by Bus Station *(Private)*
	'Babylon', 15-17 King Street *(Private)*
	'Caffe Nero', King Street *(Caffe Nero)*
	'Chicago Rock Café', High Street *(Private)*
	'Liquid', Lockmeadow Centre *(Private)*
	'Muggleton Inn', High Street *(JDW)*
	'Nandos', 29 Earl Street *(Nandos)*

'Society Rooms', Week Street *(JDW)*
Gala Bingo, Lower Stone Street *(Gala)*
Maidstone Bowl, King Street *(AMF)*
CP Maidstone YMCA, Melrose Close *(YMCA)*
CP Maidstone Gateway, Civic Centre

Staplehurst   Staplehurst Station, Platform 1 *(SouthEastern)*

Medway

Chatham	Capstone Farm Country Park
	Luton Recreation Ground, Capstone Road (8.00-18.00)
	Chatham Station, Platform 2 *(SouthEastern)*
	Pentagon, Ground Level *(Private)*
	'Nandos', Dickens World, Leviathan Way *(Nandos)*
	'Old Ash Tree', 136 Rainham Road *(Spirit)*
	Gala Bingo, High Street *(Gala)*
Cliffe	The Buttway (8.00-18.00)
Gillingham	Canterbury Street (M+F) (8.00-18.00)
	Riverside Country Park
	Sappers Walk, High Street
	Strand, Pier Road (8.00-18.00, later in summer)
	Gillingham Station, Platforms 1/2 & 3 *(SouthEastern)*
	Priestfield Stadium (7) *(Gillingham FC)*
CP	Medway Park Leisure Centre *(Private)*
Hempstead	Hempstead Valley Centre (2) *(Private)*
Hoo	Stoke Road
Lower Upnor	The Waterfront
Parkwood	Parkwood Green (M+F) (8.00-18.00)
Rainham	Shopping Precinct, Longley Road (8.00-18.00)
	Rainham Station, Platform 1 *(SouthEastern)*
Rainham M2	Medway Services, M2 J4-5 *(Moto)*
Rochester	Acorn Wharf Coach Park
	Castle Gardens (8.00-18.00, later in summer)
	Northgate (8.00-18.00, later in summer)
	'Golden Lion', High Street *(JDW)*
CP	Rochester Community Hub, Eastgate High St
Strood	Newark Yard (8.00-18.00)
	'McDonalds', Commercial Road *(McDonalds)*

	Gala Bingo, Chariot Way *(Gala)*
Twydall Green	Shopping Centre (M+F) (8.00-18.00)
Walderslade	'Sherwood Oak', Robin Hood Lane *(Spirit)*

Mid Sussex

Burgess Hill	Janes Lane Recreation Ground Pavilion
	St Johns Park Pavilion, Park Road
	The Martlets Shopping Centre, by Library
Copthorne	'Hedgehog', Effingham Road *(Marstons)*
Cuckfield	Cuckfield Recreation Ground (April-September)
	Broad Street Car Park *(Parish Council)*
Devils Dyke	by Devils Dyke Hotel *(Private)*
East Grinstead	Cantelupe Road
	King Street Car Park
	Mount Noddy Recreation Ground
	Norton House
	'Caffe Nero', High Street *(Caffe Nero)*
	'Old Mill', Dunnings Road *(Harveys)*
	'Ounce & Ivy Bush', The Atrium *(JDW)*
Handcross	'Red Lion', High Street *(Private)*
Hassocks	Adastra Park, Keymer Road
Haywards Heath	Orchards Shopping Centre Car Park
	Victoria Park, South Road (F)
	'The Heath', 47 Sussex Road *(Harveys)*
Lindfield	Denmans Lane Car Park *(Parish Council)*

Mole Valley

Ashtead	Memorial Car Park, off High Street
Bookham	Lower Shott Car Park, off A246
Box Hill	A24 Car Park, opp Burford Bridge Hotel *(Surrey CC)*
Dorking	St Martins Walk, Church Square *(Private)*
Leatherhead	Swan Shopping Centre
	Leatherhead Station *(Southern)*
	'Edmund Tylney', High Street *(JDW)*
	'Penny Black', North Street *(Youngs)*

Reigate & Banstead

Banstead	High Street Car Park (8.00-19.00) Lady Neville Recreation Park, Avenue Road (8.00-19.00) 'The Woolpack', High Street *(Private)*
Earlswood	Earlswood Lakes, Woodhatch Road (7.30-17.00)
Horley	Consort Way 'Jack Fairman', Victoria Road *(JDW)*
Merstham	Aldersted Heath Caravan Site *(Caravan Club)*
Redhill	Station Road, by McDonalds Redhill Station, Platform 3 *(Southern)* 'The Sun', London Road *(JDW)*
Reigate	Bell Street, by supermarket (8.00-19.00)
Walton-on-the-Hill	'The Chequers', Chequers Road *(Youngs)*

Rother

Battle	Market Square, by Supermarket Mount Street Car Park Normanhurst Court Caravan Site *(Caravan Club)*
Bexhill	Devonshire Square East Parade Egerton Park Little Common Roundabout Manor Barn, by Car Park Marina, Channel View East

---

Visit our online shop

For products and books that
open doors to independent living.

www.disabilityrightsuk.org

	Normans Bay (Easter-October)
	Polegrove Grandstand
	Sidley
	West Parade
Burwash	Car Park
Camber	Central Car Park (Easter-October)
	West Car Park (Easter-October)
Iden	Village Hall *(Hall Committee)*
Pett	Pett Level Car Park
	Fairlight Wood Caravan Park *(Caravan Club)*
Robertsbridge	Car Park
Rye	Gun Gardens
	Lucknow Place
	Station Approach, Crownfield
	The Strand
Sedlescombe	Car Park
Winchelsea	Winchelsea Beach
	Winchelsea Town

Doing IT Differently

Information to help everyone regardless of disability, take advantage of information technology (IT) and computers. Includes advice on how to choose and use a computer, and how to adapt it to suit your needs.

Available to order from our online shop
www.disabilityrightsuk.org

For more information on public facilities, why not telephone for more details before you travel?

Please telephone for all enquiries:

Rother
District Council

01424 787 000

Runnymead

Chertsey	off Guildford Street

Sevenoaks

Edenbridge	Market Yard Car Park *(Town Council)*
Farningham	'Pied Bull', High Street *(Private)*
Ide Hill	Wheatsheaf Hill, by Village Hall *(Parish Council)*
	'Woodman', Whitley Row *(Spirit)*
Kemsing	St Edith's Hall, High Street *(Parish Council)*
North Kirby	Westminster Field, The Street *(Parish Council)*
Otford	High Street *(Parish Council)*
Penshurst	High Street *(Parish Council)*
Riverhead	'Bullfinch' *(Private)*
Sevenoaks	Bus Station, High Street
	Lower St Johns Car Park *(Town Council)*
	The Vine House *(Town Council)*
	Sevenoaks Station, Concourse *(SouthEastern)*
	'Oak Tree', High Street *(Barracuda)*
	'Slug & Lettuce', High Street *(Private)*
	'The Sennockian', High Street *(JDW)*
Shoreham	St Andrews Wood, Rangers Lodge
	High Street *(Parish Council)*
Sundridge	'White Horse', Main Road *(Private)*
Swanley	Swanley Park, New Barn Road *(Town Council)*
Westerham	Fullers Hill *(Parish Council)*

Shepway

Cheriton	Somerset Road
Densole	Blackhorse Farm Caravan Club Site *(Caravan Club)*
Dymchurch	High Street
	Sea Wall (Summer only)
Folkestone	Bouverie Square
	Leas Cliff Hall, The Leas
	Radnor Park, Cheriton Road
	Roman Remains, East Cliff (Summer)

	Sunny Sands, Coronation Parade (Summer)
	The Stade, Folkestone Harbour
	Toll Gate, Lower Sandgate Road
	Folkestone Central Station, Booking Hall *(SouthEastern)*
	'Samuel Peto', Rendezvous Street *(JDW)*
	Folkestone Campus, Dickens Building *(K College)*
	Folkestone Campus, Martin Building *(K College)*
	Folkestone Campus, Telford Building *(K College)*
CP	Eurotunnel Passenger Terminal *(Eurotunnel)*
Greatstone	Jolly Fisherman, Coast Drive
Hawkinge	'Mayfly', Spitfire Way *(Marstons)*
Hythe	Chapel Street
	Cinque Ports, Stade Street
	Marine Parade, Saltwood Gardens
	Prospect Road
Lydd	Coronation Square
Lydd-on-Sea	Lade Car Park
St Mary's Bay	High Knocke Car Park (Summer only)
West Hythe	Daleacres Caravan Club Site *(Caravan Club)*

Spelthorne

Ashford	Church Road, by MSCP
Laleham	Laleham Park, Pavilion Kiosk
Shepperton	Shepperton Lock, Towpath
Staines	Memorial Gardens, opp. Debenhams
	Staines Station *(SW Trains)*
	Elmsleigh Shopping Centre (2) *(Private)*
	'Blue Anchor', High Street *(Private)*
	'Nandos', Two Rivers Retail Park *(Nandos)*
	'Que Pasa', Tillys Lane *(Marstons)*
	'The George', High Street *(JDW)*
Sunbury-on-Thames	Walled Garden
	Sunbury Cross Shopping Centre *(Private)*

Surrey Heath

| **Bagshot** | Park Street |
| **Camberley** | Knoll Road, by MSCP, behind Theatre |

	Martindale Avenue, Heatherside
	Watchetts Park (Daytime)
	The Mall Main Square *(Private)*
	'Claude du Vall', High Street *(JDW)*
	'Que Pasa', High Street *(Marstons)*
	'Yates's Bar', High Street *(Private)*
	BowlPlex, The Atrium *(Bowlplex)*
Chobham	Car Park, off High Street
Frimley	Church Road
	Frimley Green Recreation Ground (Daytime)
Lightwater	Lightwater Country Park (Dawn-dusk)

Swale

Boughton	The Street/School Lane
Faversham	Central Car Park
	Faversham Station, Platform 1/2 *(SouthEastern)*
	'Leading Light', Preston Street *(JDW)*
Leysdown-on-Sea	The Grove (Summer) (Daytime)
	The Spinney, Leysdown Road
Minster	The White House, The Broadway
Queenborough	Queenborough Park
Sheerness	Rose Street
	Tesco Store, Bridge Road *(Tesco)*
CP	Sheerness Gateway, High Street
Sittingbourne	Central Avenue
	The Forum
	Sittingbourne Station, front of Station *(SouthEastern)*
	'The Summoner', Bell Shopping Centre *(JDW)*

Tandridge

Bletchingley	'Plough', 2 High Street *(Chef & Brewer)*
Burstow	'Shipley Bridge', Antlands Lane *(Chef & Brewer)*
Caterham	Westway/Chaldon Road
	'Ladybird', Coulsdon Road *(Marstons)*
	'The Pilgrim', 32 Godstone Road *(Barracuda)*
Dormansland	Dormans High Street

Godstone	Godstone Green
	Godstone Hill, A22 Southbound
Lingfield	Godstone Road/Jenny Lane
Oxted	A25 Westbound, Nags Hall Lay-by
	Ellice Road Car Park
	Station Road West
	Oxted Station *(Southern)*
	'Oxted Inn', Station Road West *(JDW)*
Warlingham	Leas Road/Westhall Road
Whyteleafe	Recreation Ground, Hillbury Road
	Station Road Car Park

Thanet

Birchington	Alpha Road Car Park (Daytime)
	Minnis Bay Car Park (Daytime)
Broadstairs	Albion Street Car Park (Summer only) (Daytime)
	Broadstairs Harbour (Daytime)
	Clock Tower, Victoria Promenade (Daytime)
	Croft's Place Car Park (Daytime)
	Hopeville Avenue, St Peters (Daytime)
	Joss Bay (Easter-September) (Daytime)
	Broadstairs Station, Platform 1 *(SouthEastern)*
	'Nandos', Westwood Cross *(Nandos)*
Cliftonville	'Wheatsheaf', Northdown Park Road *(Greene King)*
Kingsgate	'Captain Digby', Whiteness Road *(Private)*
Margate	Buenos Ayres, Marine Terrace (Daytime)

Is pleased to support
Disability Rights UK

Become a member
Help us realise our vision and
make your voice count.

www.disabilityrightsuk.org

College Walk (Daytime)
Harbour Arm (Daytime)
Harold Road (Daytime)
CP Thanet Gateway, Cecil Street (Office hrs)
The Centre Shopping Mall (Daytime)
The Oval Bandstand (Events only)
West Bay Promenade (Daytime)
Margate Station, Platform 1 *(SouthEastern)*
'Mcdonalds',95 High Street *(McDonalds)*
'Yates's Bar', Cecil Square *(Private)*
Margate Magistrates Court *(Courts Service)*

Ramsgate	Bathing Station (Easter-Sepember) (Daytime)
	Cavendish Street (Daytime)
	East Pier Yard (Daytime)
	King George VI Memorial Park (Park hrs)
	Screaming Alley, off Grange Road (Daytime)
	Ramsgate Station, Concourse *(SouthEastern)*
	'Hotel de Ville', 45 Grange Road *(Private)*
	'McDonalds', 13 King Street *(McDonalds)*
	'Sovereign', 32 Harbour Street *(Private)*
Westgate	St Mildred's Bay (Daytime)
	Station Road (Daytime)

Tonbridge & Malling

Borough Green	High Street, Village Hall
East Peckham	The Pound, Snoll Hatch Road
Hadlow	Court Lane, A26 junction
	'Two Brewers', Maidstone Road *(Harveys)*
Larkfield	Leybourne Lakes Country Park (Park hrs)
	Martin Square
Snodland	Rocfort Road, Car Park
Tonbridge	Angel Centre
	Castle Street
	Haysden Country Park (Park hrs)
	Priory Road
	Race Course Sportsground (Park hrs)
	CP Tonbridge Gateway, Castle Street (Office hrs)
	Tonbridge Station, Platform 3 *(SouthEastern)*

	'Humphrey Bean', High Street *(JDW)*
	'Vauxhall Inn', Vauxhall Lane *(Spirit)*
West Malling	King Street, off High Street
	West Malling Station, Platform 1 *(SouthEastern)*
Wrotham	High Street

Tunbridge Wells

Cranbrook	Crane Lane
	'White Horse', Carriers Road *(Greene King)*
Goudhurst	Balcombes Hill Car Park
	Bedgebury National Pinetum *(Forestry Commission)*
Hawkhurst	Ockley Road
Paddock Wood	Commercial Road Car Park East
Sissinghurst	The Street
Southborough	London Road, by Silk Restaurant
	Pennington Grounds, Pennington Road
Tunbridge Wells	Calverley Park (7.00-Dusk)
	Camden Centre, Market Square (Centre hrs)
	Crescent Rd Car Park (7.00-20.00, shorter on Sunday)
	Dunorian Park (7.00-Dusk)
	Grosvenor Recreation Ground (7.00-dusk)
	Hawkenbury Recreation Ground (7.00-dusk)
	Kent & Sussex Cemetery, Benhall Mill Rd (Cemetery hrs)
	St Johns Recreation Ground Pavilion (7.00-dusk)
CP	Tunbridge Wells Gateway, Grosvenor Rd (Office hrs)
	Union House, nr. Pantiles (7.00-18.00)
	Wellington Rocks, The Common
	Tunbridge Wells Station, Platform 1 *(SouthEastern)*
	Corn Exchange, Sussex Mews, Pantiles *(Private)*
	Royal Victoria Place, nr. Shopmobility *(Private)*
	Sainsbury Supermarket, Linden Park Road *(J Sainsbury)*
	'Beau Nash', Mount Ephraim *(Private)*
	'Gourmet Burger Kitchen', Mount Pleasant Road *(Private)*
	'Opera House', Mount Pleasant Road *(JDW)*
	'Pitcher & Piano', 35 Church Road *(Marstons)*
	'Robin Hood', Sandhurst Road *(Private)*
	'Wagamama', Mount Pleasant Road *(Private)*

Waverley

Cranleigh	Cricket Green, Guildford Road *(Parish Council)* Village Way Car Park *(Parish Council)*
Farncombe	Broadwater Park, Summers Road North Street
Farnham	Central Car Park, Victoria Road *(Town Council)* Farnham Station, Platform 1 *(SW Trains)* 'Slug & Lettuce', 9 East Street *(Private)*
Frensham	Frensham Great Pond Visitor Centre, Bacon Lane
Godalming	Crown Court, High Street Winkworth Arboretum *(National Trust)* 'Jack Phillips', High Street *(JDW)* 'Slug & Lettuce', 54 High Street *(Private)*
Haslemere	High Street Car Park Haslemere Station *(SW Trains)* 'Swan Inn', High Street *(JDW)*
Witley	Witley Common Centre *(National Trust)*

Wealden

Alfriston	The Dene Car Park The Willows Car Park
Birling Gap	Car Park *(National Trust)*
Crowborough	Council Offices (Office hrs)
East Hoathly	'Foresters Arms', South Street *(Harveys)*

Hailsham	Council Offices (Office hrs)
	St Marys Walk *(Private)*
Heathfield	Station Road Car Park
Isfield	'Halfway House', Rose Hill *(Harveys)*
Mayfield	South Street Car Park
Pevensey	Pevensey Castle Car Park
Pevensey Bay	Sea Road (8.00-18.00)
Polegate	High Street
Stone Cross	Glyndley Garden Centre *(Private)*
Uckfield	Uckfield Bus Station *(Private)*
	Tesco Store, Bell Farm Road *(Tesco)*
Wadhurst	Commemoration Hall, High Street (8.00-18.00)
Willingdon	The Triangle, A22

Woking

Byfleet	Recreation Ground, Stream Close
Horsell	Wheatsheaf Common, Chobham Road
Knaphill	High Street
Mayford	Mayford Village Hall
Sheerwater	Recreation Ground, Blackmore Crescent
West Byfleet	Lavender Road
	West Byfleet Station *(SW Trains)*
Woking	Addison Road
	Heathside Car Park (Mon-Sat, daytime)
	Victoria Way MSCP
	Woking Station, Platforms 1 & 4/5 *(SW Trains)*
	'Café Giardino', Wolsey Walk *(Private)*
	'Herbert Wells', Chertsey Road *(JDW)*
	'O'Neills', Crown Square *(M&B)*
	'Rat & Parrot', Chertsey Road *(Private)*
	'RSVP', Chertsey Road *(Spirit)*
	'Station', Chettsey Road *(Spirit)*
	'Wheatsheaf Hotel', Chobham Road *(Private)*
	'Yates's Bar', Chobham Road *(Private)*
	Gala Bingo, Church Street East *(Gala)*

Worthing

Findon	Findon Road, nr Library (Daytime)
Highdown	Highdown Gardens, A259 (Daytime)
West Worthing	George V Avenue, by Post Office (Mon-Sat, daytime)
Worthing	Brooklands, Western Road Car Park (Daytime)
	Pier (Summer) (Daytime)
	Promenade, by Lido (Daytime)
	Promenade, opp. Dome (Daytime)
	Sea Lane Car Park (Daytime)
	Victoria Park (Daytime)
	Buckingham Road MSCP *(NCP)*
	High Street MSCP, Guildbourne Centre *(NCP)*
	Worthing Station, Platform 3 *(Southern)*
	'Caffe Nero', South Street *(Caffe Nero)*
	'Que Pasa', Chapel Road *(Marstons)*
	'Sir Timothy Shelley', Chapel Road *(JDW)*
	'Three Fishes', 56 Chapel Road *(JDW)*
	Gala Bingo, Rowlands Road *(Gala)*

SOUTHERN ENGLAND

Aylesbury Vale

Aston Clinton		'Duck Inn', London Road *(Private)*
Aylesbury		Anchor Lane Car Park (7.00-19.30)
		Friarscroft Car Park (8.30-19.30)
		Upper Hundreds Car Park (7.30-19.30)
		Vale Park (7.30-19.30)
		Aylesbury Cemetery (Cemetery hrs) *(Town Council)*
		Aylesbury Bus Station, Friars Square *(Private)*
		Aylesbury Station, Platform 3 *(Chiltern Trains)*
		Friars Square Shopping Centre, 3rd Floor *(Private)*
		'Chicago Rock Café', Exchange Street *(Private)*
		'Cotton Wheel', Jackson Road *(Private)*
		'Litten Tree', Kingsbury Court *(Private)*
		'New Zealand', Buckingham Road *(Private)*
		'Slug & Lettuce', Exchange Street *(Private)*
		'The Harrow', Cambridge Street *(Private)*
		'Weavers', Park Street *(Private)*
Bedgrove		'Buckinghamshire Yeoman', Cambourne Avenue *(Private)*
Buckingham		Moreton Road (7.30-22.00)
		Swan Pool & Leisure Centre *(Private)*
Stoke Mandeville		Bucks CC Sports & Social Club *(Private)*
Swanbourne		'Betsey Wynne', Mursley Road *(Private)*
Wendover		Library Car Park (7.30-19.30)
		Ellesborough Golf Club, Butlers Cross *(Private)*
Winslow		Greyhound Lane, Car Park (8.00-17.00)
Worminghall	CP	Thornley Hall Centre *(Private)*

Basingstoke & Deane

Basingstoke		Castons Yard, off New Road
		New Road, by Red Lion Lane
		War Memorial Park, by Pavilion (Park hrs)
		Worting Road, Cemetery
	CP	Basingstoke Discovery Centre (Library hrs) *(Hants CC)*
		Basingstoke Station, Platforms 1 & 2 *(SW Trains)*
		Festival Place, Car Park A *(Private)*

NATIONAL KEY SCHEME GUIDE 2013

	Festival Place, Library Square *(Private)*
	Festival Place, Wesley Walk *(Private)*
CP	The Malls Shopping Centre *(Private)*
	Debenhams Store, Festival Place *(Debenhams)*
	'Bakers', Winchester Street *(Private)*
	'Burger King', Festival Place *(Private)*
	'Lloyds Bar', Festival Place *(JDW)*
	'Maidenhead Inn', Winchester Street *(JDW)*
	'Nandos', Festival Place *(Nandos)*
	'Wagamama', Festival Place *(Private)*
	'Yates's Bar', London Street *(Private)*
	Gala Bingo, Basingstoke Leisure Park *(Gala)*
Eastrop	Eastrop Park
Kempshott	Old Down Close
	Stratton Park
Kingsclere	Swan Street
Overton	Winchester Street, Community Car Park
St Mary Bourne	Bourne Meadow, opp. Village Hall
Tadley	Mulfords Hill
Whitchurch	Bell Street, Car Park

Bracknell Forest

Ascot	'The Foresters', London Road *(Beefeater)*
Bracknell	Birch Hill Shopping Parade
	Brooke House, High Street
	Bus Station
	Hedgehog Park, Birch Hill (Park hrs)
	High Street MSCP, Level 4 (Car Park hrs)
	Jocks Lane Park, Binfield Road (Café hrs)
CP	Look Out Discovery Centre (Centre hrs)
	Bracknell Station, Platform 1 *(SW Trains)*
	Princess Square Shopping Centre *(Private)*
	'Admiral Cunningham', Priestwood Court Road *(Private)*
	'Downshire Arms', Downshire Way *(Beefeater)*
	'Old Manor', Church Road *(JDW)*
	'Woodcutters', Bere Road *(Private)*
	Hollywood Bowl *(Private)*
	Odeon Cinema, The Point *(Odeon)*

Crowthorne		Napier Road
Sandhurst		Sandhurst Memorial Park, Yorktown Road (Park hrs)
		'Wellington Arms', Yorktown Road *(Private)*
Warfield		'Shepherds House', Moss End *(Spirit)*

Cherwell

Ardley M40	CP	Cherwell Valley Services M40 J10 *(Moto)*
Banbury		Bridge Street, by Town Hall
		Bus Station
		Horsefair
		Southam Road Cemetery **(Daytime)** *(Town Council)*
		Banbury Station, upper level *(Chiltern Trains)*
		Debenhams Store, Castle Quay *(Debenhams)*
		'Fleur-de-Lis', Broad Street *(JDW)*
		'Que Pasa', High Street *(Marstons)*
		'The Exchange', High Street *(JDW)*
		'Yates's Bar', Parsons Street *(Private)*
Bicester		Victoria Road, Claremont Car Park
		'Penny Black', Sheep Street *(JDW)*
		'Yates's', Sheep Street *(Private)*
Kidlington		Watts Way Car Park, off High Street

Chiltern

Amersham on the Hill	Woodside Close, off Sycamore Road (Daytime)
Chalfont St Giles	High Street (Daytime)
Chalfont St Peter	High Street
Chesham	Star Yard Car Park (Daytime)
	Lowndes Park (Park hrs) *(Town Council)*
Great Missenden	Link Road (Daytime)
Little Chalfont	Snells Wood Car Park (Daytime)
Old Amersham	Dovecote Meadow, Car Park (Daytime)
Prestwood	High Street, Car Park (Daytime)

East Hampshire

Alton	CP	Lady Place Car Park
		Turk Street Car Park
		Alton Community Centre *(Private)*

	Alton Station *(SW Trains)*
	'Wey Bridge', High Street *(Barracuda)*
	Alton Sports Centre, changing rooms *(DC Leisure)*
Blendworth	Blendworth Lane Car Park
Bordon	Forest Shopping Centre *(Private)*
Clanfield	'Rising Sun', North Lane *(Private)*
East Meon	'Izaak Walton, High Street *(Private)*
Grayshott	Headley Road Car Park
Holybourne	'White Hart', London Road *(Private)*
Liphook	Parish Council Office, Midhurst Road *(Parish Council)*
Liss	Rake Road, behind Community Centre
	Lower Mead Shops *(Private)*
Petersfield	behind Rams Walk
	Central Car Park
	St Peters Road
	Petersfield Station, Platform 2 *(SW Trains)*
	Rams Walk *(Private)*
Rowlands Castle	'Robin Hood', The Green *(Private)*
Selborne	Car Park, behind Selborne Arms
West Meon	'West Meon'. A32/A273 *(Marstons)*
Whitehill	A325, by Guadaloupe Car Park

Eastleigh

Bishopstoke	Bishopstoke Road, Playing Fields
Chandlers Ford	The Precinct, Winchester Road
	Chandlers Ford Station, Booking Hall *(SW Trains)*
Eastleigh	Bus Station Concourse
	Lakeside Park
	Eastleigh Station, Booking Hall *(SW Trains)*
	'Chamberlayne', 105 High Street *(Marstons)*
	'Nandos', Swan Centre *(Nandos)*
	'Wagon Works', Southampton Road *(JDW)*
	AMF Bowl, Swan Centre *(AMF)*
Hamble	Foreshore Car Park *(Parish Council)*
Hedge End	Lower Northam Road *(Town Council)*

Netley	Abbey Hall, Victoria Road (Hall hrs) *(Parish Council)*
	Royal Victoria Country Park, Tea Rooms *(Hants CC)*
Southampton Airport	Southampton Airport Station, Booking Hall *(SW Trains)*
West End	Itchen Valley Country Park
	Chapel Road *(Parish Council)*

Fareham

Fareham	Fareham Cemetery, Wickham Road (Cemetery hrs)
	Trinity Street
	Fareham Station *(SW Trains)*
	Fareham Shopping Centre, by Shopmobility *(Private)*
	Fareham Shopping Centre, Thackery Mall *(Private)*
	'Crown Inn', West Street *(JDW)*
	'Lord Arthur Lee', West Street *(JDW)*
	Fareham Leisure Centre, changing area *(Private)*
Hill Head	Cliff Road, nr. Sailing Club
	Meon Shore
	Monks Hill Car Park
	Salterns Lane Car Park
Locksheath	Lockswood Centre
Park Gate	Middle Road, by shops
Portchester	Castle Street Car Park
	Waterside Lane, Portchester Castle Car Park
Sarisbury Green	Holly Hill Woodland Park
Stubbington	Stubbington Green
Titchfield	Barry's Meadow, Southampton Hill
Warsash	Passage Lane

Gosport

Gosport	Falkland Gardens
	Jamaica Place
	Ordinance Road
	'The Star', High Street *(JDW)*
	St Vincent Leisure Centre, Mill Lane *(College)*
Lee-on-Solent	Marine Parade Central, Car Park
	Marine Parade East
Stokes Bay	Central

Gilkicker
No. 2 Battery

Hart

Eversley Cross	'Frog & Wicket' *(Private)*
Fleet	Fleet Station, Platform 2 *(SW Trains)* Hart Shopping Centre *(Private)* 'Prince Arthur', Fleet Road *(JDW)*
Hartley Wintney	Car Park, off High Street *(Parish Council)*
Odiham	'Waterwitch', Colthill *(Private)*

Havant

Bedhampton	Bidbury Mead Recreation Ground
Cowplain	Mission Lane Car Park Recreation Ground, Padnell Avenue
Emsworth	Recreation Ground, Horndean Road South Street Car Park
Havant	Havant Park, Havant Parade Staunton Country Park *(Hants CC)* Havant Bus Station, Elm Lane *(Private)* Havant Station, Platform 1 *(SW Trains)* Meridian Centre, nr. Library *(Private)* 'Parchment Makers', Park Road East *(JDW)*
Hayling Island	Bosmere Road (Summer only) Central Beachlands Chichester Avenue Eastoke Corner Elm Grove Ferry Point Nab Car Park Station Road West Beachlands Car Park
Langstone	Ship Inn
Leigh Park	Greywell Car Park
Purbrook	Purbrook Heath Recreation Ground
Warblington	Warblington Cemetery, Church Lane (Cemetery hrs)
Waterlooville	Swiss Road

Waterlooville Cemetery, Hulbert Road (Cemetery hrs)
'Woodpecker', 179 London Road *(Spirit)*

Isle of Wight

Bembridge	Harold Lewis Day Centre, High Street *(Parish Council)* Whitecliff Bay Holiday Park (2) *(Private)*
Brading	High Street, Car Park
Brighstone	Warnes Lane Car Park *(Parish Council)*
Carisbrooke	High Street Car Park
Colwell	Colwell Chine Road Car Park
Compton Bay	Military Road Car Park (April-October)
Cowes, East	Osborne Road, by Town Hall
Cowes, West	Cross Street, off High Street Medina Road Mornington Road, opp. Princes Green Park Road, Recreation Ground Cowes Parade *(Trustees)*
Freshwater	Moa Place
Godshill	Car Park, High Street
Gurnard	Shore Road
Lake	Lake Cliff Gardens (April-October) *(Parish Council)* New Road/High Street *(Parish Council)*
Newport	Church Litten, South Street Car Park Post Office Lane

	Sea Close Park
	'William Coppin', Coppins Bridge *(JDW)*
CP	County Hall
CP	Riverside Centre, The Quay
Ryde	Appley Park, Garden Walk
	Eastern Esplanade
	Lind Street, by Town Hall
	Puckpool Park
	St Johns Road
	Western Esplanade
	Ryde Esplanade Station *(SW Trains)*
	Ryde Pier Head Station *(SW Trains)*
	'S Fowler & Co', Union Street *(JDW)*
Sandown	Battery Gardens
	Eastern Gardens
	Pier Street (M+F)
	St John's Road Car Park
Seaview	Ropewalk *(Private)*
Shanklin	Falcon Cross Road
	Skew Bridge, Lake Cliff Gardens
	The Esplanade (Daytime)
	Tower Cottage Gardens
	Shanklin Station, Platform *(SW Trains)*
St Helens	The Duver (May-September)
	St Helens Green *(Parish Council)*
Ventnor	Botanic Gardens
	Eastern Esplanade (M+F) (Daytime)
	Marlborough Road (M+F) (Daytime)
	Pound Lane
Wootton	Car Park, off Brannon Way *(Parish Council)*
Yarmouth	Bridge Road
	High Street, opp. Common
Yaverland	Culver Parade Car Park

Milton Keynes

Bletchley	Albert Street *(Parish Council)*
	Bletchley Station, Booking Hall *(London Midland)*
	Agora Shopping Centre *(Private)*
	Bletchley Leisure Centre *(Private)*
Caldecotte	'Caldecotte Arms', Bletchern Way *(Spirit)*
Milton Keynes Central	Coachway Milton Keynes, J14 M1 *(National Express)*
	Milton Keynes Station, Platform 3 *(London Midland)*
CP	The Centre:MK *(Private)*
	John Lewis Store *(John Lewis)*
	'All Bar One', Midsummer Boulevard *(Private)*
	'City Limits', Xscape Village *(Spirit)*
	'Moon Under Water', Avebury Boulevard *(JDW)*
	'Nandos', Queens Court *(Nandos)*
	'Nandos', The Hub *(Nandos)*
	'Nandos', Xscape *(Nandos)*
	'Rat & Parrot', Theatre Quarter *(Spirit)*
	'Revolution', Xcape Complex *(Private)*
	'Secklow Hundred', Midsomer Boulevard *(JDW)*
	'Slug & Lettuce', Savoy Crescent *(Private)*
	'Slug & Lettuce', Theatre District *(Private)*
	'Wetherspoons', Bouverie Square *(JDW)*
	Cineworld, Xscape *(Private)*
	City Limits Arcade, Xscape *(Private)*
	Xscape, Marlborough Gate *(Private)*
Newport Pagnell	Market Hill *(Town Council)*
	Lovat Hall, Silver Street *(Baptist Church)*
Olney	Market Square *(Town Council)*
Purbeck	Stantonbury Campus Leisure Centre *(Private)*
Shenley	'Burnt Oak', Shenley Brook End *(Marstons)*
Stony Stratford	Silver Street *(Town Council)*
	'The Crown', Market Square *(Private)*
Woburn Sands	High Street *(Parish Council)*
Wolverton	Wolverton Station *(London Midland)*
Woughton on the Green	'Ye Olde Swan', Newport Road *(Spirit)*

New Forest

Barton-on-Sea	Barton Court Avenue/Marine Drive
Beaulieu	Car Park, Palace Lane
Blackfield	Lepe Country Park *(Hants CC)*
Bransgore	Betsy Lane Car Park
	New Forest Caravan Club Site *(Caravan Club)*
Brockenhurst	Fibbards Road Car Park
	Brockenhurst Station *(SW Trains)*
	Black Knowl Caravan Club Site *(Caravan Club)*
Burley	Car Park, Chapel Lane
Calshot	Calshot Spit
Dibden	Applemore Health & Leisure, Claypits Lane (Centre hrs)
	Clayfields Community Hall (Hall hrs) *(Parish Council)*
Fawley	Car Park, School Road
Fordingbridge	Roundhill Car Park
	Sandy Balls Holiday Park *(Private)*
Hythe	Hythe Pier, Prospect Place
Keyhaven	Nature Reserve Car Park
Lymington	Bath Road Car Park
	New Street
	Powlett Road, M&S Car Park
	Quay Road
	'Six Bells', 47 St Thomas Street *(JDW)*
Lyndhurst	Car Park, High Street (2)
Milford-on-Sea	Hordle Cliff Car Park
	Hurst Road, Car Park
	Sea Road, Car Park
New Milton	Recreation Ground, Old Milton Road
	Station Road Car Park
Ringwood	Ringwood Furlong Car Park
Totton	Cemetery Car Park, Eling Hill
	Eling Recreation Ground, Bartram Road
	Library Road
	Winsor Road

Oxford

Cowley	Barns Road
	'William Morris', Cowley *(JDW)*
Oxford	Bury Knowle Park, Headington
	Castle Street (Daytime)
	Cowley Road
	Diamond Place, off Banbury Road, Summerstown
	Gloucester Green Bus Station
	Hinksey Park, Abingdon Road
	Market Street
	Oxpens Coach Park
	Speedwell Street (March-October)
	St Clements Car Park
	Westgate Car Park, Level 4
	Botanic Garden, Rose Lane *(University)*
	Oxford Station, Concourse *(Gt Western)*
	Debenhams Store, Magdalen Street *(Debenhams)*
	'All Bar One', Oxford Castle *(Private)*
	'Four Candles', George Street *(JDW)*
	'Jongleurs', Hythe Bridge Road *(Private)*
	'Nandos', Cowley Road *(Nandos)*
	'Swan & Castle', Castle Street *(JDW)*
	'The Victoria', 90 Walton Street *(Private)*
	'Yates's Bar', George Street *(Private)*
	Students Union, Headington Campus *(OBU)*
CP	Shopmobility, Westgate Car Park *(Shopmobility)*

Portsmouth

Cosham	Wootton Street
	'First Post', High Street *(JDW)*
Fratton	Clarkes Road (6.45-18.30)
	Fratton Station *(SW Trains)*
	'John Jacques', Fratton Road *(JDW)*
	'KFC', Fratton Way *(KFC)*
Hilsea	Hilsea Lido
	'McDonalds', Ocean Retail Park *(McDonalds)*
North End	Derby Road
	'Sir John Baker', London Road *(JDW)*
	Mountbatten Centre, changing area *(Private)*

Old Portsmouth	Point Battery
	White Hart Road
Paulsgrove	Marsden Road (Mon-Sat, 6.30-18.00)
Port Solent	'Sir Alec Rose', The Boardwalk *(JDW)*
Portsmouth City Centre	Bransbury Park (6.30-19.30)
	Central Library, Guildhall Square (2) (Library hrs)
	College Park
	Guildhall Square (Daytime)
	Milton Park (6.30-19.15)
	Paradise Street
	Tangiers Road
	The Hard Interchange
	Portsmouth & Southsea Station, Low Level *(SW Trains)*
	Portsmouth Harbour Station, Platform 1 *(SW Trains)*
	Morrisons Store, Anchorage Road *(Morrisons)*
	'All Bar One', Gunwharf Quays *(Private)*
	'Bar 38', Gunwharf Quays *(Private)*
	'Isambard Kingdom Brunel', Guildhall Walk *(JDW)*
	'Jongleurs', Gunwharf Quays *(Private)*
	'KFC', 250 Commercial Road *(KFC)*
	'La Tasca', Gunwharf Quays *(Private)*
	'Nandos', Gunwharf Quays *(Nandos)*
	Tiger Tiger', Gunwharf Quays *(Private)*
	'Trafalgar', Edinburgh Road *(JDW)*
	'Wagamama', Gunwharf Quay *(Private)*
	'White Swan', Guildhall Walk *(JDW)*
	'Yates's Bar', Guildhall Walk *(Private)*
Southsea Central	Albert Road
	Highland Road (6.30-17.00)
	Richmond Place
CP	Southsea Library, Palmerston Road (Library hrs)
	Debenhams Store, Palmerston Road *(Debenhams)*
	'Slug & Lettuce', 80 Palmerston Road *(Private)*
Southsea Seafront	Canoe Lake, St Helens Parade
	Castlefield (April-September)
	Clarence Pier
	D-Day Museum Car Park (9.00-17.00)
	Eastney Esplanade
	South Parade Kiosk

St Georges Road
Pyramids Gym, Clarence Esplanade *(Private)*

Reading

Burghfield M4	Reading East Services, M4 Juncts 11-12 *(Moto)*
Caversham	St Martins Precinct, behind Waitrose
	'Baron Cadogan', Prospect Street *(JDW)*
Reading	Broad Street Mall
	Cemetery Junction
	Cintra Park Pavilion
	Queens Road Car Park
	Thames Side Promenade, Richfield Avenue
	Town Hall, Blagrave Street
	Reading Station, Concourse & Platform 3 *(Gt Western)*
	Debenhams Store, The Oracle *(Debenhams)*
	'All Bar One', Kings Road *(Private)*
	'Back of Beyond', Kings Road *(JDW)*
	'Bar 38', Oracle Centre *(Spirit)*
	'Cape', Friar Street *(Barracuda)*
	'Hope Tap', Friar Street *(JDW)*
	'Jongleurs', Friar Street *(Private)*
	'Monks Retreat', Friar Street *(JDW)*
	'Nandos', 30 Friar Street *(Nandos)*
	'Nandos', Riverside, The Oracle *(Nandos)*
	'Old Orleans', The Oracle *(Private)*
	'O'Neill's', Blagrave Street *(M&B)*
	'Pavlov's Dog', St Mary's Butts *(Private)*
	'Pitcher & Piano', 18 Friar Street *(Marstons)*
	'Revolution', 12 Station Road *(Private)*
	'Slug & Lettuce', The Oracle *(Private)*
	'Walkabout', Wiston Terrace *(Private)*
	'Yates's Bar', Friar Street *(Private)*
Southcote	Prospect Park, Tilehurst Road
Tilehurst	Kentwood Hill, by Whitehouse
	'The Bear', Park Lane *(Spirit)*
Whitley	Whitley Street

Rushmoor

Aldershot	Aldershot Park, Guildford Road (Park hrs)
	High Street Car Park
	Manor Park, High Street/Ash Road
	Princes Gardens , High Street
	Aldershot Bus Station, Station Road *(Private)*
	Aldershot Station, Platform 1 *(SW Trains)*
	Wellington Shopping Centre *(Private)*
	'KFC', 17 Union Street *(KFC)*
	'McDonalds', 23 Union Street *(McDonalds)*
Farnborough	King George V Playing Fields, Car Patk
	Farnborough Main Station, Platform 2 *(SW Trains)*
	Princes Mead Shopping Centre *(Private)*
	'The Squirrel', 125 Park Road *(Private)*
	'Tilly Shilling', The Meads *(JDW)*
North Camp	High Street

Slough

Langley	Langley Station *(Gt Western)*
	Langley Campus *(East Berks College)*
Slough	Brunel Bus Station
	Station Approach
	The Grove, Slough High Street
	Slough Station, Platform 2 *(Gt Western)*
	Observatory Shopping Centre *(Private)*
	Queensmere Centre *(Private)*
	'Moon & Spoon', High Street *(JDW)*
	'Nandos', Queensmere Centre *(Nandos)*
	'Newt & Cucumber', High Street *(Private)*

South Buckinghamshire

Beaconsfield	Windsor End, Old Town *(Town Council)*
	'Revolution', Maxwell Road *(Private)*
Burnham	Jennery Lane Car Park *(Parish Council)*
Denham	Wyatts Covert Caravan Club Site *(Caravan Club)*
Farnham Common	Beaconsfield Road Car Park
	'Royal Oak', Beaconsfield Road *(Spirit)*
Iver	Iver Flowerland Garden Centre *(Private)*

South Oxfordshire

Didcot	Didcot Parkway Station, Platform 2 *(Gt Western)*
	Orchard Centre *(Private)*
Dorchester	Bridge End
Goring	Wheel Orchard Car Park, Station Road
Henley	Greys Road
	Kings Road
	Station Road
	Mill Meadows, Mill Road *(Town Council)*
	'Catherine Wheel', Hart Street *(JDW)*
	Four Oaks Caravan Club Site *(Caravan Club)*
Thame	Cattlemarket
	Market House
Wallingford	Cattlemarket Car Park
	Riverside (April-October)
	St Albans Car Park, off High Street
Watlington	Church Street *(Parish Council)*

Southampton

Bitterne		Maytree Road, Bitterne Precinct
		Bitterne Leisure Centre, changing rooms
Lordshill		Gala Bingo, Lordshill Retail Park *(Gala)*
Portswood		Westridge Road
		'Varsity', Portswood Centre *(Barracuda)*
Shirley		'Bright Water Inn', Shirley Road *(JDW)*
		'Malvern Tavern', 290 Winchester Road *(Spirit)*
	CP	Freemantle Community Centre *(Private)*
Southampton City Centre		East Park Pavilion (Daytime)
		Kingsland Square, St Mary's
		Mayflower Park
		Southampton City Art Gallery (Gallery hrs)
		Southampton Cent. Station, Platforms *(SW Trains)*
		The Mall Marlands Shopping Centre *(Private)*
	CP	West Quay Shopping Centre *(Private)*
		Debenhams Store, Queensway *(Debenhams)*
		'Admiral Sir Lucius Curtis', Ocean Village *(JDW)*
		'Giddy Bridge', London Road *(JDW)*

'Jongleurs', Bargate *(Private)*
'Que Pasa', 104 Above Bar Street *(Marstons)*
'Revolution', 28 Bedford Place *(Private)*
'Slug & Lettuce', 103 Above Bar Street *(Private)*
'Standing Order', The High Street *(JDW)*
'Varsity', 67/75 London Road *(Barracuda)*
'Yates's Bar', Above Bar Street *(Private)*
CP Eddie Read Swimming Complex *(Private)*

Weston
Mayfield Park
Weston Shore, Car Park
Chamberlayne Leisure Centre, Weston Lane

Woolston
Portsmouth Road, by toll booths

Test Valley

Andover
Borden Gate Car Park (Daytime)
Chantry Centre MSCP
George Yard Car Park (Daytime)
Andover Station *(SW Trains)*
'John Russell Fox', High Street *(JDW)*

Ower
'Vine Inn', Romsey Road *(Spirit)*

Romsey
Bus Station Car Park, Broadwater Road

Stockbridge
High Street (8.00-18.00)

Vale of White Horse

Abingdon
Abbey Meadow (Easter-September)
Charter Car Park
Hale Meadow Car Park

Cumnor
CP 'The Vine', 11 Abingdon Road *(Private)*

Faringdon
Southampton Street Car Park

Grove
'Grove Lock' *(Fullers)*

North Hinksey
Elms Court, Chapel Way, A35

Wantage
Manor Recreation Ground
Portway Car Park

West Berkshire

Aldermaston	The Wharf (April-September) (8.00-18.00)
Hungerford	Church Street (8.00-18.00)
Kintbury	Station Road (8.00-18.00)
Newbury	Pembroke Road MSCP (8.00-18.00)
	Snelsmore Common Country Park (Daytime)
	The Wharf (8.00-18.00)
	Newbury Station, Platform *(Gt Western)*
	CP Kennet Centre *(Private)*
	Parkway Shopping Centre *(Private)*
	Weavers Walk *(Private)*
	Sainsbury's Store, Hectors Way *(Sainsbury)*
	'Lock Stock & Barrel', Northbrook Street *(Fullers)*
	CP Northcroft Leisure Centre *(Private)*
	Vue Cinema, Kennet Centre *(Private)*
Pangbourne	River Meadow (April-September) (8.00-18.00)
	Station Road (8.00-18.00)
Thatcham	Broadway (8.00-18.00)
	The Kingsland Centre *(Private)*

Working for West Berkshire

West Berkshire Council is a Local Authority based in Newbury. The Council provides a wide range of services across the district from Social Care to Environmental Health and Planning. We also have a number of support functions including Finance, Legal and Human Resources. This variety of services mean that there are a number of differing recruitment opportunities available from office based roles to roles out working with the public. As well as permanent vacancies the Council is also able to offer volunteering, work placements and apprenticeships in many areas.

West Berkshire Council supports Equal Opportunity of employment, and positively encourages applications from people in under represented groups such as people with disabilities or from a minority ethnic group.

For further information on the Council or to see our vacancies please go to:

www.westberks.gov.uk/jobsandcareers

West Oxfordshire

Bampton	Town Hall, Market Square
Burford	Guildenford Car Park
	High Street
	Burford Caravan Club Site *(Caravan Club)*
Carterton	Black Bourton Road, Car Park
Charlbury	Spendlove Centre (Daytime)
	Charlbury Station *(Gt Western)*
Chipping Norton	New Street, Car Park
	Town Hall, Market Place
Eynsham	Back Lane Car Park
	Oxford Road Playing Field
Witney	Langdale Gate
	The Leys [Closed at present] (Daytime)
	'Company of Weavers', Market Square *(JDW)*
CP	Windrush Leisure Centre
Woodstock	Hensington Road Car Park
	Bladon Chains Caravan Club Site *(Caravan Club)*

Winchester

Bishops Waltham	Central Car Park, Houchin Street
Colden Common	CP Marwell Wildlife *(Private)*
Denmead	Kidmore Lane Car Park
New Alresford	Station Road
Wickham	Station Road
	Rooksbury Park Caravan Club Site *(Caravan Club)*
Winchester	Abbey Gardens
	Brooks Shopping Centre, Upper Parking Level
	Chesil Street MSCP
	Jewry Street
	Market Lane
	Middle Brook Street
	St Catherines Park & Ride
	Tower Street Car Park
	Worthy Lane Coach Station/Car Park
	Winchester Station, Platform 2 *(SW Trains)*

Debenhams Store, High Street *(Debenhams)*
'Bishop on the Bridge', High Street *(Fullers)*
'Old Gaol House', Jewry Street *(JDW)*
'Pitcher & Piano', 57 Colebrook Street *(Marstons)*
'Slug & Lettuce', The Square *(Private)*
Morn Hill Caravan Club Site *(Caravan Club)*

Windsor & Maidenhead

Ascot	Station Hill
	Ascot Station, Platform 1 *(S W Trains)*
Cookham	Sutton Road Car Park
Eton	Eton Court Park
Hurley	Hurley Riverside Park *(Private)*
Maidenhead	Nicholsons MSCP, by Shopmobility (7.30-18.00)
	Providence Place, Northern Rotunda
	Maidenhead Station *(Gt Western)*
	'Bar 38', Grenfell Island *(Spirit)*
	'Bear', High Street *(JDW)*
	'Greyhound', Queen Street *(JDW)*
CP	Magnet Leisure Centre
Sunninghill	High Street
Taplow	Taplow Station *(Gt Western)*
Windsor	Bachelors Acre, off Victoria Street
	Coach Park (8.00-18.00)
	Home Park, off Romney Lock Road
	River Street Car Park
	Windsor Leisure Centre (Centre hrs)
	Windsor & Eton Central Station *(Gt Western)*
	Windsor & Eton Riverside Station, Concourse *(SW Trains)*
	'All Bar One', Windsor Royal Station *(Private)*
	'King & Castle', Thames Street *(JDW)*
	'Nandos', Thames Street *(Nandos)*
	'Windlesora', William Street *(JDW)*
	Windsor Campus *(East Berks College)*

Wokingham

Barkham	'Ye Olde Leathern Bottle', Barkham Road *(Spirit)*
Twyford	Twyford Station, Platform *(Gt Western)*
Wokingham	'Gig House', Denmark Street *(JDW)*
	Gala Bingo, Easthamstead Road *(Gala)*

Wycombe

Bourne End	Wakeman Road
Flackwell Heath	Straight Bit
Hazlemere	Beaumont Way
	Park Parade
High Wycombe	Easton Street MSCP
	Pauls Row (Daytime)
	'Nandos', Eden Shopping Centre *(Nandos)*
	'The Falcon', Cornmarket *(JDW)*
	'William Robert Loosley', Oxford Road *(JDW)*
	AMF Bowl, Eden Centre *(AMF)*
Marlow	Central Car Park, Crown Lane
	Pound Lane
	Marlow Library (Library hrs) *(Bucks CC)*
Princes Risborough	Horns Lane Car Park
West Wycombe	Hill Road

Bath & North East Somerset

Bath City Centre	Charlotte Street Car Park
	Charlotte Street, Car Park entrance
	Henrietta Park, Henrietta Street
	Parade Gardens, Grand Parade (Park hrs)
	Riverside Coach Park, Avon Street
	Royal Victoria Park, Pavilion, Royal Avenue
	Royal Victoria Park, Play Area, Upper Bristol Rd
	Seven Dials, Monmouth Road
	Sydney Gardens, Sydney Place
	Victoria Art Gallery (Gallery hrs)
	Bath Spa Station, Platforms 1 & 2 *(Gr Western)*
	'King of Wessex', James Street *(JDW)*
	'Nandos', 5-10 St James Street West *(Nandos)*
	'Revolution', York Buildings, George Street *(Private)*
	Gala Bingo, Sawclose *(Gala)*
Bath, Beechen Cliff	Alexandra Park, Shakespeare Avenue
Bath, Combe Down	Bradford Road
Bath, Lambridge	Alice Park, Gloucester Road
	Larkhall Square
Bath, Lansdown	Approach Golf Course, Weston Road
Bath, Odd Down	Park & Ride site

Bath, Oldfield Park	Monksdale Road
	Shaftesbury Road
Bath, Twerton	Dominion Road
Bath, Weston	Weston High Street, nr. Shops
Batheaston	Car Park, off London Road *(Parish Council)*
Keynsham	Ashton Way Car Park
	Memorial Park
CP	Keynsham Leisure Centre *(Private)*
Midsomer Norton	Gullock Tyning Sports Centre Car Park
	The Island, High Street
Paulton	Red Lion Car Park, High Street *(Parish Council)*
Peasedown St John	Greenlands Road, car park by shops
Saltford	Shallows Car Park, Picnic Area

Bournemouth

Boscombe & Southbourne	Ashley Road Bus Station
	Boscombe Gardens (Daytime)
	Boscombe Overcliff Gardens (April-September)
	Fisherman's Walk, Southbourne
	Hengistbury Head, Double Dykes
	Seabourne Road, opp Pokesdown Station
	Southbourne Crossroads (Daytime)
	Tuckton Road, nr. Belle Vue Road
	Wick Lane Car Park, Tuckton
	'Sir Percy Florence Shelley', Christchurch Road *(JDW)*
	'Yates's Bar', Dean Park Crescent *(Private)*
Bournemouth	East Overcliffe, opp. Carlton Hotel
	Firbank Road/Charminster Road (2)
	Glen Fern Road Car Park
CP	Lower Gardens, Exeter Crescent
	Poole Hill, The Triangle
	Richmond Gardens MSCP (Daytime)
	Travel Interchange, by Asda
	West Overcliffe, nr. West Hill Road
	Westover Road, by Information Bueau
	Bournemouth Station, Platform 2/3 *(SW Trains)*
	Debenhams Store, The Square *(Debenhams)*
	'Christopher Creek', Holdenhurst Road *(JDW)*

	'Moon in the Square', Exeter Road *(JDW)*
	'Nandos', Showrooms East, Castlepoint *(Nandos)*
	'Slug & Lettuce', 4/15 Bourne Avenue *(Private)*
	'Walkabout', Old Christchurch Road *(Private)*
	'Old Fire Station', Holdenhurst Road (2) *(Bournemouth Univ.)*
Bournmouth Seafront	Alum Chine, Bournemouth
	Bedford Beach, Southbourne
	Boscombe East
	Boscombe West
	Bournemouth East
	Bournemouth Pier
	Bournemouth West
	Coasters, nr Bournemouth Pier
	Durley Chine, Bournemouth
Kinson Green	Millhams Road (Daytime)
CP	Pelham Park Leisure Centre *(Private)*
CP	Kinson Hub, Wimborne Road
Wallisdown	Old Mulberry Close, Aldi Car Park
	'Kings Arms', 252 Wallisdown Road *(Marstons)*
Westbourne	Milburn Road Car Park
Winton	Leslie Road (Daytime)
	'Parkstone & Heathlands', Wimborne Road *(JDW)*
	Gala Bingo, Wimborne Road *(Gala)*

Bristol

Ashton	Ashton Road
Bedminster	Bridgwater Road, Bedminster Down (Daytime)
	East Street
	Victoria Park (Park hrs)
	'Robert Fitzharding', Cannon Street *(JDW)*
Bristol City Centre	Albion Marina (Daytime)
	Castle Park, Broadweir (Park hrs)
	Colston Avenue (8.00-19.00)
	St James Barton (Daytime)
	Wapping Wharf, Redcliff (Daytime)
	Bristol Temple Meads Station (3) *(Gr Western)*
CP	Cabot Circus Shopping Centre *(Private)*
	The Galleries Bristol, Broadmead *(Private)*

'Bay Horse', Lewins Mead *(Spirit)*
'Commercial Rooms', Corn Street *(JDW)*
'Green House', College Green *(Spirit)*
'Jongleurs', Baldwin Street *(Private)*
'Knights Templar', Temple Quay *(JDW)*
'Nandos', Cabot Circus *(Nandos)*
'Pitcher & Piano', Cannons Road *(Marstons)*
'Que Pasa', Corn Street *(Private)*
'Revolution', Old Fish Market, St Nicholas Street *(Private)*
'Slug & Lettuce', 26 St Nicholas Street *(Private)*
'V-Shed', The Waterfront *(JDW)*
'Walkabout', Corn Street *(Private)*
Bristol Aquarium, Anchor Road *(Private)*
Baltic Wharf Caravan Site *(Caravan Club)*

Clifton City Museum, Queens Road (Museum hrs)
Clifton Downs, by Gorge
'All Bar One', Berkeley Square *(Private)*
'The Berkeley', Queens Road *(JDW)*
'The Hill', Cotham Hill *(Private)*
'W G Grace', 71-75 Whiteladies Road *(JDW)*

Doing Work Differently

Explores practical solutions to real questions related to work. This guide can help you overcome barriers and shows how small adjustments can make a big difference.

Available to order from our online shop
www.disabilityrightsuk.org

Bristol City Council
fully supports
Disability Rights UK

0117 922 2100
www.bristol.gov.uk

Fishponds	Fishponds Park (Daytime)
	Morrisons Store, Fishponds Road *(Morrisons)*
	'Van Dyke Forum', 748 Fishponds Road *(JDW)*
	Gala Bingo, Fishponds Road *(Gala)*
Knowle	Redlatch Park (Park hrs)
Montpellier	St Andrews Park (Park hrs)
Redfield	'St George's Hall', Church Road *(JDW)*
Southmead	Greystoke Avenue (Daytime)
Stoke Bishop	Sea Wall, Durdham Down (Daytime)
	Stoke Road, by Water Tower (Daytime)
Witchurch	CP South Bristol Community Hospital *(NHS)*

Cheltenham

Cheltenham	Bath Terrace, off Bath Road
	Imperial Square, by Town Hall
	Montpellier Gardens
	Pittville Park
	Royal Well Road, by Municipal Offices
	Royal Well, nr. Bus Station

Cheltenham Spa Station *(Gt Western)*
CP Beechwood Shopping Centre *(Private)*
Sainsbury's Store, Tewkesbury Road *(Sainsbury)*
'All Bar One', 18 Montpellier Walk *(Private)*
'Bank House', Clarence Street *(JDW)*
'Moon Under Water', Bath Road *(JDW)*
'Nandos', The Brewery, St Margarets Road *(Nandos)*
'Que Pasa', Clarence Street *(Marstons)*
'Revolution', Clarence Parade *(Private)*
'Yates's Bar', Crescent Terrace *(Private)*

Christchurch

Christchurch	Bridge Street (8.00-dusk)
	Christchurch Quay (8.00-dusk)
	Saxon Square, off High Street (8.00-18.00)
Friars Cliffe	Promenade by Beach Café (Café hrs)
Highcliffe	Highcliffe Cliff Top (Café hrs)
	Recreation Ground, Wharncliffe Road (8.00-dusk)
	Sea Corner, Lymington/Waterford Roads (8.00-dusk)
Mudeford	Mudeford Recreation Ground, Ledbury Road (8.00-dusk)
	Quay Head
Mudeford Sandbank	Toilet Block 3, nr. Ferry Pontoon
	Toilet Block 5, nr. Black House (March-October)
Purewell	Purewell Cross Roads (8.00-dusk)

Cotswold

Bibury	London Road (Daytime)
Bourton-on-the-Water	Church Rooms (Daytime)
	Rissington Road Car Park (Daytime)
Chipping Campden	Sheep Street (Daytime)
Cirencester	Brewery Car Park (Daytime)
	Forum Car Park (Daytime)
	London Road (Daytime)
	Lorry Park (Daytime)
	Abbey Grounds (Apr-Oct) (Daytime) *(Town Council)*
	Cirencester Park Caravan Club Site *(Caravan Club)*
Fairford	High Street (Daytime)

Lechlade	Burford Road (Daytime)
Moreton-in-Marsh	High Street (Daytime)
	Moreton-in-Marsh Caravan Club Site *(Caravan Club)*
Northleach	Market Place (Daytime)
Stow-on-the-Wold	Market Square (Daytime)
	Maugersbury Rd Car Park (Daytime)
Tetbury	Chipping Street (Daytime)
	West Street (Daytime)

East Dorset

Astley Heath	CP	Moors Valley Country Park
Corfe Mullen		Towers Way
Ferndown		Pennys Walk
		'Night Jar', Victoria Road *(JDW)*
		'Pure Drop', 457 Wimborne Road East *(Marstons)*
Verwood		Ferret Green
West Moors		Park Way
West Parley		Christchurch Road

COTSWOLD CHARM—CHIPPING CAMPDEN

3 Four Star Cottages with level access
Ewe Pen sleeps M3i - en suite wetroom, sleeps 5
Lower Chapter— sleeps 2
George Barn—en suite wetroom, sleep 4, available April '13

T: (01386) 840164 Mob/Text: 0788 964 9812
E: info@cotswoldcharm.com www.cotswoldcharm.com
Contact: Michael Haines

East Dorset District Council

Is pleased to support
Disability Rights UK

Wimborne Minster	Cook Row
	Hanham Road South Car Park
	'Man in the Wall', West Borough *(JDW)*

Forest of Dean

Broomsgreen	Memorial Hall *(Hall Committee)*
Cinderford	Heywood Road
Coleford	Railway Drive Car Park
Drybrook	High Street *(Parish Council)*
Dymock	Ledbury Road *(Parish Council)*
Littledean	Silver Street
Lydbrook	New Road
Lydney	Newerne Street Car Park
Mitcheldean	High Street Car Park
Newent	Lewell Street, High Street
Newnham-on-Severn	Riverside Car Park
Woolaston	Peters Cross Picnic Area

Gloucester

Gloucester	Berkeley Street
	Gloucester Bus Station
	Gloucester Park (Park hrs)
	Kings Square
	Westgate Street Car Park
	Gloucester Station *(Gt Western)*
	Eastgate Shopping Centre *(Private)*
	Debenhams Store, Kings Square *(Debenhams)*
	'Avenue', 227 Bristol Road *(Marstons)*
	'Sloans', Brunswick Road *(Private)*
	'The Regal', St Aldate Street, Kings Square *(JDW)*
	'Varsity', Northgate Street *(Barracuda)*
	'Water Poet', Eastgate Street *(JDW)*
	Gala Bingo, Peel Centre *(Gala)*
Kingsholm	Javelin Park & Ride *(Glos CC)*
Matson	Robinswood Hill Country Park

| Quedgeley | Waterwells Park & Ride *(Glos CC)* |
| | 'Haywain', Bristol Road *(Marstons)* |

Mendip

Frome	Market Yard Car Park, Justice Lane
	Merchants Barton Car Park *(Town Council)*
	Victoria Park *(Town Council)*
	Frome Station *(Gt Western)*
Glastonbury	St Johns Car Park
	Magdalene Street *(Town Council)*
Shepton Mallet	Commercial Road Car Park
	Collett Park, Park Road *(Town Council)*
Street	Southside Car Park
	Clarkes Village (3) *(Private)*
	'The Lantokay', High Street *(JDW)*
Wells	Union Street Car Park
	Bus Station, Princes Road *(City Council)*
	Recreation Ground, Silver Street *(City Council)*
	Town Hall Buildings (8.00-18.00) *(City Council)*
	'Kings Head', High Street *(Private)*

North Dorset

Blandford Forum	Corn Exchange (Centre hrs) *(Town Council)*
	Marsh & Ham Car Park *(Town Council)*
	The Tabernacle, by Post Office *(Town Council)*
Gillingham	High Street Car Park *(Town Council)*
Shaftesbury	Bell Street Car Park *(Town Council)*
	Town Hall, ground floor (Town Hall hrs) *(Town Council)*
Stalbridge	Station Road Car Park *(Town Council)*
Sturminster Newton	Station Road, by Car Park *(Town Council)*

North Somerset

Clevedon	Chalet Conveniences, Seafront
	Station Road
	'Crab Apple Inn', Southern Way *(Private)*
Nailsea	Glassmaker, Crown Glass Place *(JDW)*

Portishead	Lake Grounds, Esplanade Road (8.00-20.00)
	Wyndham Way Car Park
Uphill	Links Road
Weston-super-Mare	Boulevard, by Library (8.00-19.45)
	Grove Park Car Park (8.00-18.00)
	Locking Road 4 Car Park (8.00-20.00)
	Marine Parade, opp. Grand Atlantic Hotel
	Marine Parade, Oxford Street
	Marine Parade, Richmond Street
	Marine Parade, Sanitorium
	Rozel Seafront (8.00-20.00)
	Sand Bay Bus Terminal
	Weston-super-Mare Station *(Gt Western)*
	'Dragon Inn', Meadow Street *(JDW)*
	'Yates's Bar', Regent Street *(Private)*
	Country View Hiliday Park *(Private)*
Wick St Lawrence	'Ebdon', Lilac Way *(Marstons)*
Worle	The Maltings, High Street
	'Summerhouse', Parkway *(Marstons)*

Poole

Branksome	Branksome Chine, Beach Car Park
	Branksome Recreation Ground
	Courts, Poole Road
Broadstone	Macaulay Road
	'Blackwater Stream', Lower Blandford Road *(JDW)*

Canford Heath	The Pilot Car Park, Adastral Road
	Haymoor Bottom Shopping Centre *(Private)*
Hamworthy	Ashmore Avenue, Hamworthy Park
	Blandford Road, by Co-op
	Lake Pier, Lake Drive (8.00-18.00, longer in summer)
Holton Heath	Sandford Holiday Park *(Private)*
Parkstone	Alexandra Park Recreation Ground
	Jubilee Road
	Viewpoint, Constitution Hill
Poole	Chapel Lane
	Haven Ferry, Panorama Road
	Kingland Road Bus Station
	Newfoundland Drive, Baiter Recreation Ground
	Poole Park, Central Park Café
	Poole Park, West Gate (8.00-18.00, longer in summer)
	Whitecliff Recreation Centre
	Poole Station *(SW Trains)*
	Dolphin Square *(Private)*
	'Lord Wimborne', Lagland Street *(JDW)*
	'Nandos', Tower Park *(Nandos)*
	'Shah of Persia', 173 Longfleet Road *(Marstons)*
	'Slug & Lettuce', 35/37 High Street *(Private)*
	'Yates's Bar', High Street *(Private)*
	BowlPlex, Tower Park *(Bowlplex)*
Sandbanks	Banks Road, Sandbanks Pavilion
	Shore Road, Beach Pavilion
The Quay	Quay Visitors Car Park
	Watch Station, nr. Lifting Bridge
	Dolphin Quays *(Private)*
	'The Quay', The Quay *(JDW)*
Upton Country Park	Upton Heritage Centre
	Upton Park Car Park (8.00-18.00, longer in summer)

Purbeck

Corfe Castle	West Street
	Castle Ticket Office *(National Trust)*
Norden	Park & Ride Car Park *(Swanage Rlwy)*
Studland	Beach Road

	Knoll Car Park *(National Trust)* Middle Beach *(National Trust)* Shell Bay *(National Trust)*
Swanage	Burlington Chine *(Town Council)* Heritage Centre (Daytime) *(Town Council)* Herston *(Town Council)* Shore Road *(Town Council)* Haycraft Caravan Site *(Caravan Club)*
Wareham	Howards Lane Hunters Moon Caravan Site *(Caravan Club)*
Worth Maltravers	Car Park

Sedgemoor

Axbridge	Moorland Street
Berrow	Hurn Lane Caravan Club Site *(Caravan Club)*
Brean Sands	Brean Leisure Park *(Private)* Holiday Resort Unity *(Private)*
Bridgwater	Taunton Road Angel Place Shopping Centre *(Private)* 'Carnival Inn', St Mary Street *(JDW)*
Bridgwater M5	Bridgwater Services *(Moto)*
Burnham-on-Sea	Apex Park (Daytime) Oxford Street Car Park (Daytime) South Esplanade, Information Centre (Daytime) Tourist Information Centre Car Park (Daytime) 'Reeds Arms', Pier Street *(JDW)* 'The Railway', College Street *(Greene King)*
Cheddar	Dagshole (Daytime) Station Road, by School (Daytime) Cheddar Caravan Club Site *(Caravan Club)*
Highbridge	Bank Street Car Park (Daytime)
Winscombe	'Stag & Hounds', Bristol Road *(Marstons)*

South Gloucestershire

Alveston	'Ship Inn', Thornbury Road *(Private)*
Aust M48	Severn View Services *(Moto)*

Charfield		Memorial Hall
Cribbs Causeway		'Nandos', Unit 208 *(Nandos)*
Downend		Westerleigh Road (7.30-19.00)
Filton		Church Road
Hanham		Conham River Park
		Laburnham Road Car Park
		'Jolly Sailor', High Street *(JDW)*
		'Nandos', Aspect Leisure Park *(Nandos)*
Kingswood	CP	Kingswood Civic Centre, High Street (Office hrs)
		Kingswood Park, High Street
		Moravian Road (M+F)
		Kings Chase Shopping Centre *(Private)*
		'Kingswood Colliers', Regent Street *(JDW)*
Mangotsfield		St James Street Car Park (M+F)
Patchway	CP	Patchway Hub, Rodway Road (Office hrs)
Severn Beach		Beach Road
Staple Hill		Page Park (M+F) (7.30-19.00)
		Page Road (M+F) (7.30-19.00)
		'Staple Hill Oak', High Street *(JDW)*
Stoke Gifford		Bristol Parkway Station (2) *(Gt Western)*
		'Bailey's Court Inn' *(Marstons)*
Thornbury		St Marys Shopping Centre *(Private)*
		'White Lion', High Street *(Marstons)*
Warmley		by A420 & Bristol-Bath Cycleway
		Station Yard, High Street
Wick		Golden Valley Shopping Centre *(Private)*
Winterbourne		Flaxpits Lane
Yate		Yate Shopping Centre *(Private)*
		'Fox', Broad Lane *(Marstons)*
		'Thorn's Farm', 11-17 South Parade *(JDW)*

South Somerset

Bruton	Grove Alley
Castle Cary	Millbrook Gardens Car Park
	Castle Cary Station *(Gt Western)*

Chard	Bath Street
	Boden Street
	'The Cerdic', Fore Street *(JDW)*
	Five Acres Caravan Club Site *(Caravan Club)*
CP	Magdalen Farm, Winsham *(Private)*
Crewkerne	South Street
Ilminster	Shudrick Lane (Daytime)
	'Stonemasons', Harts Close *(Marstons)*
Somerton	Cox's Yard Car Park, West Street *(Town Council)*
Stoke-sub-Hamdon	Ham Hill
Wincanton	Memorial Hall Car Park (7.00-19.00)
	Carrington Way Car Park *(Town Council)*
	Churchfields *(Town Council)*
	Wincanton Racecourse Caravan Club Site *(Caravan Club)*
Yeovil	Bus Station, Earle Street (M+F)
	Petters Way Car Park
	Recreation Centre, Mudford Road (7.00-19.00)
	Peter Street *(Town Council)*
	Quedam Centre *(Private)*
	'William Dampier', Middle Street *(JDW)*

Stroud

| Berkeley | Marybrook Street |
| Cainscross | Westward Road Car Park |

contributing towards an overall improvement in physical and mental wellbeing

STROUD DISTRICT COUNCIL
www.stroud.gov.uk

For more information on accessibility
to our 12 public conveniences
please visit

www.stroud.gov.uk/docs/environment/
toilets.asp

or call 01453 754549

Dursley	Castle Street Car Park (Daytime)
	May Lane Car Park (Daytime)
Kingswood	Rectory Road *(Parish Council)*
Minchinhampton	Bell Lane
Nailsworth	Old Market Bus Station
Painswick	Stamages Lane
	St Mary's Street *(Town Council)*
Stonehouse	High Street Car Park
Stroud	Bedford Street
	Brunel Mall MSCP (7.30-18.00)
	Stratford Park, Car Park (Daytime)
	'Lord John', Russell Street *(JDW)*
	'Old Nelson', Stratford Road *(Brewers Fayre)*
Wotton under Edge	Rope Walk (Daytime)

Swindon

Bridgemead		Sainsbury's Store, Bridgemead *(Sainsbury)*
		'Manor Farm' *(Marston)*
Covingham		Dorcan Way (Mon-Sat, daytime)
	CP	Dorcan Recreation Centre
Gorse Hill		Chapel Street
Highworth		Brewery Street Car Park
		Highworth Recreation Centre (Centre hrs)
Lechlade		Riverside Park [from Easter 2013] *(Private)*
Middleleaze	CP	Saltway Centre
South Swindon		Barbury Castle Park
		Coate Water Country Park (Park hrs)
Swindon Town Centre	CP	Brunel Centre, Market Place
		Bus Station, New Bridge Street (Station hrs)
		Town Arts Centre, Regent Circus (Centre hrs)
		Town Gardens, Westlecot Street (Park hrs)
		Victoria Road, Old Town
		Swindon Station, Platform 1 *(Gt Western)*
		The Brunel Centre *(Private)*
		Debenhams Store, The Parade *(Debenhams)*
		House of Fraser Store, Brunel Centre *(House of Fraser)*

'Bell Hotel', Club Bar, Old Town *(Private)*
'Dockle Farmhouse', Bridge End Road *(JDW)*
'Groves Company Inn', Fleet Street *(JDW)*
'Revolution', Bridge Street *(Private)*
'Sir Daniel Arms', Fleet Street *(JDW)*
'The Savoy', Regent Street *(JDW)*
Gala Bingo, Greenbridge Retail Park *(Gala)*
CP Oasis Leisure Centre *(Private)*

West Swindon	Link Centre (2) (Centre hrs)
	Lydiard Park, Visitor Centre (Park hrs)
	West Swindon Centre, Town Square
Wroughton	Wharf Road (unsuitable for wheelchair users)

Taunton Deane

Bishops Lydeard	Mount Street
	Bishops Lydeard Station *(W Somerset Rlwy)*
Taunton	Canon Street Car Park (8.00-20.00)
	Castle Green (M only)
	Castle Walk (F only) (8.00-18.00)
	Flook House, Station Road (8.00-20.00)
	French Weir Recreation Area (8.00-20.00)
	High Street MSCP (8.00-20.00)
	Paul Street (8.00-20.00)
	Taunton Bus Station
	Victoria Park (6.00-18.00)
	Vivary Park (8.00-sunset)
	Wilton Lands, nr. Golf Club (8.00-20.00)
	Taunton Station *(Gt Western)*
	Debenhams Store, North Street *(Debenhams)*
	Sainsbury's Store, Heron Gate *(Sainsbury)*
	'Coal Orchard', Bridge Street *(JDW)*
	'Perkin Warbeck', East Street *(JDW)*
	'Pitcher & Piano', Corporation Street *(Marstons)*
	'Que Pasa', High Street *(Marstons)*
	'Yates's Bar', High Street *(Private)*
Wellington	Longforth Road
	North Street Car Park
	Wellington Park (Park hrs)
Wiveliscombe	North Street

Tewkesbury

Alderton	Village Hall *(Private)*
Churchdown	Parish Council Offices, Parton Road *(Parish Council)*
Tewkesbury	Spring Gardens *(Town Council)* Tewkesbury Abbey Caravan Club Site *(Caravan Club)*
Twigworth	'Twigworth', Tewkesbury Road *(Spirit)*
Winchcombe	Back Lane Car Park *(Town Council)*

West Dorset

Abbotsbury		Back Street Beach *(Private)*
Beaminster		Fleet Street
Bridport		South Street Car Park West Street Car Park Eype Picnic Area *(SW Highways)* 'The Greyhound', East Street *(JDW)*
	CP	Bridport Leisure Centre *(Private)*
Buckland Newton		Village Hall *(Parish Council)*
Burton Bradstock		Village Hive Beach *(National Trust)*
Cerne Abbas		Long Street
Charmouth		Foreshore Village Car Park
Chideok		Seatown

Dorchester	Maumbury Road, Car Park
	Top o'Town Car Park
	Trinity Street Car Park
	Tudor Arcade Car Park (Trading hrs)
	Kingston Pond, A35 *(SW Highways)*
	Dorchester South Station *(SW Trains)*
	Antelope Walk *(Private)*
	'Royal Oak', High West Street *(JDW)*
	Crossways Caravan Club Site *(Caravan Club)*
Lyme Regis	Broad Street
	Charmouth Road (Summer)
	Holmbush
	Monmouth Beach Car Park
	Marine Parade (Summer) (**Daytime**) *(Town Council)*
	Woodmead Car Park *(Town Council)*
Sherborne	Culverhayes Car Park
	Digby Road
	Old Market Yard Car Park
West Bay	East Beach (Summer)
	The Mound
	Visitors Centre
	Groves Garden Centre *(Private)*
West Bexington	Beach Car Park

West Somerset

Blue Anchor	Seafront, Central
Dulverton	Lion Stables Car Park
	Exmoor House Caravan Club Site *(Caravan Club)*
Dunster	Dunster Steep Car Park
Exebridge	Lakeside Caravan Club Site *(Caravan Club)*
Kilve	Kilve Beach Car Park
Minehead	Blenheim Gardens (Seasonal)
	Summerland Road Car Park
	Warren Road, Arcade
	Warren Road, opp. Butlins
	Minehead Station *(W. Somerset Rlwy)*
	'Duke of Wellington', Wellington Square *(JDW)*
	Minehead Caravan Club Site *(Caravan Club)*

Porlock	Central Car Park (Seasonal)
	Doverhay Road Car Park
Tarr Steps	Tarr Stepps Car Park *(National Park)*
Watchet	Harbour Road
	Market Street Car Park
Wheddon Cross	Rest & Be Thankful Car Park *(Parish Council)*
Williton	Car Park, Killick Way

Weymouth & Portland

Portland	Easton Gardens
	Ferrybridge Car Park
	Portland Bill Car Park (Daytime)
Weymouth	Brunswick Terrace
	Cove Street, Hope Square
	Lodmoor Car Park
	Nothe Gardens, Barrack Road (Daytime)
	Swannery Car Park, Radipole Park Drive (Daytime)
	The Esplanade
	Lower St Alban Street MSCP *(Private)*
	Weymouth Station *(SW Trains)*
	Debenhams Store, New Bond Street *(Debenhams)*
	Jubilee Business Park, Café *(Private)*
	'Que Pasa', St Thomas Street *(Marstons)*
	'The Swan', St Thomas Street *(JDW)*
	'William Henry', Frederick Place *(JDW)*
	'Yates's Bar', St Thomas Street *(Private)*
	Gala Bingo, Crescent Street *(Gala)*
CP	Beach Rescue Centre

Wiltshire

Amesbury	'The Bell', 13-15 Salisbury Street *(JDW)*
	Central Car Park, Salisbury Street
Bradford-on-Avon	St Margaret's Car Park (Daytime)
	Station Approach Car Park (Daytime)
Calne	The Pippin (Daytime)
Castle Combe	The Street (Daytime)

Chippenham		Bath Road Car Park (Daytime)
		Borough Parade (Daytime)
		Monkton Park (Daytime)
		Sainsbury's Store, Bath Road *(Sainsbury)*
		'Bridge House', Borough Parade *(JDW)*
	CP	Olympiad Leisure Centre *(DC Leisure)*
Cricklade		off High Street (Daytime)
Devizes	**CP**	Hillworth Park (8.00-dusk)
		The Green
		West Central Car Park
	CP	Hillworth Park, by Office (8.00-dusk) *(Town Council)*
		'Silk Mercer', St Johns Street *(JDW)*
Downton		The Borough
Lacock		Red Lion Car Park *(National Trust)*
Leigh Delamere M4		Leigh Delamere Services Eastbound *(Moto)*
		Leigh Delamere Services Westbound *(Moto)*
Marlborough		George Lane
Melksham		Bath Road Car Park (Daytime)
		Church Street Car Park (Daytime)
		Town Square (Daytime)
		'The Bear', 3 Bath Road *(JDW)*
Mere		Salisbury Street Car Park
Pewsey	**CP**	Pewsey Library, Aston Close (Library hrs)
Royal Wootton Bassett		Boroughfields Car Park (Daytime)
Salisbury		Central Car Park (Daytime)
		Coach Station
		Culver Street (Daytime)
		Market Square
		Bemerton Recreation Ground *(City Council)*
		Churchill Gardens *(City Council)*
		Lush House, Crane Street *(City Council)*
		Victoria Park (Park hrs) *(City Council)*
		Salisbury Cathedral, off Cloisters *(Cathedral)*
		Salisbury Station, Platforms 2 & 4 *(SW Trains)*
		Old George Mall Shopping Precinct *(Private)*
		Debenhams Store, Market Place *(Debenhams)*
		'Kings Head', Bridge Street *(JDW)*

	Gala Bingo, Endless Street *(Gala)*
	Hillside Caravan Club Park *(Caravan Club)*
	Husdons Field Campsite
Tisbury	The Avenue (Daytime)
Trowbridge	Trowbridge Park (Daytime)
	Trowbridge Station *(Gt Western)*
	'Albany Palace', Park Road *(JDW)*
	'Sir Isaac Pitman', Market Place *(JDW)*
	Ashton Building, Trowbridge Campus *(Wiltshire College)*
	Cheverell, Trowbridge Campus *(Wiltshire College)*
	Kennet Building, Trowbridge Campus *(Wiltshire College)*
CP	County Hall, Bythesea Road
Warminster	Central Car Park (Daytime)
	Warminster Park (Daytime)
	Warminster Station *(Gt Western)*
	Longleat Caravan Club Site *(Caravan Club)*
CP	Warminster Civic Centre
Westbury	High Street Car Park
	Warminster Road Car Park
	Westbury Station, Platform 1 *(Gt Western)*
Wilton	Market Place (Daytime)

Cornwall

Bodelva	CP	Eden Project *(Private)*
Bodmin		Lanivet Car Park
		Dennson Road *(Town Council)*
		Fair Park *(Town Council)*
		Priory Park *(Town Council)*
		Bodmin Parkway Station *(Gt Western)*
		'Chapel an Gansblydhen', Fore Street *(JDW)*
Boscastle		Cobweb Car Park
Bude		Crackington Haven
		Crooklets Beach Car Park
		Poughill
	CP	Summerleaze Beach
	CP	Summerleaze Car Park
		The Crescent Car Park
		Widemouth Bay
		Duckpool, National Trust Car Park *(National Trust)*
Callington		New Road
Calstock		The Quay
Camborne		Camborne Park
		Gurneys Lane
		Rosewarne Car Park
		Camborne Station *(Gt Western)*
Camelford		Enfield Park
Coverack		Car Park (M+F)
Delabole		High Street
Downderry		Main Road
Falmouth		'Packet Station', The Moor *(JDW)*
	CP	Ships & Castle Leisure Centre *(Private)*
Gunnislake		by Car Park (M+F) (Daytime)
Gunwalloe		Church Cove (Easter-September)
Gwithian		Godrevy *(National Trust)*
		Godrevy Park Caravan Site *(Caravan Club)*

Hayle		Foundry Square
Helford		Car Park
Helston		Coinagehall Street
		Trengrouse Way
		Park View, Old Cattle Market *(Private)*
Kilkhampton		Market Square Car Park
Kingsand		behind Halfway House (F only)
Kynance Cove		Car Park *(National Trust)*
Lanlivery	CP	Vitalise Churchdown Resource Centre *(Private)*
Lanner		Playing Field *(Parish Council)*
Launceston		Cattle Market
		Walkhouse Car Park
Lelant Saltings		Park & Ride
Liskeard		Sungirt Car Park
		Westbourne Car Park
		Liskeard Station *(Gt Western)*
Lizard		The Green Car Park
Looe		Guildhall
		Hannafore
		Millpool
		Seafront
		Looe Caravan Club Site *(Caravan Club)*
Marazion		Station Car Park
Menheniot		East Road *(Parish Council)*
Minions		Location details not available
Mullion		Cove (Easter-September)
		Village Car Park
Newquay		Newquay Station *(Gt Western)*
		'Sailors Arms', Fore Street *(Private)*
		'The Cribbar', 11-19 Gover Lane *(JDW)*
		'Towan Blystra', Cliff Road *(JDW)*
		'Walkabout', The Crescent *(Private)*
Padstow		Council Offices Car Park
		Link Road Car Park
		South Quay

Padstow Coast		Constantine Beach Car Park
		Corys Shelter (F only)
		Harlyn Beach
		Porthcothan Beach
		Trevone Beach
		Treyaron Beach
Pelynt		Village Hall *(Parish Council)*
Pendeen		Boscaswell (F only) (Daytime)
Penzance		Alexandra Gardens
		Jennings Street
		Penalverne, nr. St Johns Hall
		Tourist Information Centre
		Wherrytown, Bedford Bolitho Gardens
		Penzance Station *(Gt Western)*
		Wharfside Shopping Centre *(Private)*
	CP	Bread Street Gallery *(Private)*
		'Tremenheere', Market Place *(JDW)*
	CP	Lescudjack Centre, Penmere Close *(Private)*
Poldhu		Beach (Easter-September)
Polperro		Fishna Bridge
Polruan		St Saviours
Polzeath		Daymer Beach
		New Polzeath Car Park
		opp. The Beach
Pool	CP	Heartlands, Dudnance Lane *(Private)*
Port Isaac		Clifftop Car Park
		Fish Cellars, Roscarrick Hill
Porthallow		Porthallow Beach

Porthcurno		Car Park
Porthleven		Shute Lane
Portreath		Beach Road
Portscatho		Merrose Farm Caravan Site *(Caravan Club)*
Praa Sands		Car Park
Praze-an-Beeble		The Square
Redruth		Fairfield (Events only) New Cut Car Park Redruth Station, Platform 2 *(Gt Western)*
Rejerrah		Monkey Tree Holiday Park *(Private)*
Rose		Treamble Valley Caravan Site *(Caravan Club)*
Saltash		Bellevue Car Park Longstone Park (M+F) (Daytime)
Sennen Cove		Car Park (Summer)
St Austell	**CP**	Priory Road Car Park St Austell Station *(Gt Western)* 'Rann Wartha', Biddicks Court *(JDW)*
St Ives		Porthmeor Car Park (Daytime) Sloop Car Park (Daytime) Station Car Park (Daytime) Trenwith Car/Coach Park (Daytime) West Pier (Daytime) 'Hain Line', Treganna Place *(JDW)*
St Just		Lafrowda Close Car Park
St Keverne		The Square
St Merryn		Harlyn Road
St Teath		Car Park, opp. White Hart
Tintagel		Bossinney Fore Street, Trevenna Square The Castle Trerammett Visitor Centre Trewethhett Farm Caravan Site *(Caravan Club)*
Torpoint		Antony Road Thanckes Park

		Ferry Queuing Lanes *(Tamar Crossings)*
Trebarwith		Trebarwith Strand
Truro		Truro Station, Platform 2 *(Gt Western)*
		'Barley Sheaf', Old Bridge Street *(Private)*
		'Try Dower', Lemon Quay *(JDW)*
Wadebridge	**CP**	Camel Trail, Eddystone Road
		Egloshaye Road
		Goldsworthy Way Car Park
		The Platt

East Devon

Axminster		West Street Car Park (8.00-19.00, later in summer)
Beer		Jubilee Gardens (8.00-19.00, later in summer)
Branscombe		Beach Car Park (8.00-19.00, later in summer)
Budleigh Salterton		Brook Road Car Park (F only) (8.00-19.00, later in summer)
Exmouth		Bus/Rail Station (8.00-19.00, later in summer)
		Elizabeth Hall Grounds (8.00-19.00, later in summer)
		Esplanade, Lifeboat (Summer) (8.00-22.00)
		Foxholes Car Park (8.00-19.00, later in summer)
		Imperial Grounds (8.00-19.00, later in summer)
		Maer Park (Summer) (8.00-22.00)
		Manor Gardens, by Town Hall (8.00-19.00, later in summer)
		Phear Park (8.00-19.00, later in summer)
		'Powder Monkey', The Parade *(JDW)*
Honiton		King Street (8.00-19.00, later in summer)
		Lace Walk (8.00-19.00, later in summer)
		Turks Head Picnic Site
	CP	Newholme, Northcote Lane *(Private)*
Otterton		The Square
Ottery St Mary		The Flexton, Town Centre (8.00-19.00, later in summer)
Seaton		Chine, by West Walk Esplanade (Summer) (8.00-22.00)
		Harbour Road Car Park (8.00-19.00, later in summer)
		Marsh Road, by Town Hall (8.00-19.00, later in summer)
		Seaton Hole (Summer) (8.00-22.00)
Sidford		Sidford (8.00-19.00, later in summer)
Sidmouth		Connaught Gardens (8.00-19.00, later in summer)

Market Place (8.00-19.00, later in summer)
Port Royal (8.00-19.00, later in summer)
Triangle (8.00-19.00, later in summer)
Woolbrook, Long Park (8.00-19.00, later in summer)
Putts Corner Caravan Club Site *(Caravan Club)*

Exeter

Exeter City Centre	Blackboy Road
	Ennerdale Way
	King William Street
	Musgrave Row
	Paris Street
	The Quay
	Exeter St Davids Station *(Gt Western)*
	'Butlers', Mary Arches Road *(Spirit)*
	'George's Meeting House', Fore Street *(JDW)*
	'Nandos', 32/3 Princess Hay *(Nandos)*
	'Pitcher & Piano', Queen Street *(Marstons)*
	'The Imperial', New North Road *(JDW)*
	'Walkabout', Fore Street *(Private)*
CP	Princesshay Shopping Centre *(Private)*
Exeter St Thomas	Cowick Barton Playing Fields
	Cowick Street Railway Arch
	St Thomas Pleasure Ground
	Okehampton Street
	'Sawyers Arms', Cowick Street *(JDW)*
Heavitree	Fore Street
	Heavitree Park
Matford	Park & Ride
Polsloe	Hamlin Lane
	'Railwayman', Pinhoe Road *(Spirit)*
Topsham	Fore Street
	Topsham Quay
Whipton	Pinhoe Road, near shops

Isles of Scilly

St Mary's	Old Weslyan Chapel, Garrison Lane

Mid Devon

Bampton		Luke Street
Chawleigh		Village Hall (Daytime)
Crediton		Market Street
		Newcombes Meadow
		'General Sir Redvers Buller', High Street *(JDW)*
Cullompton		Station Road
	CP	The Hayridge, Exeter Hill *(Devon CC)*
Down St Mary		A377 Morchard Road Picnic Area
Hemyock		Culmbridge Road, by Parish Hall
Sampford Peverell		Recreation Ground
		Tiverton Parkway Station *(Gt Western)*
Tiverton		Lowman Green (7.00-19.00)
		Market Car Park (7.00-19.00)
		Peoples Park (7.00-19.00)
		Phoenix Lane
		Westexe South
		Canal Basin Car Park *(Devon CC)*
		'White Ball Inn', Bridge Street *(JDW)*

North Devon

Barnstaple	Old Cattlemarket Car Park
	Pilton Park
	North Devon Library & Record Office, Tuly St (Library hrs) *(Devon CC)*
	Rock Park (Daytime) *(Town Council)*
	Barnstaple Station *(Gt Western)*
	Green Lanes Shopping Centre *(Private)*
	Sainsbury's Store, Gratton Way *(Sainsbury)*
	'Panniers', Boutport Street *(JDW)*
	'Water Gate', The Strand *(JDW)*
Braunton	Caen Street Car Park
Combe Martin	Kiln Car Park
Croyde	Croyde Beach
	Croyde Parish Hall
	Down End Car Park
Ilfracombe	Bicclescombe Park

	Brimlands, Hillsborough Car Park
	Hele Beach
	The Cove
	The Pier
	Town Council Offices
	Wilder Road Car Park
Instow	Marine Drive Car Park
	Sandy Lane
Mortehoe	Station Road Car Park
	Danage Barton Caravan Club Site *(Caravan Club)*
Saunton	Beach Toilets
South Molton	Pannier Market (Daytime)
Woolacombe	Red Barn
	Willingcott Caravan Club Site *(Caravan Club)*

Plymouth

Crown Hill	'KFC', Crown Hill Retail Park *(KFC)*
	'Tamar', Moorshead Road *(Spirit)*
Devonport	Ferry Approach Lanes *(Tamar Crossings)*
Lipson	Freedom Park (Café hrs)
Marsh Mills	Copypool Park & Ride
Mawnamead	Hartley Park
Milehouse	'Britannia Inn', Wolseley Road *(JDW)*
Mount Wise	Mutton Close (May-September)
Mutley	Mutley Plain (Daytime)
	'Mannamead', Mutley Plain *(JDW)*
Plymouth City Centre	Armada Way, by Sundial (Daytime)
	Barbican, Quay (Daytime)
	Bretonside Bus Station (7.00-20.00)
	Civic Centre Foyer, Royal Parade (Office hrs)
	Hoe Promenade (Daytime)
	Midland House, Notte Street (Office hrs)
	Phoenix Wharf Car Park, The Hoe
	Plymouth Market, Cornwall Street (Market hrs)
	Tavistock Road, by City Library (Daytime)
	Tinside Lido, The Barbican (Centre hrs)
	West Park, West Hoe (Daytime)

Devon Housing Aid Centre, Mayflower Street *(Shelter)*
Plymouth Station, Platform 4 *(Gt Western)*
Debenhams Store, Royal Parade *(Debenhams)*
House of Fraser Store, Royal Parade *(House of Fraser)*
'All Bar One', Princess Street *(Private)*
'Discovery Café', Eastlake Street *(Private)*
'Gog & Magog', Southside Street *(JDW)*
'Hogs Head', Royal Parade *(Private)*
'Nandos', Barbican Leisure Park *(Nandos)*
'Revolution', Derrys Cross *(Private)*
'Union Rooms', Union Street *(JDW)*
'Varsity', Derrys Cross *(Barracuda)*
'Walkabout', Derry's Cross *(Private)*
'Watering Hole', Quay Road *(Private)*
'Yates's Bar', Royal Parade *(Private)*
Gala Bingo, Derrys Cross *(Gala)*
Vue Cinema, Barbican Leisure Park (M+F) *(Private)*

CP Drake Circus Shopping Centre *(Private)*
CP Plymouth Highbury Trust, Outland Road *(Private)*

Plympton	The Ridgeway, Plymco Car Park (Daytime)
Plymstock	Dean Hill (Daytime)
St Budeaux	Wolseley Road
Stoke	Masterman Road (Daytime)
Stonehouse	Cremyll Street (Daytime)
	Devil's Point (Daytime)
Tamar Bridge	Bridge Car Park, A38 *(Tamar Crossings)*
Turnchapel	Lawrence Road, Mountbatten Car Park (Daytime)
West Hooe	Jennycliff Car Park (Daytime)

South Hams

Modbury	Broad Park Caravan Site *(Caravan Club)*
Stoke Gabriel	Ramslade Caravan Club Site *(Caravan Club)*
Stokenham	Start Bay Caravan Club Site *(Caravan Club)*
Totnes	Totnes Station *(Gt Western)*

Teignbridge

Abbotskerswell		bottom of Church Path
Ashburton		Kingsbridge Lane Car Park
Bovy Tracey		Station Road Car Park
Buckfastleigh		Coach Park
Dawlish		Barton Hill
		Boat Cove (Daytime)
		Sandy Lane Car Park (Daytime)
		The Lawn, by Tourist Information Centre
		Dawlish Station *(Gt Western)*
Dawlish Warren		Beach Road Car Park
		Sea Front
Newton Abbot	CP	Cricketfield Car Park (8.00-18.00, later in summer)
		Decoy Country Park, Car Park
		Market Walk
		Newfoundland Way
		Station Road
		Newton Abbot Station, Platform 3 *(Gt Western)*
		'Richard Hopkins', Queen Street *(JDW)*
Shaldon		The Strand
Starcross		The Strand (Summer) (Daytime)
Teignmouth		Brunswick Street
		Lower Brook Street (Daytime)
		Teignmouth Station, Platform 1 *(Gt Western)*
Widecombe		The Green Car Park

Teignbridge

DISTRICT COUNCIL
South Devon

For more information on toilet facilities and access, why not telephone before you travel?

Please telephone for all enquiries:

01626 215 838

Disability Rights UK

Visit our online shop

For products and books that open doors to independent living.

www.disabilityrightsuk.org

Torbay

Brixham	Bank Lane (Daytime)
	Brixham Harbour (Daytime)
	Shoalstone Beach (April-October) (9.00-19.00)
	Berry Head *(Coast & Countryside Trust)*
	'The Vigilence', 5 Bolton Street *(JDW)*
	Hillhead Holiday Park *(Caravan Club)*

Paignton
Broadsands Beach (Daytime)
Goodrington Central (Daytime)
Paignton Central (Daytime)
CP Paignton Library, Great Western Road (Library hrs)
Palace Avenue (8.00-20.00)
Parkside/Victoria Square (Daytime)
Preston Bus Shelter (9.00-19.00)
Preston North, Marine Drive (Daytime)
'Isaac Merritt', Torquay Road *(JDW)*
'Noahs Ark', Totnes Road *(Private)*
Gala Bingo, Temperance Street *(Gala)*
Quaywest Central *(Private)*
CP Occombe Farm, Community Kitchen *(Private)*
CP ROC Point, Hyde Road

Torquay
Abbey Meadows (April-October) (9.00-19.00)
Beacon Quay (Daytime)
Corbyn Head (April-October) (9.00-19.00)
Factory Row, off Union Street (Daytime)
Lymington Road, Coach Station (Daytime)
Meadfoot Beach (April-October) (9.00-19.00)
Oddicombe Beach (April-October) (9.00-19.00)

is committed to being accessible to all
www.torbay.gov.uk/disability

Old Town Hall, Union Street (Daytime)
Seafront Complex (Daytime)
St Marychurch Town Hall, Car Park (7.00-21.00)
Vaughan Parade (Daytime)
Cockington Car Park *(Private)*
Torquay Station *(Gt Western)*
Fleet Walk Centre *(Private)*
'Babbacombe Inn', Babbacombe Down *(Private)*
'Bar Med', Fleet Walk Centre *(Private)*
'Hogs Head', Union Street *(Private)*
'London Inn', The Strand *(JDW)*
'Manor Inn', Market Street *(Private)*
'Shiraz', Vaughan Parade *(Private)*
'Yates's Bar', Swan Street *(Private)*
Torquay Bowl, Torwood Street *(AMF)*

Torridge

Appledore	Churchfields Car Park (Daytime)
Bideford	Bideford Quay
	Victoria Park (Daytime)
Bradworthy	The Square
Halwill Junction	Playing Field
Holsworthy	North Road
Torrington	South Street (Daytime)
	The Commons (Daytime)
Westward Ho!	Main Putting Green (Daytime)
	Slipway, Maritime Station (Daytime)
Winkleigh	Castle Street

West Devon

Chagford	Jubilee Rooms, nr. Car Park (Hall hrs)
Meldon	Meldon Quarry Station *(Dartmoor Rlwy)*
Okehampton	Fairplace, George Street
	Market Street, by Taxi Rank
	Okehampton Station *(Dartmoor Rlwy)*

Princetown	Information Centre Car Park
Tavistock	Bedford Car Park, Tavistock Wharf (8.30-18.00)
	Guildhall Car Park
Yelverton	Roundabout

EASTERN ENGLAND

Babergh

Chelmondiston		Pin Mill *(Landscape Group)*
East Bergholt		Flatford Visitor Centre *(Landscape Group)*
		Red Lion Car Park *(Landscape Group)*
Lavenham		Prentice Street Car Park *(Town Council)*
		Cock Inn Car Park *(Landscape Group)*
Long Melford		Cordell Road *(Landscape Group)*
		The Green *(Landscape Group)*
Rodbridge		Rodbridge Picnic Site [Under review] *(Suffolk CC)*
Sudbury		'Grover & Allen', 68 North Street *(JDW)*
		'Maldon Grey', Cots Lane *(Greene King)*
	CP	Kingfisher Leisure Centre *(Private)*

Basildon

Basildon	Basildon Library, St Martins Sq (Library hrs) *(Essex CC)*
	Basildon Station, Booking Hall *(C2C)*
	Eastgate Shopping Centre (3) *(Private)*
	Market Square *(Private)*
	'The Towngate', Westgate Park, Fodderwick *(Spirit)*
	'Moon on the Square', Market Square *(JDW)*
	'Nandos', Eastgate *(Nandos)*
	'Nandos', Festival Leisure Park *(Nandos)*
	'Yates's Bar', Swan Street *(Private)*
	Nethermayne Campus, B Block *(South Essex College)*
	Eastgate Business Centre *(Private)*
Billericay	'Blue Boar', High Street *(JDW)*
	'Red Lion', 113 High Street *(Marstons)*
Laindon	Shopping Centre (M+F) (Mon-Sat, 9.00-16.30)
	Laindon Station, Platform 3 *(C2C)*
Pitsea	Pitsea Station, Booking Hall *(C2C)*
Wickford	Woodford Road (Mon-Sat, 9.00-16.30)
	Downtown Youth Centre (Centre hrs) *(Essex CC)*
	Wickford Station *(Greater Anglia)*

The Willows Shopping Centre *(Private)*
Royal British Legion Club, Runwell Road *(RBL)*

Bedford

Bedford	Allhallows Bus Station (8.00-17.45)
	St Pauls Square (Mon-Sat, 8.00-17.15)
	Bedford Station, Platform 1 *(Capital Connect)*
	Debenhams Store, High Street *(Debenhams)*
	'Bankers Draft', High Street *(JDW)*
	'Bar Chameleon', St Pauls Square *(Private)*
	'Nandos', 3 High Street *(Nandos)*
	'Pilgrim's Progress'', Midland Road *(JDW)*
	Corn Exchange
CP	River Street MSCP
East Bedford	Priory Country Park (9.30-17.00, later in summer)
	Russell Park (8.00-18.00, later in summer)
Harrold	Harrold Country Park (8.30-17.30)

Braintree

Braintree	Victoria Street Bus Park
	Braintree Library, Fairfield Road (Library hrs) *(Essex CC)*
	Braintree Station, Ticket Office *(Greater Anglia)*
	'Baileys Café Bar', High Street *(Marstons)*
	'Picture Palace', Fairfield Road *(JDW)*
	'Silk Worm', High Street *(Barracuda)*
CP	Charles Leeks House, Coggeshall Rd *(Mencap)*
Castle Hedingham	Memorial Lane

Become a member

Help us realise our vision and make your voice count.

www.disabilityrightsuk.org

Jackson
& Kelly Ltd

Is pleased to support
Disability Rights UK

Finchingfield	Stephen Marshall Avenue
Witham	Witham Library, Newland Road (Library hrs) *(Essex CC)* Witham Station *(Greater Anglia)* 'Battesford Court', Newland Street *(JDW)*

Breckland

Attleborough	Queens Square, Car Park (Daytime) *(Town Council)*
Dereham	Barwells Court, Market Place *(Town Council)*
Roudham Heath	Rest Area *(Highways Authority)*
Swaffham	The Shambles, Market Place *(Town Council)*
Thetford	Bridge Street Car Park *(Town Council)* Cage Lane *(Town Council)* Castle Park, Castle Street *(Town Council)* 'Red Lion'. Market Place *(JDW)*
Watton	St Giles Car Park (Daytime) *(Town Council)*

Brentwood

Brentwood	Brentwood Station
CP	High Street (7.00-16.00) 'Nandos', High Street *(Nandos)* 'Slug & Lettuce', 78 High Street *(Private)*
CP	Brentwood Centre, Doddinghurst Road (2) *(Private)*
Ingatestone	Market Place (Mon-Sat, 8.00-18.00)
Shenfield	Shenfield Station, Platform 3 *(Greater Anglia)*
West Horndon	West Horndon Station, Ticket Hall *(C2C)*

Broadland

Acle	The Street, by Kings Head
Ranworth	The Staithe, opp. The Maltsters (April-October)
Salhouse	Salhouse Broad Car Park (April-October)
Thorpe St Andrew	River Green, Yarmouth Road (April-October)

Broxbourne

Broxbourne	Deaconsfield, High Street Old Mill Meadows Car Park *(Lee Valley RPA)*
Cheshunt	Grundy Park, Turners Hill (Daytime)

Pindar Car Park *(Lee Valley RPA)*
'King James', Turners Hill *(JDW)*

Hoddesdon	Town Centre, Amwell Street (Daytime)
Waltham Cross	Car Park, High Street (M+F) (Daytime) 'Moon & Cross', High Street *(JDW)*

Cambridge

Cambridge	Arbury Court (8.00-19.00) Barnwell Road (8.00-16.00) Cherry Hinton Hall (8.00-19.00) Chesterton Recreation Ground (8.30-19.00) Chesterton Road (8.00-18.00) Drummer Street (8.00-20.00) Gonville Place (8.00-20.00) Jesus Green, nr. Chesterton Road footbridge (8.00-18.00) Kings Hedges Recreation Ground (April-Oct) (8.00-19.00) Lamas Land, nr. Paddling Pool (8.30-19.00) Lion Yard Shopping Centre (8.30-20.00) Nightingale Recreation Ground (8.00-19.00) Quayside, off Bridge Street (8.30-20.00)

Doing Careers Differently

Packed with useful information, this guide includes stories from disabled people who have built satisfying careers, from part-time flexible work to a first-time management role and beyond.

Available to order from our online shop
www.disabilityrightsuk.org

CAMBRIDGE
CITY COUNCIL

For information on Shopmobility and public toilets:

Visit our website
www.cambridge.gov.uk

or contact our customer service centre:
Telephone 01223 458282

Romsey Recreation Ground (8.00-18.00)
Silver Street, by bridge (8.00-19.00)
Cambridge Station, Platform 1 *(Greater Anglia)*
Grafton Centre, by Shopmobility *(Private)*
Grafton Centre, Eden Hall *(Private)*
Debenhams Store, Grafton Centre *(Debenhams)*
'McDonalds', Rose Crescent *(McDonalds)*
'Nandos', 33 St Andrews Street *(Nandos)*
'Nandos', Cambridge Leisure Park *(Nandos)*
'Revolution', Downing Street *(Private)*
'The Regal', St Andrews Street *(JDW)*
Helmore Building, East Road (3) *(Anglia Ruskin University)*
Corn Exchange (2)
Mumford Theatre *(Anglia Ruskin University)*
Cherry Hinton Caravan Site *(Caravan Club)*
CP Cambridge Shopmobility, Grand Arcade Car Park *(Private)*

Castle Point

Benfleet
Rectory Road, Car Park
Richmond Hall
Tarpot Car Park, Rushbottom Lane
Benfleet Station, Platform 1 *(C2C)*

Canvey Island
Lubbins Car Park, Eastern Esplanade

Central Bedfordshire

Arlesey
'Old Oak', Church Lane *(Private)*

Biggleswade
Market Square Bus Station *(Town Council)*
CP Saxon Pool & Leisure Centre *(Private)*

Clophill
'Flying Horse', The Green *(Private)*

Dunstable
Ashton Square Car Park
'First & Last', Church Street *(Private)*
'Gary Cooper', Grove Park *(JDW)*
'Highwayman', London Road *(Private)*
'KFC', White Lion Retail Park *(KFC)*
'Old Sugar Loaf', High Street North *(Spirit)*

Houghton Regis
Bedford Square

Leighton Buzzard
Leighton Buzzard Library (Library hrs)
West Street MSCP
Waterbourne Walk Car Park (Trading hrs) *(Town Council)*

		Rushmere Country Park, by Stockgrove Centre *(Trust)*
		Leighton Buzzard Station *(London Midland)*
Potton		Brook End, nr. Market Square *(Town Council)*
Sandy		Bedford Road Recreation Ground (Park hrs)
Shefford		Northbridge Street *(Town Council)*
Stotfold		Brook Street Car Park *(Town Council)*
Toddington M1	CP	Toddington Services *(Moto)*

Chelmsford

Boreham		'Grange', Main Road *(Private)*
Chelmsford		Admirals Park, near footbridge (Daytime)
		Central Park, by Bowls Pavilion (Park hrs)
		Dovedale Sports Centre (Centre hrs)
		Hylands Park, by car park
		Lionmead Park, Sandford Road (Daytime)
		Oaklands Park (Park hrs)
		Shopmobility, Market Road (Daytime)
		County Hall E Block (Office hrs) *(Essex CC)*
		Chelmsford Station *(Greater Anglia)*
		The Meadows Shopping Centre *(Private)*
		Debenhams Stor, High Street *(Debenhams)*
		Ladbrokes Bookmakers, Clematis Tye *(Ladbrokes)*
		Sainsbury's Store, Springfield *(Sainsbury)*
		'Baroosh Restaurant', Moulsham Road *(Private)*
		'Escedra', 219 Moulsham Street *(Private)*
		'Golden Fleece', Duke Street *(Private)*
		'Ivory Peg', New London Road *(JDW)*
		'Nandos', Grays Brewery Yard *(Nando)*
		'Purple Lounge', Springfield Rd *(Private)*
		'The Cross', Springfield Road *(Private)*
		'Thomas Mildmay', Springfield Road *(JDW)*
		'Wildwood', The Meadows *(Private)*
		Ashby House, Bishop Hall Road *(Angia Ruskin University)*
		Odeon Cinema, Kings Head Walk *(Odeon)*
		Tenpin, Widford Industrial Estate *(Private)*
	CP	Adult Community Learning *(Essex CC)*
	CP	Market Road
Galleywood		Watchouse Road, by shops *(Parish Council)*

South Woodham Ferrers	South Woodham Ferrers Leisure Centre (Centre hrs) *(Town Council)*
	Starz Youth Centre, Trinity Square (Centre hrs)
	William de Ferrers Adult Education Centre (Centre hrs) *(Essex CC)*
	South Woodham Ferrers Station *(Greater Anglia)*
CP	Marsh Farm, Marsh Farm Road *(Private)*
Writtle	'Horse & Groom', Writtle *(Spirit)*

Colchester

Colchester	Castle Park, behind Hollytrees
	Castle Park, by Boating Lake
	Cemetery, Mersea Road
	Colchester Bus Station, Osborne Street (Station hrs)
	High Woods Country Park
	Lion Walk
	St John's Street MSCP
	St Mary's MSCP, Balkerne Hill
	Colchester Library, Trinity Square (Library hrs) *(Essex CC)*
	Osborne Street MSCP *(NCP)*
	Colchester Station *(Greater Anglia)*
	Sir Isaac's Walk *(Private)*
	'Nandos', Head Street *(Nandos)*
	'Slug & Lettuce', 111 High Street *(Private)*
	'The Playhouse', 4 St John Street *(JDW)*
	'Yates's Bar', Head Street *(Private)*
	Gala Bingo, Osborne Street *(Gala)*
Dedham	Driftway, Playing Fields
Great Horkesley	'Yew Tree', The Causeway *(Chef & Brewer)*
Tiptree	Church Road
West Mersea	Coast Road Car Park
	High Street
	Victoria Esplanade, Willoughby Avenue (M+F)
Wivenhoe	High Street Car Park
Wivenhoe Park	Square 4, Colchester Campus *(University)*
	Students' Union *(University)*
	Sub Zero *(University)*
	University Sports Pavilion *(University)*

Dacorum

Apsley	Durrants Hill Road
Berkhamstead	Water Lane Car Park, off High Street 'Old Mill', London Road *(Spirit)* 'The Crown', High Street *(JDW)*
Hemel Hempstead	Gadebridge Park (April-September) King George V, Queensway Car Park Market Square Bus Station Woodwells Cemetery (Cemetery hrs) Nash Mills Boat Base *(Private)* Marlowes Shopping Cente *(Private)* 'Full House', The Marlowes *(JDW)*
Kings Langley	High Street (Daytime) Kings Langley Station *(London Midland)*
Ringshall	Ashridge Estate, by Visitor Centre *(National Trust)*
Tring	Market Place Car Park, High Street

East Cambridgeshire

Ely	Barton Road Car Park (8.00-18.00) Cloisters Shopping Centre (8.00-18.00) Newnham Street Car Park Sacrist Gate, by Cathedral (8.00-18.00) Ship Lane Car Park Ely Station, Platform 1 *(Greater Anglia)*
Littleport	Main Street Car Park (8.00-17.00)
Soham	Fountain Lane Car Park
Wicken Fen	Lode Lane Car Park, nr. Nature Reserve Wren Building *(National Trust)*

East Hertfordshire

Bishops Stortford	Castle Gardens Bishops Stortford Station, Platform 1 *(Greater Anglia)*
Buntingford	Bowling Green Lane
Hertford	Bircherley Green, nr. Bus Station Hartham Common, The Wash Hertford East Station *(Greater Anglia)*

	'Caffe Nero', Salisbury Square *(Caffe Nero)*
	'Six Templers', The Wash *(JDW)*
Sawbridgeworth	Bell Street Car Park
Spellbrook	'Three Horseshoes', Spellbrook Lane East *(Spirit)*
Ware	Amwell End/Broadmeads
	Priory Street *(Town Council)*

Epping Forest

Buckhurst Hill	Lower Queens Road
Epping	Bakers Lane Car Park
High Beech	Epping Forest Information Centre *(City of London)*
Hoddesdon	Dobbs Weir Car Park *(Lee Valley RPA)*
Loughton	Brook Path, High Road
	The Broadway
	Traps Hill Car Park
	'The Last Post', 227 High Road *(JDW)*
Ongar	High Street
Waltham Abbey	Quaker Lane Car Park
	High Bridge Street *(Town Council)*
	Fishers Green Car Park *(Lee Valley RPA)*
	'Bakers Arms', Stewardstone Road *(Spirit)*

Fenland

Chatteris	Furrowfields
March	Broad Street
	City Road Car Park *(Town Council)*
Whittlesey	Station Road
Wisbech	Church Terrace Car Park
	Exchange Square *(Town Council)*
	Wisbech Park *(Town Council)*
	Horsefair Shopping Centre *(Private)*
	'Wheatsheaf Inn', Church Terrace *(JDW)*

Forest Heath

Brandon	Brandon Country Park [Under review] *(Suffolk CC)*
Mildenhall	Recreation Way
	CP Mildenhall Community Resource Unit *(Private)*
Newmarket	Memorial Gardens, High Street
	Guineas Shopping Centre *(Private)*
	'Golden Lion', High Street *(JDW)*
	'White Hart', High Street *(Marstons)*

Great Yarmouth

Caister	Beach Road Car Park (Easter-October)
	High Street
	Second Avenue (Easter-October)
	Yarmouth Stadium *(Private)*
	Grasmere Caravan Park *(Private)*
Gorleston	Brush Quay
	High Street, opp. The Feathers
	Pier Head, by Ocean Rooms
	Ravine Bridge, Marine Parade
Great Yarmouth	Alpha Road/Southtown Road
	Caister Road/Beaconsfield Road
	Marina Beach (Easter-October) (7.00-21.00)
	Market Gates Precinct (M+F) (7.00-21.00)
	North Beach, Seafront
	The Conge, off Market Place
	The Jetty, Seafront
	The Tower, Marine Parade

	Great Yarmouth Station, Concourse *(Greater Anglia)*
	'Troll Cart', Regent Road *(JDW)*
CP	Marina Leisure & Fitness Centre *(Private)*
	Gt Yarmouth Racecourse Caravan Site *(Caravan Club)*
	Vauxhall Holiday Park (2) *(Private)*
Hemsby	Beach Road
Martham	Village Green
Winterton	Beach Road Car Park

Harlow

Harlow	Bus Station, Terminus Street
	Town Park, Pets Corner
	Harlow Town Station, Ticket Hall *(Greater Anglia)*
	'Nandos', The Water Gardens *(Nandos)*
	'William Aylmer', Kitson Way *(JDW)*
	'Yates's Bar', Eastgate *(Private)*

Hertsmere

Borehamwood	'Hart & Spool', Shenley Road *(JDW)*
	Gala Bingo, Boulevard Park *(Gala)*
Bushey	King George Recreation Ground
Potters Bar	Oakmere Park, High Street
	'Admiral Byng', Darkes Lane *(JDW)*
Radlett	Radlett Station, Platform 4 *(Capital Connect)*

Huntingdonshire

Grafham Water	Grafham Water Caravan Club Site *(Caravan Club)*
Huntingdon	Bus Station
	Hinchingbrooke Country Park
	Riverside Pavilion, Hartford Road
	Shopmobility, Princess St. Car Park *(Shopmobility)*
	Grammar School Walk Car Park *(Private)*
	'Cromwells Bar', 137 High Street *(Marstons)*
	Art Block, California Road *(Hunts Regional College)*
St Ives	Bus Station, Station Rd/Cattle Market
St Neots	Riverside Park Car Park
	Tebbuts Road Car Park

	'Priory', Market Square *(Marstons)*
	'Weeping Ash', New Street *(JDW)*
CP	One Leisure St Neots, Barford Road *(Private)*
West Perry	Mander Car Park *(Anglia Water)*

Ipswich

Ipswich	Alexandra Park (Park hrs)
	Bourne Park, by Depot (Park hrs)
	Chantry Park, Hadleigh Road (Park hrs)
	Christchurch Park, Lower Arboretum (Park hrs)
	Christchurch Park, Lower Park (Park hrs)
	Corn Exchange, Box Office (Office hrs)
	Holywell Park (Park hrs)
	Majors Corner
	Old Cemetery (Cemetery hrs)
	Ipswich County Library, 1st Floor *(Suffolk Libraries)*
	Ipswich Station, Platform 2 *(Greater Anglia)*
	Buttermarket Centre (2) *(Private)*
	Debenhams Store, Westgate Street *(Debenhams)*
	'Cricketers', Crown Street *(JDW)*
	'Harvester', Cardinal Leisure Park *(M&B)*
	'McDonalds', Cardinal Leisure Park *(McDonalds)*
	'Nandos', Cardinal Leisure Park *(Nandos)*
	'Old Orleans', Cardinal Park *(Private)*
	'Raven', Hening Avenue *(Marstons)*
	'Robert Ransom', Tower Street *(JDW)*
CP	Felgains Care & Mobility, Knightsdale Rd *(Private)*
CP	New SouthWest *(Suffolk CC)*
CP	Rushmere CRU, Humber Ducy Lane *(Private)*

King's Lynn & West Norfolk

Brancaster	Beach Car Park, Broads Lane
Downham Market	Wales Court, Bridge Street (M+F) (6.00-16.00)
	Downham Market Station, Platform 1 *(Capital Connect)*
Heacham	North Beach, Jubilee Road
	South Beach Road
Hilgay	Quayside (April-October)
Holme	Beach Road
Hunstanton	Bowling Green (March-October)

Bus Station, Westgate
Central Promenade, Seagate
Cliff Top, Light House Close
Esplanade Gardens
Seagate (April-October)

King's Lynn	Baker Lane Car Park (7.30-18.00)
	Bus Station
	Ferry Street Car Park (7.30-18.00)
	Gaywood Road (7.00-16.00)
	King's Lynn Station, off Platform 1 *(Capital Connect)*
	'Lattice House', Chapel Street *(JDW)*
	'Nandos', High Street *(Nandos)*
	'The Globe', King Street *(JDW)*
	King's Lynn Campus, Front Block *(Col. of W Anglia)*
Sandringham	Sandringham Country Park *(Private)*
	Sandringham Caravan Club Site *(Caravan Club)*

Luton

Luton	Bells Close Recreation Ground, Havelock Road
	Bramingham Road
	Brantwood Park
	Bus Station
	Dunstable Road, Kingsway
	Farley Hill
	Old Bedford Road, Wardown Park
	Purley Centre, Purway Close (Thursday & Saturday)
	St George's Square, Bute Street
	The Hat Factory (Centre hrs)

**King's Lynn &
West Norfolk Council**
are pleased to support
Disability Rights UK

Make a donation
Support our work with a one-off
or regular donation.

www.disabilityrightsuk.org

Luton Airport Parkway Station *(Capital Connect)*
Luton Station, Platforms 3/4 *(Capital Connect)*
The Mall Luton, Bute Square (2) *(Private)*
The Mall Luton, Central Square *(Private)*
The Mall Luton, Market Hall *(Private)*
Debenhams Store, The Mall *(Debenhams)*
'Nandos', Galaxy Centre, Bridge Street *(Nandos)*
'White House', Bridge Street *(JDW)*

Maldon

Burnham-on-Crouch	Doctor's Lane
	The Quay Riverside Park
Heybridge	Bentalls Shopping Centre *(Private)*
Maldon	Promenade Coach Park
CP	Promenade Park, Sea Wall (Park hrs)
	Kings Head Centre *(Private)*

Mid Suffolk

Barham	Barham Picnic Site [Under review] *(Suffolk CC)*
Bramford	Picnic Site, Ship Lane [Under review] *(Suffolk CC)*
Needham Market	Needham Lakes Car Park
	Barratts Lane *(Town Council)*
Stowmarket	Ipswich Street, By Regal Theatre *(Town Council)*
	Recreation Ground, Finborough Road *(Town Council)*
	Wilkes Way *(Asda)*
	'Willow Tree', 101 Ipswich Street *(JDW)*

North Hertfordshire

Ashwell	Ashridge Farm Caravan Club Site *(Caravan Club)*
Hitchin	'Que Pasa', Market Place *(Marstons)*
Letchworth	The Gallery, Openshaw Way *(Private)*
	Central Approach *(Private)*
	'Three Magnets', Leys Avenue *(JDW)*

North Norfolk

Bacton	Coast Road (March-October & weekends)
Blakeney	The Quay

Cromer	Cadogan Road
	Meadow Road Car Park
	Melbourne (March-October)
	Pier (mid March-October)
	Rocket House (Café hrs)
	Runton Road (mid March-December)
	Seacroft Caravan Club Site *(Caravan Club)*
East Runton	Beach (March-October)
Fakenham	Bridge Street
	Highfields
	Queens Road
	Fakenham Racecourse Caravan Club Site *(Caravan Club)*
Happisburgh	Cart Gap (mid March-September)
Hickling	Staithe
Holt	Albert Street
	Country Park
Horning	Swan Car Park
Hoveton	Station Road
Ludham	Ludham Bridge
	Broadlands Caravan Club Site *(Caravan Club)*
Mundesley	Marina Road
North Walsham	Car Park, New Road
Overstrand	Pauls Lane Car Park (mid March-December)
Potter Heigham	Bridge
Sea Palling	Beach Road
Sheringham	East Promenade (March-October)
	High Street
	Station Approach
	West Promenade
	Sheringham Park *(National Trust)*
Stalham	High Street
Walcott	Coast Road
Walsingham	High Street
Wells-next-the-Sea	Newgate Lane
	Quay, Beach Road

West Runton   Incleboro Field Caravan Site *(Caravan Club)*

Norwich

Drayton   'Cock Inn', Drayton High Street *(Marstons)*

Norwich   Chapelfield Gardens Park (Park hrs)
City Hall, St Peters Street (Office hrs)
Eaton Park (Park hrs)
Memorial Gardens, St Peters Street (Mon-Sat)
St Giles MSCP, St Giles Street
Waterloo Park
Wensum Park (April-October) (Park hrs)
Norwich Station, Platform 5 *(Greater Anglia)*
Anglia Square *(Private)*
Castle Mall (3) *(Private)*
Co-op Store, St Stephens Street *(Co-op)*
Debenhams Store, Orford Place *(Debenhams)*
Jarrolds Store, London Street *(Private)*
'All Bar One', Tombland/Upper King Street *(Private)*
'Auberge', Castle Mall *(Private)*
'Bell Hotel', Orford Hill *(JDW)*
'Forget-me-Not Café', Redwell Street *(Private)*
'Glass House', Wensum Street *(JDW)*
'Henrys', Haymarket *(Private)*
'KFC', Dereham Road *(KFC)*
'KFC', Prince of Wales Road *(KFC)*
'Maid Marian', Ipswich Road *(Private)*
'Nandos', 23 Red Lion Street *(Nandos)*
'Nandos', Riverside Leisure Park *(Nandos)*
'Norwegian Blue', Riverside Leisure Park *(Spirit)*
'Queen of Iceni', Riverside Leisure Park *(JDW)*
'Revolution', 6 Queen Street *(Private)*
'Slug & Lettuce', 7/9 Queen Street *(Private)*
'The Whiffler', Boundary Road *(JDW)*
'Wagon & Horses', Dereham Road *(Private)*
'Yates's Bar', Queens Street *(Private)*
Lower Common Room, Union Building *(UEA)*
Norwich Magistrates Court *(Courts Service)*
Cinema City *(Private)*
Norfolk Showground Caravan Club Site *(Caravan Club)*

Peterborough

Peterborough	Car Haven Car Park (Daytime)
	Northminster MSCP (Daytime)
	St Peters Arcade, Bridge Street
	Peterborough Station, Platforms 2 & 5 *(East Coast)*
	'College Arms', The Broadway *(JDW)*
	'Drapers Arms', Cowgate *(JDW)*
	'Moorhen', West Lake Avenue, Hampton Vale *(Marstons)*
	Peterborough Bowl *(AMF)*
	Ferry Meadows Caravan Site *(Caravan Club)*
CP	Mencap Business Support Centre, Hampton *(Private)*

Rochford

Ashingdon	Ashingdon Recreation Fields
	'Victory Inn', 385 Ashingdon Road *(Private)*
Great Wakering	High Street
Hockley	Hockley Road Car Park
	Hockley Woods Car Park
Hullbridge	Pooles Lane
Rayleigh	Crown Hill
	'Roebuck', High Street *(JDW)*
	'Travellers Joy', Down Hall Road *(Greene King)*
	Warehouse Centre *(Private)*
Rochford	Back Lane
	Rochford Station *(Greater Anglia)*
	'Anne Boleyn', Southend Road *(Private)*
Southend Airport	Southend Airport Station, Platform *(Stobbart Rail)*
Wallasea Island	Riverside Village Holiday Park *(Private)*

South Cambridgeshire

Cambourne	'Monkfield Arms', Cambourne Village *(Marstons)*
Linton	'Dog & Duck' *(Private)*
Milton	Milton Country Park *(Private)*
	Enterprise Building, Cambridge Campus *(Col. of W Anglia)*

South Norfolk

Diss	Meres Mouth, by Tourist Information Centre
Harleston	Bullock Fair Close Car Park
Hingham	Market Place
Loddon	Church Plain
Long Stratton	Swan Lane Car Park
Wymondham	Market Place

Southend-on-Sea

Chalkwell	CP	Chalkwell Esplanade, opp. Station
		Chalkwell Park, London Road
Leigh-on-Sea		Belfairs Park, Eastwood Road North
		Bell Wharf, Old Leigh High Street
		Eastwood Park, Rayleigh Road
		Elm Road, between Rectory Road & Broadway
		Sutherland Boulevard/London Road
		Leigh-on-Sea Station, Concourse *(C2C)*
		'Sarah Moor', Elm Road *(Marstons)*
		'The Elms', 1060 London Road *(JDW)*
Shoeburyness		East Beach Car Park, George Street (Events only)
		Ness Road
		Shoebury Common, Car Park
		Shoebury Park, Elm Road
	CP	Shoeburyness Leisure Centre
Southchurch		Southchurch Hall Park, Woodgrange Drive
		Southchurch Park, Liftsan Way
		'White Horse', Southchurch Road *(Spirit)*
Southend	CP	City Beach, Marine Parade
		Dalmatia Road, nr. Southchurch Road
	CP	Marine Parade, opp. The Ship
		Pitmans Close
		Priory Park, Victoria Avenue
		Seaway Car Park, Queensway (M+F)
		Pier Gardens *(Private)*
		Southend Central Station, Concourse *(C2C)*
		Southend Victoria Station *(Greater Anglia)*
		The Royals Shopping Centre *(Private)*

	Victoria Shopping Centre *(Private)*
	Debenhams Store, The Royals *(Debenhams)*
	'Nandos', 24 London Road *(Nandos)*
	'Slug & Lettuce', 6-8 Southchurch Road *(Private)*
	'The Bell', Southend Arterial Road *(Private)*
	'Varsity', Chichester Road *(Barracuda)*
	Student Union, Elmer Approach *(University of Essex)*
	Mecca Bingo, Greyhound Shopping Park *(Mecca)*
	Roots Hall Stadium *(Southend Utd FC)*
Thorpe Bay	Thorpe Esplanade (April-October)
Westcliff	London Road/Hamlet Court Road
	Western Esplanade, by Café

St Albans

Chiswell Green	'Three Hammers', Watford Road *(Private)*
Harpenden	'Silver Cup', 5 St Albans Road *(Private)*
	'The George', High Street *(Private)*
London Colney	High Street
Redbourne	High Street Car Park
Sandridge	High Street Car Park
St Albans	Alban Arena Car Park (M+F) (Daytime)
	Alban Arena, Foyer (Centre hrs)
	Clarence Park, Bowling Green (Park hrs)
	Clarence Park, Ornamental Gardens (Park hrs)
	Drovers Way, Car Park
	Hatfield Road Cemetery (Cemetery hrs)
	Park Street
	The Ridgeway, Marshalswick
	Tourist & Information Centre, Town Hall (Centre hrs)
	Verulamium Changing Rooms (M+F)
	Verulamium Park, Causeway (M+F) (Daytime)
	Westminster Lodge Running Track
	Jubilee Centre, Church Street *(Private)*
	The Maltings Shopping Centre *(Private)*
	'Cross Keys', Chequer Street *(JDW)*
	'Inn on the Park', Verulamium Park *(Private)*
	'Nandos', Chequer Street *(Nandos)*
	'Peahen', 14 London Road *(Private)*
	'Waterend Barn', St Peters Street *(JDW)*

| Wheathampstead | East Lane Car Park
'The Bull', High Street *(Private)*
'Wicked Lady', 15 Normansland *(Private)* |

St Edmundsbury

Bury St Edmunds	Abbey Gardens, Angel Hill Bus Station Hardwick Heath, Hardwick Lane Nowton Park, Nowton Road West Stow Country Park (Park hrs) Bury St Edmunds Station *(Greater Anglia)* **CP** Arc Shopping Centre *(Private)* 'Corn Exchange', Abbeygate Street *(JDW)*
Clare	Clare Castle Country Park
Haverhill	Council Offices (Office hrs) East Town Park (Park hrs) Jubilee Walk Recreation Ground, Recreation Road 'Drabbet Smock', Peas Hill *(JDW)*

Stevenage

| Stevenage | Fairlands Valley Park, Sailing Centre
Town Square
Stevenage Station, inside ticket gate *(Capital Connect)*
Westgate Shopping Centre, 1st Floor *(Private)*
'KFC', Stevenage Leisure Park *(KFC)*
'Nandos', Kings Way Leisure Park *(Nandos)*
'Standard Bearer', The Plaza *(JDW)*
'Standing Order', High Street *(JDW)*
'The Proverbial', 76 High Street *(Barracuda)*
'White Lion', 68 High Street *(Greene King)* |

Suffolk Coastal

Aldeburgh	Fort Green Moot Hall West Lane
Bawdsey	The Ferry
Dunwich	Dunwich Beach Coastguard Cottages, Dunwich Heath *(National Trust)*

Felixstowe		Bath Tap, Bath Hill
		Beach Station Road
	CP	Crescent Road Car Park
		Golf Road Car Park
		Langer Park
		Manor Road Car Park
		Ranelagh Road Car Park
		Spa Pavilion
		The Dip
		Town Hall

Framlingham	Crown *&* Anchor Lane

Leiston	Sizewell Road (Daytime)
	Dinsdale Road (Daytime) *(Town Council)*

Martlesham	'Red Lion', Main Road *(Chef & Brewer)*

Orford	Quay Street Car Park *(Parish Council)*

Saxtead	The Green

Sizewell	Sizewell Beach Car Park

Thorpeness	The Mere

Walberswick	Village

Wickham Market	Crafters Car Park

Woodbridge	Brook Street
	Jetty Lane
	Elmhurst Park *(Town Council)*
	Kingston Field *(Town Council)*

Tendring

Brightlingsea	Promenade Way Car Park
	Station Road
	Waterside

Clacton	High Street Car Park
	Lower Promenade, Ambleside (May-October)
	Lower Promenade, West Greensward
	Magdalen Green, Old Road/Coppins Road
	Pier Gap, Bottom Promenade
	Rosemary Road, opp. The Grove
	Westcliff, Middle Promenade, nr. Pier
	Clacton Station *(Greater Anglia)*

	'McDonalds', Pier Avenue *(McDonalds)* 'Moon & Starfish', Marine Parade East *(JDW)* Flicks Cinema, Pier Avenue *(Private)* Gala Bingo, Pier Avenue *(Gala)*
Dovercourt	Lower Marine Parade Milton Road Car Park West End Lane
Frinton	Esplanade, opp. Connaught Avenue Greensward Kiosk, nr. Golf Club Lower Promenade, opp. Cambridge Road Old Way
Harwich	Main Road, by High Lighthouse
Holland-on-Sea	Holland Gap, nr. Car Park Ipswich Road, nr. Car Park Middle Promenade, opp. Queensway (May-October) 'Roaring Donkey', Holland Road *(Greene King)*
Jaywick	Meadow Way/Tamarisk Way
Manningtree	Market Site, Brook Street
Parkeston	Harwich International Station, Platform 1 *(Greater Anglia)*
Walton-on-the-Naze	Coronation Car Park, Princes Esplanade (May-October) Jubilee Beach, Lower Promenade (May-October) Mill Lane Walton-on-Naze Station *(Greater Anglia)* Walton Pier *(Private)*

Three Rivers

Rickmansworth	Aquadrome, Frogmoor Lane (Dawn-dusk) 'Pennsylvanian', High Street *(JDW)*
CP	Old Town Hall, High Street *(Mencap)*

Thurrock

Aveley	Belhus Park Golf & Country Club *(Private)*
Chafford Hundred	Chafford Hundred Station, Booking Hall *(C2C)* 'Treacle Mine', Lodge Lane, *(Private)*
Grays	Grays Beach Riverside Park, Thames Road *(Private)* Grays Station *(C2C)* Grays Shopping Precinct *(Private)*

	CP	Woodview Campus, E Block *(South Essex College)*
		Woodview Campus, Learning Resource Centre *(South Essex College)*
		Blackshots Leisure Centre, Blackshots Lane *(Private)*
	CP	Grays Community Resource Centre *(Private)*
Lakeside		Debenhams Store, Lakeside Centre *(Debenhams)*
		'Las Iguanas', The Broadwalk *(Private)*
		'Nandos', Lakeside Pavilion *(Nandos)*
		'Wagamama', The Boardwalk *(Private)*
Little Thurrock		Tyrrells Hall Club, Dock Road *(Private)*
North Stfford		'Dog & Partridge', High Road *(Private)*
Purfleet		'Royal Hotel', London Road *(Spirit)*
South Ockendon	CP	South Ockendon Locality Base
Stanford-le-Hope		East Thurrock Community Association *(Private)*
	CP	Stanford Base, The Sorrells *(Private)*
Tilbury		Tilbury Town Station, Platform 1 *(C2C)*
		Tilbury Community Assn Leisure Centre *(Private)*
West Thurrock M25		Thurrock Services, A1306 *(Moto)*

Uttlesford

Saffron Walden	Library, Market Square (Library hrs) *(Essex CC)*
	'The Temeraire', High Street *(JDW)*
Stansted Airport	Terminal, Airside by Frankie & Bennies *(Airport)*
	Terminal, Airside by Wetherspoons *(Airport)*
	Terminal, Landside, by 'Bridge Bar' *(Airport)*

Watford

Garston	North Watford Cemetery (Cemetery hrs)
	Orbital Community Centre, Garston *(Private)*
	Hollywood Bowl, Woodside Leisure Park *(AMF)*
	Watford Leisure Centre, Woodside *(Private)*
Watford	Charter Place Market
	Watford Colosseum, Town Hall (Hall hrs)
	Holywell Community Centre, Chaffinch Lane *(Private)*
	Watford Junction Station, Booking Hall *(London Midland)*
	Harlequin Shopping Centre *(Private)*
	'Bar Naz', 135 The Parade *(Private)*

'Café Maximo Bar', High Street *(Private)*
'Caffe Nero', High Street *(Caffe Nero)*
'Chicago Rock Café', The Parade *(Private)*
'Colombia Press', High Street *(JDW)*
'Destiny Night Club', The Parade *(Private)*
'Essex Arms', Langley Way *(Private)*
'Moon Under Water', High Street *(JDW)*
'Nandos', 42 The Parade *(Nandos)*
'O'Neills', The Parade *(M&B)*
'Que Pasa', 58 High Street *(Marstons)*
'Reflex', The Parade *(Private)*
'Revolution', 48/50 High Street *(Private)*
'Southern Cross', Langley Road *(Spirit)*
'The Flag', Station Road *(Private)*
'Walkabout', The Parade, High Street *(Private)*
'Sportz Academy', The Parade *(Private)*
Vicarage Road Stadium, hospitality area *(Watford FC)*

Waveney

Beccles	Blyburgate Car Park
	Hungate Car Park
	Yacht Station, The Quay
	'Kings Head', Newmarket *(JDW)*
Bungay	Priory Lane
	Bungay Pool, changing area *(Private)*
Halesworth	Thoroughfare Car Park
	Halesworth & District Museum *(Trust)*
Kessingland	Church Road
	Heathland Beach Caravan Park (3) *(Private)*
	White Horse Beach Caravan Club Site *(Caravan Club)*
Lowestoft	Gordon Road
	Jubilee Parade North (Summer)
	Kensington Gardens, A12
	Kirkley Cenetery
	Lowestoft Cemetery, Normanston Drive
	Pakefield Street
	Sparrow's Nest Park (Daytime)
	Triangle Market, High Street
	Lowestoft Library, Clapham Rd South *(Suffolk Libraries)*

Oulton Broad	Nicholas Everitt Park (Daytime)
Southwold	Church Green
	The Harbour, Ferry Street
	The Pier

Welwyn Hatfield

Cuffley		Northaw Great Wood
Hatfield		Hatfield Leisure Centre (Centre hrs)
		Hatfield Swim Centre (2) (Centre hrs)
		Galleria Shopping Centre *(Private)*
		'Nandos', Unit 66 The Galleria *(Nandos)*
	CP	Briars Pavilion, Briars Lane
Welwyn Garden City		Campus East (Office hrs)
		Campus West (Office hrs)
		Stanborough Lakes North, by Play Area
		Stanborough Lakes South behind Café
		Stanborough Lakes, South
		Howard Centre, 1st Floor (2) *(Private)*
		Commons Wood Caravan Club Site *(Caravan Club)*
	CP	Woodcot Centre, off Ridgeway

Amber Valley

Alfreton	Cemetery, Rogers Lane (8.00-16.30)
	Leabrooks Cemetery
	'Wagon & Horses', King Street *(JDW)*
CP	Genesis Family Entertainment Centre *(Private)*
Belper	Belper Cemetery
	River Gardens, Matlock Road
Duffield	'Bridge Inn', Duffield Bank *(Marstons)*
Heanor	'Red Lion', Derby Road *(JDW)*
CP	Shipley Country Park Visitor Centre *(Derbys CC)*
Ripley	'Red Lion', Market Place *(JDW)*
South Normanton	'Boundary', Lea Vale, Broadmeadows *(Marstons)*

Ashfield

Hucknall	Market Place, Ogle Street (7.00-19.00)
	'Bowman', Nottingham Road *(Spirit)*
	'Pilgrim Oak', High Street *(JDW)*
Huthwaite	Columbia Street
Kirkby-in-Ashfield	Station Street (7.00-19.00)
	'The Regent', Kingsway *(JDW)*
Sutton-in-Ashfield	Idlewells Shopping Centre *(Private)*
	'Picture House', Fox Street *(JDW)*

Bassetlaw

Blyth A1(M)	Blyth Services A1(M)/A614 *(Moto)*
Clumber Park	Cricket Ground *(National Trust)*
	Near Conservation Centre *(National Trust)*
	Clumber Park Caravan Site *(Caravan Club)*
Retford	Bus Station, waiting room (Station hrs)
	Chancery Lane (Daytime)
	Chapelgate (Mon-Sat, daytime)
	Retford Station *(East Coast)*
	'Broadstone', The Square *(Private)*
	'Dominie Cross', Market Place *(JDW)*
	'Litten Tree', Chapelgate *(Private)*
Worksop	73, Bridge Street
	Gateford Road (Mon-Sat, daytime)
	Priory Shopping Centre (Shopping hrs)
	'Half Moon', Whitwell Common *(Private)*
	'Liquorice Gardens', Newcastle Street *(JDW)*
	'Litten Tree', Victoria Square *(Private)*
	'Lock Keeper', Sandy Lane *(Marstons)*
	'Three Legged Stool', Raymoth Lane *(Private)*
	'Top House', Park Street *(Private)*
	'White Lion', Park Street *(JDW)*
	CP Worksop Library *(Notts CC)*

Blaby

Blaby	Johns Court, Waitrose Car Park
Glen Parva	'Glen Parva Manor', The Ford *(Marstons)*
Kirby Muxloe	'Castle Hotel', Main Street *(Spirit)*
Whetstone	'Old Vicarage', 123 Enderby Road *(Marstons)*

Bolsover

Bolsover	Cavendish Walk (Mon-Sat, daytime)
Shirebrook	CP Carter Lane Day Centre *(Derbys CC)*

Boston

Boston	Cattle Market Car Park, Bargate

	Central Park
	Lincoln Lane
	'Moon Under Water', High Street *(JDW)*
CP	Princess Royal Sports Arena *(Private)*

| Leverton | Picnic Area, off A52 |

Broxtowe

Beeston	Beeston Fields Recreation Ground, Central Avenue
	Broadgate Park, High Road
	Leyton Crescent Recreation Ground (Attendant hrs only)
	Weirfields Recreation Ground, Canal Side
	'Last Post', Foster Avenue/Chilwell Road *(JDW)*
CP	Bramcote Leisure Centre, Derby Road

| Chilwell | 'Charlton Arms', High Road *(Spirit)* |

| Eastwood | Coronation Park, Plumtre Way |
| | Nottingham Road, by Library |

| Kimberley | Main Street |

Stapleford	Ilkeston Road Recreation Ground
	Queen Elizabeth Park, Toton Lane
	The Roach
	'Admiral Sir John Warren', 97 Derby Road *(JDW)*

| Toton | Manor Farm Recreation Ground, High Road |

Charnwood

| Anstey | The Nook Car Park (Mon-Sat, 8.00-18.00) *(Parish Council)* |

| Barrow-on-Soar | High Street Car Park [Closed at present] (8.00-16.30) *(Parish Council)* |

| Birstall | Stonehill Avenue (Mon-Sat, daytime) *(Parish Council)* |

| Hathern | Kings Arms, Derby Road *(Marstons)* |

Loughborough	Biggin Street (Thurs & Sat, 8.00-18.00)
	Charnwood Water (8.00-18.00)
	Market Yard (Daytime)
	Outwoods Park (Park hrs)
	Queens Park (Park hrs)
	Sainsbury's Store, Greenclose Lane *(Sainsbury)*
	'Amber Rooms', The Rushes *(JDW)*
	'Moon & Bell', Wards End *(JDW)*

	'Revolution', Baxtergate *(Private)*
	'Varsity', Market Street *(Barracuda)*
Markfield	'Copt Oak', Whitwick Road *(Marstons)*
Markfield M1	Leicester Services, M1/A50 *(Moto)*
Quorn	Station Road *(Parish Council)*
Shepshed	Hallcroft (Daytime) *(Town Council)*
Sileby	King Street (6.30-18.00) *(Parish Council)*
Syston	Melton Road Car Park *(Town Council)*
Woodhouse Eaves	Main Street *(Parish Council)*

Chesterfield

Brimington	High Street
Chesterfield	Beetwell Street Coach Station
	Pavements Centre (Shopping hrs)
	Queens Park, North Lodge (Daytime)
	Chesterfield Station, Platform 1 *(East Midlands Trains)*
	Vicar Lane Shopping Centre *(Private)*
	Sainsbury's Store, Rother Way *(Sainsbury)*

	'Crooked Spire', Church Way *(Marstons)*
	'Portland Hotel', West Bars *(JDW)*
	'Spa Lane Vaults', St Marys Gate *(JDW)*
	'Yates's Bar', Burlington Street *(Private)*
Hollingwood	'Hollingwood Hotel', Private Drive *(Marstons)*
Newbold	Holmebrook Valley Park (Dawn-dusk)
Old Whittington	by Swanwick Memorial Hall
Poolsbrook	Poolsbrook Country Park (Dawn-dusk)
Somersall	Somersall Park, Somersall Lane
Staveley	Market Place Car Park (Dawn-dusk)
Tapton	Tapton Park (Dawn-dusk)
Whittington Moor	Duke Street, off Sheffield Road

Corby

Corby		Boating Lake, Cottingham Road (Park hrs)
		Market Walk, Queens Square *(Private)*
		Willow Place Shopping Centre *(Private)*
		'Harpers Brook', Butland Road *(Marstons)*
		'Samuel Lloyd', Rockingham Rd/Gretton Rd *(JDW)*
		'Spread Eagle', Oakley Road *(Marstons)*
	CP	Corby International Swimming Pool
East Carlton		East Carlton Countryside Park (Park hrs)

Daventry

Braunston		'Boat House', London Road *(Marstons)*
Brixworth	**CP**	Brixworth Country Park, Mackintosh Centre (Centre hrs) *(County Council)*
Daventry		Daventry Country Park, by Visitor Centre (Centre hrs)
		New Street
		'Queen of Hearts', Ashby Fields *(Marstons)*
		'Saracen's Head', Brook Street *(JDW)*

Derby

Allenton	Allenton Market (Market days)
Derby	Arboretum, Rosehill Street
	Bold Lane Car Park
	Chaddesdon Park, Chaddesdon Lane

Darley Park, by Café
Darley Playing Fields
Markeaton Park, nr Craft Village
Munday Play Centre
Quad, Market Place (Centre hrs)
Rowditch Recreation Ground
The Spot, London Rd/Osmaston Rd (8.00-17.00)
Victoria Street
Derby Station, Platforms 1 & 4 *(East Midlands Trains)*
CP Westfield Derby Shopping Centre *(Private)*
'Babington Arms', Babington Lane *(JDW)*
'Fat Cat', Friar Gate *(Private)*
'Nandos', 15/16 Market Place *(Nandos)*
'Old Orleans', Pride Parkway *(Private)*
'Pitcher & Piano', Friargate *(Marstons)*
'Revolution', Wardwick *(Private)*
'Slug & Lettuce', Irongate *(Private)*
'Sodabar', Friar Gate *(Private)*
'Standing Order', Irongate *(JDW)*
'Varsity', Friar Gate *(Barracuda)*
'Walkabout', Market Place *(Private)*
'Yates's Bar', Irongate *(Private)*
Derby College Sports Centre *(College)*
Pride Park Stadium *(Derby County FC)*

Littleover	Burton Road Shops
Oakwood	'Kings Corner', Lime Lane *(Marstons)*

Derbyshire Dales

Ashbourne	Bus Station
	Recreation Ground
	Shaw Croft Car Park
	Mappleton Lane Car Park *(National Park)*
	'Stepping Stones', Carnation Way, A52 *(Marstons)*
Ashford-in-the-Water	Village
Bakewell	Agricultural Business Centre
	Granby Road
	Recreation Ground
	Riverside
Baslow	Village

	Chatsworth Park Caravan Club Site *(Caravan Club)*
Bradwell	Village
Cromford	Memorial Gardens
Darley Dale	Station Road
Dovedale	Dovedale Car Park *(National Park)*
Eyam	Village
Hartington	Village
Hathersage	Village
Kirk Ireton	Blackwall Plantation Caravan Club Site *(Caravan Club)*
Matlock	Artists Corner
	Bus Station
	Hall Leys Play Area
	Hall Leys, Roadside
	'The Crown', Crown Square *(JDW)*
	CP Arc Leisure, Bakewell Road *(Private)*
Matlock Bath	North Parade
	Pavilion
Middleton Top	Picnic Site *(Derbyshire CC)*
Middleton-by-Youlgreave	Village
Monsal Head	Village
Over Haddon	Village
Parsley Hay	Cycle Hire Centre, A515 *(Private)*
Rowsley	'Grouse & Claret', Station Road *(Marstons)*
Thorpe	Village
Tideswell	Tideswell Dale *(National Park)*
Winster	Village
Wirksworth	Barmcote Croft Car Park

East Lindsey

Anderby Creek	Sandy Lane (Daytime)
Burgh le Marsh	Market Place (Daytime)
Chapel St Leonards	Bus Station, Sea Rd (Daytime in winter) *(Parish Council)*
	Chapel Point (Summer) (7.00-20.00) *(Parish Council)*
	South Road *(Parish Council)*

	Trunch Lane (Summer) (7.00-20.00) *(Parish Council)*
Conningsby	Castle Lane Car Park (Daytime)
Horncastle	St Lawrence Street (Daytime)
CP	Horncastle Swimming Pool
Huttoft	Huttoft Bank
Ingoldmells	Bus Station, Church Street (Daytime)
	Sea Lane, Joe's Beach Bar (Summer) (9.00-24.00)
Louth	Bus Station, Church Street (Daytime)
	Eastgate, by Market Hall (Daytime)
	Hubbards Hill *(Trust)*
CP	Meridian Leisure Centre, Wood Lane
Mablethorpe	Central Promenade (Summer) (7.00-20.00)
	Dunes Gardens, Quebec Road (Daytime)
	Queens Park (Summer & weekends) (Daytime)
	Seacroft Road Bus Station (Daytime)
	Seaview Car Park (Summer) (7.00-20.00)
	Bohemia (Summer) (Daytime) *(Town Council)*
	Golf Rd (Summer & weekends) (Daytime) *(Town Council)*
	North End (Summer & weekends) (Daytime) *(Town Council)*
	South Promenade, by Coral Café (Summer) *(Town Council)*
North Somercotes	Playing Field (Closed at night in winter) *(Parish Council)*
Skegness CP	Briar Way (Daytime)
	Lumley Square (Daytime)
	North Parade (Summer) (7.00-20.00)
	Princes Parade (Summer & Winter weekends) (Daytime)
	Tower Esplanade (Daytime)
	Tower Gardens (Daytime)
	Skegness Station *(East Midlands Trains)*
	'Red Lion', Roman Bank *(JDW)*
	Embassy Centre, Upper Foyer *(Private)*
Spilsby	Market Place (Daytime)
Sutton-on-Sea	by Sandilands Golf Course (Daytime)
	Pleasure Gardens, York Road (Daytime)
	Hawthorn Farm Caravan Club Site *(Caravan Club)*
Wainfleet	Brooks Walk (Daytime)
Winthorpe	Sandfields, Roman Bank (Summer) (7.00-20.00)

Woodhall Spa	Spa Road (Daytime)
	Jubilee Park (Easter-October) *(Parish Council)*
Wragby	Market Place (Daytime)

East Northamptonshire

Higham Ferrers	Wharf Road (Daytime) *(Town Council)*
Irthlingborough	High Street (Daytime) *(Town Council)*
Oundle	St Osyth's Lane (Daytime) *(Town Council)*
Raunds	Marshals Road *(Town Council)*
Rushden	Duck Street (Mon-Sat, 8.00-17.00) *(Town Council)*
	Newton Road (8.00-17.00) *(Town Council)*
Thrapston	Oundle Road (Daytime) *(Town Council)*

Erewash

Borrowash	Victoria Avenue, Supermarket Car Park
Breaston	Blind Lane
	'Bulls Head', Wilsthorpe Road *(Marstons)*
Draycott	Markets Street/Derby Street
Ilkeston	Gallows Hill
	Market Place, Bath Street
	Station Road
CP	Ilkeston Co-op Store, Market Place *(Private)*
	'Moon & Sixpence', Market Place *(Spirit)*
	'Observatory', Market Place *(JDW)*
Long Eaton	Hall Grounds
	Long Eaton Station
	Market Trader
	Orchard Street
	Trent Lock
	West Park Pavilion
	'Twitchel Inn', Clifford Street *(JDW)*
Sandiacre	Longmoor Lane
Sawley	'Bell Inn', Tamworth Road *(Private)*
Trowell M1	Trowell Services, J25/26 *(Moto)*

Gedling

Arnold	Arnot Hill Park (Kiosk hrs)
	Burnt Stump Park Car Park
	Redhill Cemetery (Cemetery hrs)
	Wood Street
	'Burnt Stump', Burnt Stump Road *(Marstons)*
	'Friar Tuck', Gedling Road *(Spirit)*
	'The Ernehale', Nottingham Road *(JDW)*
Bestwood	Bestwood Country Park, Alexandra Lodge *(Notts CC)*
Burton Joyce	'Wheatsheaf Inn', Main Street *(Spirit)*
Calverton	St Wilfreds Square
Carlton	Cavendish Road, nr. Cemetery
Gedling	'Chesterfield Arms', Main Road *(Spirit)*
Mapperley	'Woodthorpe Top', Woodthorpe Road *(JDW)*
Stoke Bardolph	'Ferry Boat Inn' *(Spirit)*

Harborough

Little Bowden	Recreation Ground
Lutterworth	George Street Car Park *(Town Council)*
	'Elms', St John's Business Park *(Marstons)*
Market Harborough	The Commons Car Park
	Welland Park, Welland Park Road
	Market Harborough Station, Platform 1 *(East Midlands Trains)*
	'Peacock', St Mary's Place *(Marstons)*
	'Sugar Loaf', High Street *(JDW)*

High Peak

Buxton	Market Place (7.00-19.00)
	Pavilion Gardens Car Park
	Pavilion Gardens, Boating Lake
	Sylvan Car Park
	Grin Low Country Park *(Derbys CC)*
	'Wye Bridge House', Fairfield Road *(JDW)*
	Grin Low Caravan Club Site *(Caravan Club)*
Castleton	Losehill Caravan Club Site *(Caravan Club)*
Chapel-en-le-Frith	'Fallow Deer', Foresters Way *(Marstons)*

Glossop	Manor Park
	Market Place
	Glossop Station *(Northern Rail)*
	'Norfolk Arms', High Street *(Holts)*
Hayfield	Hayfield Countryside Centre
	Sett Valley Trail Car Park *(Derbys CC)*
	Bowden Bridge Car Park *(National Park)*
Whaley Bridge	Market Street

Hinckley & Bosworth

Barwell	Top Town, Shilton Road
Hinckley	Ashby Road Cemetery (Cemetery hrs)
	Hollycroft Park (Park hrs)
	Leisure Centre, Coventry Road (Centre hrs)
	Station Road
	'Baron of Hinckley', Regent Street *(JDW)*
	'Hinckley Knight', Watling Street *(Private)*
Newbold Vernon	Methodist Church Car Park, Main Street *(Church)*

Kettering

Burton Latimer	Churchill Way Car Park
Kettering	Kettering Station, Platform 1 *(East Midlands Trains)*
	Newlands Shopping Centre *(Private)*
	'Earl of Dalkeith', Dalkeith Place *(JDW)*
	'Nandos', Kettering Business Park *(Nandos)*
	'Park House', Kettering Business Park *(Marstons)*
	'Trading Post', 10 Bignall Court *(Marstons)*
	Gala Bingo, High Street *(Gala)*
	CP The Shop, God Street *(Private)*
Rothwell	Squires Hill

Leicester

Leicester	Abbey Park, Abbey Park Road (Park hrs)
	Aylestone Hall Gardens
	Aylestone Leisure Centre, Foyer & 1st Floor (Centre hrs)
	Belgrave Road, by Flyover
	Braunston Park, Cort Crescent (Park hrs)
	Clarendon Road, by Library
	Cossington Street, by Recreation Ground

De Montfort Hall, Foyer (Hall hrs)
East Park Road, Spinney Hill Park
Evington Library, Evington Lane (Library hrs)
Fosse Library/Community Centre, Mantle Rd (Centre hrs)
Foundary Square, Belgrave Gate
Humberstone Park, Uppingham Road (Park hrs)
Infirmary Square
Knighton Lane East, opp Leisure Centre
Knighton Park, Palmerston Road (Park hrs)
Leicester Market (Trading hrs)
New Walk Museum & Gallery (Museum hrs)
St Barnabas Library, French Road (Library hrs)
St Margaret Pastures Sports Centre (Centre hrs)
St Margarets Bus Station (Station hrs)
The Oak Centre, Benbow Rise (Centre hrs)
Thurcaston Road
Victoria Park (Park hrs)
Welford Road, Nelson Mandela Park
Western Park, Hinckley Road (Park hrs)
Leicester Station, Platforms 2 & 4 *(East Midlands Trains)*
'Almanack', Bath House Lane *(Private)*
'Café Rouge', Highcross *(Private)*
'Corn Exchange', Market Place *(JDW)*
'Cricketers', Grace Road *(Private)*
'Gynsils', Leicester Road, Glenfield *(Spirit)*
'Heathley Park', Groby Road *(Spirit)*
'High Cross', High Street *(JDW)*
'Jongleurs', Granby Street *(Private)*
'Last Plantagenet', Granby Street *(JDW)*
'Nandos', 50 Granby Street *(Nandos)*
'Nandos', Freemans Leisure Park *(Nandos)*
'Nandos', Highcross *(Nandos)*
'Old Horse' 198 London Road *(Private)*
'Owl & Pussycat', Melton Road *(Spirit)*
'Revolution', New Walk *(Private)*
'Reynard', Market Street *(Private)*
'Varsity', 146 London Road *(Barracuda)*
'Varsity', 8 Friar Lane *(Barracuda)*
'Wagamama', Highcross *(Private)*
'Yates's Bar', Belvoir Street *(Private)*
Campus Centre, The Gateway *(De Montfort Univ)*

CP Clephan Building, The Gateway *(De Montfort Univ)*
Continuing Studies, Freemans Park Campus *(Leicester Col)*
CP Hawthorn Building, The Gateway *(De Montfort Univ)*
CP Hugh Aston Building, The Gateway *(De Montfort Univ)*
CP St Margarets Campus, Grafton Place *(Leicester Col)*
Students' Union, The Gateway *(De Montfort Univ)*
Kingpower Stadium *(Leicester City FC)*
Leicester Tigers Stadium *(Leicester RUFC)*
CP Apex House, Charles Street *(Private)*
CP Mosaic, Oak Spiney Park *(Private)*

Lincoln

Lincoln

Castle Square
City Bus Station, by Shopmobility
Hartsholm Country Park, Visitor Centre
Lucy Tower Street
Tentercroft Street
Westgate, nr. Union Road
CP Yarborough Leisure Centre (Centre hrs)
Lincoln Station, Platform 5 *(East Midlands Trains)*
'Lincolnshire Poacher', Bunkers Hill *(Marstons)*
'Nandos', Brayford Wharf North *(Nandos)*
'Revolution', Park Street *(Private)*
'Slug & Lettuce', 22/28 High Street *(Private)*
'Square Sail', Brayford Wharf North *(JDW)*
'The Forum', Silver Street *(JDW)*
'The Ritz', High Street *(JDW)*
'Varsity', Guildhall Street *(Barracuda)*
'Walkabout', High Street *(Private)*
'Yates's Bar', High Street *(Private)*
CP The Showroom, Tritton Road *(Private)*

Mansfield

Mansfield

Bus Station, Walkden Street
Four Seasons Shopping Centre
Mansfield Town Hall, Market Place
Mansfield Station *(East Midland Trains)*
'Ravensdale', Sherwood Hall Road *(Marstons)*
'Rufford', Chesterfield Road South *(Marstons)*

	'Rushley', Nottingham Road *(Marstons)*
	'Sir John Cockle', Sutton Road *(Marstons)*
	'Swan', Church Street *(Marstons)*
	'The Courthouse', Market Place *(JDW)*
	'Widow Frost', Leeming Street *(JDW)*
	'Yates's Bar', Leeming Street *(Private)*
	Gala Bingo, Albert Street *(Gala)*
Mansfield Woodhouse	Rose Lane
Warsop	High Street Car Park

Melton

Melton Mowbray	Cattle Market (Market days)
	St Mary's Way
	Wilton Road
	'Kettleby Cross', Wilton Road *(JDW)*
CP	Melton Mowbray Mencap, Chapel Street *(Mencap)*
CP	Melton Carnegie Museum *(Leics CC)*

Newark & Sherwood

Bilsthorpe	'Copper Beech', Kirklington Road *(Private)*
Clipstone	Vicar Water Country Park Visitor Centre (Daytime)
Edwinstowe	Mansfield Road, by Village Hall
	Sherwood Forest Country Park Visitor Centre (Centre hrs) *(Notts CC)*
Farnsfield	'White Post', High Street *(Marstons)*
Gunthorpe	'Anchor Inn', Main Street *(Private)*
	'Unicorn Hotel', Gunthorpe Bridge *(Private)*
Kelham	Kelham Hall Civic Suite, Carriage Court (Hall hrs)
Laxton	Dovecote Inn Car Park (Dawn-dusk)
Lowdham	Southwell Road/Main Street
New Balderton	'The Grove', London Road *(Private)*
Newark	Castle Grounds, Gilstrap Building (Daytime)
	London Road Car Park
	Sconce & Devon Park, Boundary Road
CP	St Mark's Place (Daytime)
	Tolney Lane, Riverside Park
	Newark Northgate Station *(East Coast)*

Buttermarket *(Private)*
'Atrium', Castle Gate *(Private)*
'Sir John Ardene', Church Street *(JDW)*

Ollerton	Sherwood Heath Information Centre (Centre hrs)
	Rufford Country Park, The Abbey (Park hrs) *(Notts CC)*
Rainworth	'Robin Hood', Southwell Road East *(Private)*
Rufford	'Rose Cottage', Old Rufford Road *(Private)*
Southwell	Church Street Car Park

North East Derbyshire

Ashover	'Crispin Inn', Church Street *(Private)*
Clay Cross	Market Street *(Parish Council)*
Dronfield	Cliffe Park, Callywhite Lane *(Town Council)*
Grassmoor	'Boot & Shoe', North Wingfield Road *(Private)*

North East Lincolnshire

Cleethorpes	CP	Boating Lake, Kings Road (8.00-18.00, later in summer)
		Kingsway, nr. Leisure Centre
		Sea Road
		St Peter's Avenue, off Car Park
		Cleethorpes Station *(Transpennine)*
		'The Wellow', Kings Road *(Greene King)*
		Pleasure Island *(Private)*
Grimsby		Garibaldi Street (Mon-Fri, 8.30-17.30)
		Market Hall (Mon-Fri, 8.30-17.30)
		Grimsby Town Station *(Transpennine)*
		Freshney Place Shopping Centre *(Private)*
		'Bradley Inn', Bradley Crossroads *(Private)*
		'DN 31', Victoria Street *(Private)*
		'Ice Barque', Frederick Ward Way *(JDW)*
		'The Parity', Old Market Place *(Barracuda)*
		'Yarborough Hotel', Bethlehem Street *(JDW)*
		'Yates's Bar', Riverhead *(Private)*
		Great Grimsby Swimming Pool, Scartho Road
		Grimsby Leisure Centre *(Private)*
Immingham		Kennedy Way, off Car Park
	CP	Immingham Civic Offices (Office hrs) *(Town Council)*

New Waltham	'Harvest Moon'. Station Road *(Private)*
Stallingborough	'Green Man', Station Road *(Private)*
Waltham	Waltham Windmill and Grounds 'Kings Head', High Street *(Private)*

North Kesteven

| North Hykeham | CP | North Kesteven Leisure Centre *(Private)* |
| Sleaford | | Money's Yard, Carre Street (Daytime) *(Town Council)*
'Packhorse Inn', Northgate *(JDW)* |

North Lincolnshire

Barton-on-Humber	Baysgarth Park, Brigg Road Humber Bridge Viewing Area Market Place
Belton	Picnic Area, off A161
Brigg	Barnard Avenue/ Bigby High Road Cary Lane Elsham Country Park, Car Park *(Private)*
Epworth	Chapel Street Car Park
Haxey	Vinehall Road/High Street
Owston Ferry	High Street
Scunthorpe	Ashby High Street, Car Park Dunstall Street Car Park Frodingham Road/Doncaster Road Normanby Hall Car Park Normanby Hall Country Park Parishes MSCP, by Shopmobility Scunthorpe Station *(Transpennine)* 'Blue Bell Inn', Oswald Road *(JDW)* Scunthorpe Bowl, Warren Road *(AMF)*

North West Leicestershire

| Ashby-de-la-Zouch | Kilwardby Street/Derby Road
'White Hart', Market Street *(Marstons)* |
| Coalville | The Precinct, off Hotel Street
'Monkey Walk', Marlborough Square *(JDW)* |

Donington Park M1	Donington Park Services J23A M1 *(Moto)*
Moira	Moira Craft Workshops *(Private)*

Northampton

Northampton	Guildhall, St Giles Square (Office hrs)
	Central Library, Abington St (Library hrs) *(Northants CC)*
	Greyfriars Bus Station *(Private)*
	Northampton Station, Booking Hall *(London Midland)*
	Grosvenor Shopping Centre *(Private)*
	Market Walk Shopping Centre *(Private)*
CP	Weston Favel Shopping Centre (4) *(Private)*
	Debenhams Store, The Drapery *(Debenhams)*
	'Ask', St Giles Square *(Private)*
	'Auctioneers', Market Square *(Marstons)*
	'Billing Mill Restaurant', The Causeway *(Private)*
	'Chicago Rock Café', Market Square *(Private)*
	'Cordwainer', The Ridings *(JDW)*
	'Eastgate', Abington Street *(JDW)*
	'Fish Inn', Fish Street *(Spirit)*
	'Fox & Hounds', Harborough Road, Kingsthorpe *(Private)*
	'Frog & Fiddler', Harborough Road *(Private)*
	'Hart of Duston', 573 Harlestone Road, Duston *(Private)*
	'Hungry Horse', Sixfields Leisure Park *(Private)*
	'KFC', Riverside Business Park *(KFC)*
	'Moon on the Square', Market Square *(JDW)*
	'NB's', Bridge Street *(Private)*
	'Queen Eleanor', London Road, Wootton *(Spirit)*
	'Revolution', 34 Bridge Street *(Private)*
	'White Elephant', Kingley Park Terrace *(Private)*
	'Yates's Bar', The Ridings *(Private)*
CP	Northampton General Hospital *(Hospital)*
	Tenpin 10, Sixfields Leisure Park *(Private)*
	Billing Aquadrome *(Private)*
CP	Pitsford Sports Arena, Moulton College *(College)*

Nottingham

Basford	'Fox', Valley Road *(Spirit)*
Bulwell	**CP** Bulwell Riverside Centre (Centre hrs)
	Duke Street (7.00-18.00)
	CP Ken Martin Leisure Centre

Cinderhill		'Broxtowe Inn', Nuthall Road *(Private)*
Hyson Green		Hyson Green Park & Ride (7.00-18.00)
	CP	Djanogly Community Leisure Centre
	CP	Mary Potter Centre, The Boulevard
Lenton		'Nandos', Redfield Way *(Nandos)*
Nottingham City Centre	CP	Greyhound Street, Market Square (7.00-20.00)
		Broadmarsh Bus Station *(Private)*
		Nottingham Station *(East Midlands Trains)*
		Debenhams Store, Long Row *(Debenhams)*
		'Caffe Nero', 18 Wheelergate *(Caffe Nero)*
		'Company Inn', Castle Wharf *(JDW)*
		'Grove Castle Hotel', Castle Boulevard *(Spirit)*
		'Jongleurs', Castle Wharf *(Private)*
		'Joseph Else', Market Square *(JDW)*
		'KFC', Lower Parliament Street *(KFC)*
		'Liit', Market Street *(Spirit)*
		'Lloyds Bar', Carlton Street *(JDW)*
		'Nandos', Angel Row, Market Square *(Nandos)*
		'Old Dog & Partridge', Lower Parliament Street *(Spirit)*
		'Pit & Pendulum', Victoria Street *(Private)*
		'Revolution', Broad Street, Hockley *(Private)*
		'Revolution', Cornerhouse, Foreman Street *(Private)*
		'Roebuck Inn', St James Street *(JDW)*
		'Slug & Lettuce', Corner House, Foreman Street *(Private)*
		'Varsity', Peel Street *(Barracuda)*
		'Walkabout', Friar Lane *(Private)*
		S Notts College, Carlton Road Centre *(S Notts College)*
		Gala Bingo, Hucknell Road *(Gala)*
	CP	Nottingham Ice Centre *(Private)*
	CP	Nottingham Contemporary Arts Centre *(Private)*
St Ann's		Gala Bingo, St Ann's Well Road *(Gala)*
Wollaton		'Willoughby Arms', Lambourne Drive *(Spirit)*
Wollaton	CP	Wollaton Hall & Gardens

Oadby & Wigston

Great Glen		'Yews', London Road *(Spirit)*
Oadby		East Street Car Park
		'Horse & Hounds', Glen Rise *(Spirit)*
		'Lord Keeper of the Great Seal', The Parade *(JDW)*

South Wigston	Blaby Road
Wigston	Junction Road
	Peace Memorial Park
	'William Wygston', Leicester Road *(JDW)*

Rushcliffe

Ruddington	'Millers', Loughborough Road *(Spirit)*
West Bridgford	Bridgford Park, Central Avenue (Dawn-dusk)
	Trent Bridge Cricket Ground, Fox Rd Stand (2) *(Notts CCC)*
Wilford	'Ferry Inn' *(Chef & Brewer)*

Rutland

Oakham	John Street, Westgate Car Park (7.00-19.00)
CP	Church Street Car Park (7.00-18.00) *(Town Council)*
Uppingham	Market Place (7.00-19.00)

South Derbyshire

Etwall	Eggington Road (Dawn-dusk)
Melbourne	Leisure Centre (Centre hrs)
Overseal	Woodsville Road (Dawn-dusk)
Repton	'Bulls Head', High Street *(Private)*
Shardlow	'Clock Warehouse', London Road *(Marstons)*
Swadlincote	Bus Park, Civic Way (Dawn-dusk)
	East End Car Park (Dawn-dusk)
	'Sir Nigel Gresley', Market Street *(JDW)*
Swarkstone	'Crewe & Harpur', Woodshop Lane *(Marstons)*
Ticknall	Ingleby Lane, nr. Village Hall (Dawn-dusk)
	Calke Abbey, Restaurant Yard *(National Trust)*
Willington	Canal Bridge (Dawn-dusk)

South Holland

Crowland	Town Centre
	West Street
Donington	Park Lane, off A52
Holbeach	Church Street

Long Sutton		West Street
Spalding		Ayscoughfee Gardens (8.00-sunset)
		Bus Station, Winfrey Avenue
		Sheepmarket (8.00-18.00)
		Vine Street
		'Ivy Wall', New Road *(JDW)*
Sutton Bridge		Bridge Road, off A17

South Kesteven

Bourne		South Street (Trading hrs) *(Town Council)*
Deeping St James	CP	Deeping Leisure Centre, Park Road
Gonerby Moor A1		Grantham North Services *(Moto)*
Grantham		Arnoldfield Playing Field (April-September) (9.00-19.00)
		Conduit Lane
		Grantham Station, Platform 1 *(East Coast)*
		George Shopping Centre (2) *(Private)*
		'Tollemache Inn', St Peter's Hill *(JDW)*
		Gala Bingo, Trent Road *(Gala)*
Market Deeping		The Precinct *(Town Council)*
Stamford		Red Lion Square

South Northamptonshire

Brackley	Market Place
Stoke Bruerne	'Navigation', Bridge Road *(Marstons)*
Towcester	Sponne Precinct Car Park

Wellingborough

Finedon	Recreation Ground [Closed at present]
Sywell	'Overstone Manor', Ecton Lane *(Spirit)*
Wellingborough	Bassetts Park
	Commercial Way MSCP (2) (7.30-17.30)
	Market Square (7.30-18.00)
	Swanspool Gardens (7.30-dusk)
	The Embankment
	Wellingborough Station, Platform 1 *(East Midlands Trains)*
	'Red Well', Silver Street *(JDW)*
	Wellingborough Bowl, Victoria Retail Park *(AMF)*
	CP Waendel Leisure Centre *(Private)*

West Lindsey

Caistor	Town Hall Car Park
Gainsborough	Roseway Car Park
	'Sveyn Forkbeard', Silver Street *(JDW)*
Market Rasen	Willingham Wood, by Café *(Private)*

Birmingham

Acocks Green	Westley Road, by Laffertys 'Spread Eagle', Warwick Road *(JDW)*
Aston	Villa Park Stadium *(Aston Villa FC)*
Birmingham City Centre	Central Library (3) (Library hrs) Hurst Street/Queensway Coach Station, Mill Lane *(National Express)* Birmingham New Street Station *(Network Rail)* Moor Street Station *(Chiltern Trains)* Snow Hill Station, Platforms 1 & 3 *(London Midland)* Millennium Point, Curzon Street *(Private)* Pallisades Shopping Centre *(Private)* Pavilions Shopping, by Food Court *(Private)* 'All Bar One', Waters Edge, Brindley Place (M+F) *(M&B)* 'Bennetts', 8 Bennetts Hill *(Marstons)* 'Briar Rose', 25 Bennetts Hill *(JDW)* 'Dragon Inn', Hurst Street *(JDW)* 'Figure of Eight', Broad Street *(JDW)* 'Highlight', 259 Broad Street *(Private)* 'KFC', 98 Bull Street *(KFC)* 'Malt House', Brindley Place *(Spirit)* 'Nandos', R2 The New Bullring *(Nandos)* 'Nandos', The Mailbox *(Nandos)* 'Old Joint Stock', Temple Row West *(Fullers)* 'Risa', Quayside Tower, Broad Street *(Private)* 'Slug & Lettuce', Brindley Place *(Private)* 'Soloman Cutler', Regency Wharf *(JDW)* 'Square Peg', Corporation Street *(JDW)* 'The Hornet', Alum Green Road *(JDW)* 'Walkabout', Regency Wharf *(Private)* 'Wetherspoons', Paradise Place *(JDW)* International Convention Centre (2) *(Private)* Bowlplex, Broadway Plaza *(Private)* Gala Casino, Hill Street *(Gala)* National Indoor Arena, Concourse O2 Academy, New Street (2) *(Private)* Old Joint Stock Theatre, Temple Row East *(Private)*

	Symphony Hall, Broad Street (2) *(Private)*
Bournville	Linden Road Instruction Pool (Pool hrs)
CP	Cadbury World *(Private)*
Cotteridge	Pershore Road, opp. Watford Road
Digbeth	Digbeth Campus, High St Deritend *(S. Birmingham College)*
Edgbaston	Five Ways Island
	Five Ways Station *(London Midland)*
	University Station *(London Midland)*
	'Nandos', Fiveways Leisure Centre *(Nandos)*
	'Revolution', Broad Street, Fiveways *(Private)*
	County Ground *(Warwickshire CCC)*
	Grosvenor Casino, Fiveways Leisure Centre *(Private)*
Erdington	Stockland Green Leisure Centre, Slade Street (Centre hrs)
	Wilton Road/High Street
	'Charlie Hall', Barnabas Road *(JDW)*
	Gala Bingo, Streetly Road *(Gala)*
Four Oaks	Mere Green Youth & Community Centre
	Mere Green Library (Library hrs)
	'Mare Pool', 294 Lichfield Road *(JDW)*
Great Barr	Beeches Pool & Fitness Centre (Centre hrs)
	Tower Hill Library (Library hrs)
Hall Green	Sarehole Mill, Cole Bank Road (Museum hrs)
	Hall Green Campus, Cole Bank Rd (2) *(S. B'ham College)*
Handsworth	Baker Street, off Soho Road
Harborne CP	Harborne Pool Leisure Centre (4) (Centre hrs)
	High Street
	'Old House at Home', 193 Lordswood Road *(Private)*
	'Proverbial', High Street *(Barracuda)*
	Gala Bingo, Harborne High Street *(Gala)*
Highgate	Gooch Street
Hockley	Vyse Street, Jewellery Quarter
	Jewellery Quarter Station *(London Midland)*
Kings Heath	Vicarage Road
	'Pear Tree', Alcester Road South *(JDW)*
Kings Norton	Kings Norton Station *(London Midland)*
Kingstanding	Kingstanding Road

Longbridge	Calmers Community Leisure Centre (Centre hrs)
	Longbridge Station *(London Midland)*
Lozells	Boulton Road
Moseley	Alcester Road, Moseley Village
	Cannon Hill Park, off Edgbaston Road *(Trust)*
	Cannon Hill Park, Russell Road Gate *(Trust)*
	'Elizabeth of York', St Marys Row *(JDW)*
Nechells	'KFC', Star City *(KFC)*
	'Old Orleans', Star City *(Private)*
Northfield	Church Road Car Park
	Northfield Fitness Centre, Bristol Rd South (Centre hrs)
Perry Barr	Alexander Stadium, Fitness Centre (Centre hrs)
	'Arthur Robertson', Walsall Road *(JDW)*
Selly Oak	Bristol Road/Harborne Lane
	Selly Oak Station *(London Midland)*
Small Heath	Coventry Road/Regent Park Road
Sparkhill	Stratford Road, Sparkhill Park
Stetchford	Pool Way Shopping Centre
	Stetchford Cascades Leisure Centre (Centre hrs)
Stirchley	Pershore Road, opp. Hazlewell Street
Streetly	'Farmer John's', Aldridge Road *(Marstons)*
Sutton Coldfield	Boldmere Library, Boldmere Road (Library hrs)
	Boldmere Road
	Sutton Coldfield Town Hall, Reception (Hall hrs)
	The Mall Sutton Coldfield *(Private)*
	'Bishop Vesey', Boldmere Road *(JDW)*
	'Boot Inn', Rectory Road *(Spirit)*
	'Bottle of Sack', Birmingham Road *(JDW)*
	'Plough & Harrow', Slade Road, Roughley *(Marstons)*
Warmley	Crawford Street
Weoley Castle	Weoley Castle Road
Wythall	Chapel Lane Caravan Site *(Caravan Club)*
Yardley	South Yardley Library, Yardley Road (Library hrs)
	'William Tyler', 140 Church Road *(JDW)*
	Gala Bingo, Swan Centre *(Gala)*

Bromsgrove

Alvechurch		Tanyard Lane
		'Hopwood House', Redditch Road *(Marstons)*
Bromsgrove		Market Street (Daytime)
		Sanders Park
		'Golden Cross Hotel', High Street *(JDW)*
		'Slug & Lettuce', 126 High Street *(Private)*
	CP	Crown Close
Frankley M5		Frankley Services J3/4 M5 *(Moto)*
Rubery		New Road

Cannock Chase

Cannock	'Linford Arms', High Green *(JDW)*
	'Newhall Farm', Lichfield Road *(Marstons)*
	'Yates's Bar', High Green *(Private)*
	The Green Building, Cannock Campus *(S Staffs College)*
Hednesford	Cannock Chase Information Centre *(Staffs CC)*
Rugeley	'Ash Tree', Armitage Road *(Marstons)*
	'Stag's Leap', Wolseley Road *(Marstons)*
	'The Plaza', Horsefair *(JDW)*

Coventry

Ansty		'Ansty Arms', Combe Fields Road *(Spirit)*
		'Coventry Oak', Ansty Road *(Private)*
		Tenpin Coventry, Crosspoint Business Park *(Private)*
Binley		Coombe Country Park, Brinklow Road (Park hrs)
		Coombe Visitors Centre (Park hrs)
Cannon Park		De Montfort Way Shopping Centre
Chapel Fields		'Maudsley', 190 Allesley Old Road *(Private)*
Cheylesmore		Daventry Road/Cecily Road
		War Memorial Park, by Tennis Pavilion (Park hrs)
Coundon		'Holyhead', Holyhead Road *(Private)*
Coventry City Centre		Belgrade Plaza Car Park (Car Park hrs)
		Broadgate House, Broadgate (Office hrs)
		Canal Basin, St Nicholas Street
	CP	Central Library, Smithford Street (Mon-Sat, 9.00-22.00)
		Christchurch House, Greyfriars Lane (Office hrs)

Civic Centre 1, Little Park Street (Office hrs)
Civic Centre 2, Much Park Street (Office hrs)
Civic Centre 4, Much Park Street (Office hrs)
Council House, Earl Street (Office hrs)
Coventry Retail Market (Market hrs)
Spire House, New Union Street (Office hrs)
Coventry Old Cathedral, rear entrance *(Church)*
Pool Meadow Bus Station *(Centro)*
Coventry Station, Platform 1 *(Virgin Trains)*
Cathedral Lanes Shopping Centre *(Private)*
Lower Precinct Shopping Centre *(Private)*
West Orchards Shopping Centre *(Private)*
'Earl of Mercia', High Street *(JDW)*
'Flying Standard', Trinity Street *(JDW)*
'Litten Tree', 1A Warwick Row *(Private)*
'Nandos', Trinity Street *(Nandos)*
'Old Orleans', The Sky Dome *(Private)*
'Shakespeare', 18 Spon Street *(Private)*
'Yates's Bar', High Street *(Private)*
Belgrade Theatre, Belgrave Square *(Private)*
Coventry Sports & Leisure Centre, 1st floor *(Private)*
Sidney Stringer Academy Sports Centre *(Private)*

Earlsdon	Albany Road 'City Arms', Earlsdon Street *(JDW)* 'Old Clarence', Earlsdon Avenue North *(Private)*
Edgewick	Edgewick Park, Foleshill Road
Ernesford Grange	Ernesford Grange Community Sports Centre *(Private)*
Potters Green	Moat House Leisure Centre, Winston Avenue *(Private)*
Radford	Jubilee Crescent Shopping Centre
Rowleys Green	Tesco Extra, Arena Retail Park *(Tesco)* Ricoh Arena, Phenix Way *(Coventry City FC)*
Tile Hill	Tile Hill Station *(London Midland)*
Walsgrave	'KFC', 276 Walsgrave Road *(KFC)* 'Nandos', Gielug Way *(Nandos)* 'Rose & Crown', 262 Walsgrave Road *(Private)*
Wyken	Caludan Castle Sports Centre, Axholme Road *(Private)*

Dudley

Amblecote	Sainsbury's Store, Sandringham Way *(Sainsbury)*
Brierley Hill	'Corn Exchange', Amblecote Road *(Spirit)* 'Tenth Lock', 154 Delph Road *(Marstons)*
Dudley	Market Place Bus Station, Birmingham Street *(Centro)* 'Full Moon', High Street *(JDW)* 'Nandos', 2 Castlegate, Birmingham Road *(Nandos)* Gala Bingo, Castle Hill *(Gala)*
Halesowen	Bus Station, Hagley Road *(Centro)* 'William Shenstone', Queensway *(JDW)*
Kingswinford	'British Oak', 55 Stallings Lane *(Marstons)*
Lye	'Hadcroft', Grange Lane *(Marstons)*
Merry Hill	Debenhams Store, Pedmore Road *(Debenhams)* 'Abraham Darby', Merry Hill *(JDW)* 'Bar Edge', Waterfront East, Level Street *(Spirit)* 'Nandos', Food Court *(Nandos)* 'Waterfront Inn', The Waterfront *(JDW)*
Netherton	'Woodman', 45 Saltwells Road *(Marstons)*
Sedgley	Townsend Place 'The Clifton', Bull Ring *(JDW)*
Stourbridge	Court Street, off New Road **CP** Crystal Leisure Centre, Bell Street (Centre hrs) Bus Station, Foster Street *(Centro)* Stourbridge Junction Station *(London Midland)* 'Edward Rutland', High Street *(JDW)* 'Station Inn', 95 Worcester Road *(Marstons)*
Wollaston	Meridan Avenue

East Staffordshire

Barton-under-Needwood	Crowberry Lane, off Main Street
Branston	Branson Water Park 'The Gate', Main Street *(Private)*
Burton-on-Trent	Manor Croft, Market Place Shobnall Leisure Complex (Centre hrs) Station Road

	Consumer Direct, High Street (Office hrs) *(Staffs CC)*
	Octagon Shopping Centre *(Private)*
	'Albion', Shobnall Road *(Marstons)*
	'Goodridge', Station Street *(Barracuda)*
	'Lord Burton', High Street *(JDW)*
	'Mulberry Restaurant', Burton College *(College)*
	'The Cosmopolitan', High Street *(Private)*
	'The Sump', Newton Road *(Marstons)*
	'Wing Wah Restaurant', New Street *(Private)*
	Mecca Bingo, Middleway Park *(Mecca)*
CP	Meadowside Leisure Centre

Rolleston-on-Dove	'Spread Eagle', Church Road *(M&B)*
Stapenhill	Main Street
	'Crown Inn', Rosilton Road *(Marston)*
Stretton	'Mill House', Milford Drive *(Spirit)*
Tatenhill	'Horseshoe Inn', Main Street *(Marstons)*
Tutbury	Duke Street Car Park
	'Dog & Partridge', High Street *(Spirit)*
Uttoxeter	Bradley Street
	Bramshall Recreation Ground
	Trinity Road Car Park
	'Old Swan', Market Place *(JDW)*
	'Sozzled Sausage', 30 Market Place *(Private)*
	'Steeplechase', 58 Bridge Street *(Private)*
	Uttoxeter Racecourse Caravan Club Site *(Caravan Club)*
Winshill	Berry Hedge Youth Centre (Centre hrs)

Herefordshire

Colwell		British Camp
		Wyche Road
Hereford		Blackfriars Street (7.00-17.30)
		Maylord Shopping Centre (7.30-18.00)
		Union Walk, nr. Bus Station (7.30-18.00)
		Hereford Station *(Arriva Wales)*
		'Kings Fee', Commercial Road *(JDW)*
	CP	Hereford Leisure Pool
Kington		Mill Street
Ledbury		Church Lane
Leominster		Central Car Park
		Grange, off Etnam Street Car Park (7.00-17.00)
	CP	Leominster Leisure Centre
Moorhampton		Moorhampton Caravan Club Site *(Caravan Club)*
Ross-on-Wye		Croft Court Shopping Centre (8.00-17.30)
		Red Meadow Swimming Pool Car Park (8.00-17.00)
		Wye Street
		'Mail Rooms', Gloucester Road *(JDW)*
Symonds Yat		'Saracens Head', Symonds Yat East *(Private)*
Weobley		Back Lane, library car park

Lichfield

Burntwood	Sankeys Corner (9.00-17.30)
	Swan Island (9.00-17.30)
Chasetown	High Street (9.00-17.30)
Lichfield	Bus Station, Birmingham Road (7.30-17.30)
	Dam Street (9.00-17.30)
	Swan Road (9.00-17.30)
	'Acorn Inn', Tamworth Street *(JDW)*
	'Gatehouse', Bird Street *(JDW)*

Malvern Hills

Bransford	'Fox Inn', Bransford Court Lane *(Chef & Brewer)*

Great Malvern	Barnards Green (7.00-19.00)
	Grange Road
	Worcester Road
	Great Malvern Station *(London Midland)*
Hanley Swan	Blackmore Caravan Club Site *(Caravan Club)*
Malvern Link	Victoria Pavilion *(Town Council)*
Tenbury Wells	Teme Street Car Park (7.00-19.00)
Upton-upon-Severn	Hanley Road Car Park
	High Street

Newcastle-under-Lyme

Bradwell	Bradwell Crematorium (Crematorium hrs)
	Bradwell Park, Bradwell Lane
Kidsgrove	Heathcote Street (8.00-18.00)
Newcastle-under-Lyme	Chesterton Pavilion
	Hassell Street
	Keele Cemetery (Cemetery hrs)
	Merrial Street (Mon-Sat, 8.00-18.00)
	Newcastle Cemetery (Cemetery hrs)
	Silverdale Cemetery (Cemetery hrs)
	CP Newcastle Library, Iron Market (Library hrs) *(Staffs CC)*
	Sainsbury's Store, Liverpool Road *(Sainsbury)*
	'Arnold Machin', Ironmarket *(JDW)*
	'Revolution', 7 Hassell Street *(Private)*
	'Yates's Bar', Ironmarket *(Private)*
	CP Jubilee 2 Centre, Brunswick Street *(Private)*
Wolstanton	Alexandra Road, Wolstanton Marsh

North Warwickshire

Atherstone	Bus Station
Coleshill	High Street
	Coleshill Parkway Station *(London Midland)*
	'Bell Inn', Birmingham Road *(Spirit)*
Polesworth	Bridge Street Car Park
Water Orton	Birmingham Road

Nuneaton & Bedworth

Bedworth	Chapel Street (Mon-Sat, 9.00-17.30)
	Civic Hall (Hall hrs)
	Market Place (Mon-Sat, 9.00-17.30)
	'The Griffin', Griff *(Marstons)*
	'Bear & Ragged Staff', King Street *(JDW)*
Nuneaton	Bus Station (Mon-Sat 7.00-19.30, shorter on Sundays)
	Ropewalk Shopping Centre MSCP (Trading hrs)
	Town Hall, Cotton Road (Office hrs)
	Nuneaton Station *(London Midland)*
	Sainsbury's Store, Vicarage Street *(Sainsbury)*
	'Acorn', Horeston Grange *(Marstons)*
	'Felix Holt', Stratford Street *(JDW)*
CP	Stop Off Facility, Abbey Street

Redditch

Redditch	Redditch Town Hall, Walter Stranz Square (Office hrs)
	Woodrow Centre One Stop Shop, Studley Road
	Kingfisher Shopping Centre (5) *(Private)*
	'Bar 98', Alcester Street *(Private)*
	'Foxlydiate Arms', Birchfield Road *(Brewers Fayre)*
	'Rising Sun', Alcester Street *(JDW)*
	'The Abbey', Alcester Street *(Barracuda)*

Rugby

Rugby	Caldecott Park (Daytime)
	North Street Car Park
	Rugby Art Gallery, Museum & Library (2) (Library hrs)
	Visitors' Centre, Lawrence Sheriff Street (Building hrs)
	Benn Hall, Newbold Road *(DC Leisure)*
	Rugby Station, Platform 1/2 *(Virgin Trains)*
	Churchside Arcade *(Private)*
	Clock Towers Shopping Centre *(Private)*
	'Rupert Brooke', Castle Street *(JDW)*
	Frobisher Road Pavilion *(Private)*
	Gala Bingo, North Street *(Gala)*
	Ken Marriott Leisure Centre *(Private)*

Sandwell

Cradley Heath	Lower High Street Car Park (9.00-17.30)
	Cradley Heath Bus Station, Forge Lane *(Centro)*
	'Moon Under Water', High Street *(J D Wetherspoon)*
Great Barr	Scott Arms Shopping Centre, Walsall Road
	Gala Bingo, Walsall Road *(Gala)*
Oldbury	Sandwell & Dudley Station, Bromford Road (Station hrs)
	'Court of Requests', Church Street *(JDW)*
Rowley Regis	Henderson Way Car Park (9.00-17.30)
	'The Britannia', Halesowen Street *(JDW)*
Smethwick	Stoney Lane Car Park (9.00-17.30)
	Bearwood Bus Station, Adkins Lane *(Centro)*
	Smethwick Galton Bridge Station *(London Midland)*
	'Sampson Lloyd', Cape Hill *(JDW)*
Tipton	'Gospel Oak', Gospel Oak Road *(Marstons)*
Wednesbury	The Shambles
	Bus Station, Holyhead Road *(Centro)*
	'The Bellwether', Walsall Street *(JDW)*
	Gala Bingo, St James Bridge *(Gala)*
West Bromwich	Sandwell Valley Country Park
	Bus Station, Ring Road *(Centro)*
	The Hawthorns Station *(London Midland)*
	Kings Square, Sandwell Centre *(Private)*
	Queens Square Shopping Centre *(Private)*
	'Billiard Hall', St Michael's Ringway *(JDW)*

Shropshire

Albrighton	Crown Car Park
	'Crown', High Street *(Marstons)*
Bishops Castle	Station Street Car Park *(Town Council)*
Bridgnorth	Fox Corner, St John's Street
	Innage Lane Car Park
	Listley Street Car Park
	Sainsburys Store, Whitburn Street
	Castle Grounds, West Castle Street (Summer) *(Bridgnorth Town Council)*
	'Bandon Arms', Mill Street *(Marstons)*
	'Jewel of the Severn', High Street *(JDW)*

Broseley	Dark Lane Car Park
Church Stretton	Carding Mill Valley *(National Trust)*
Clee Hill	High Street, A4117 *(Parish Council)*
Clun	Newcastle Road Car Park *(Parish Council)*
Craven Arms	Shrewsbury Road *(Town Council)*
Ellesmere	Cross Street *(Town Council)*
Ford	A458 Lay-by
Highley	High Street Car Park *(Parish Council)*
Ludlow	Castle Street Car Park *(Town Council)* Smithfield Car Park *(Town Council)* Ludlow Station, Station Building *(Arriva Wales)* 'British Legion Club', Mill Street *(RBL)* 'The Squirrel'. Foldgate Lane *(Marstons)*
Market Drayton	Towers Lawn *(Town Council)* 'Hippodrome', Queen Street *(JDW)*
Much Wenlock	St Mary's Lane Car Park
Oswestry	Beatrice Street Car Park Central Car Park, English Walls Cae Glass Park *(Town Council)* 'Wilfred Owen', Willow Street *(JDW)*
Pontesbury	School Bank *(Parish Council)*
Prees Heath	Car & Lorry Park
Shifnall	Aston Street Place 'Bell', Tong *(Marstons)*
Shrewsbury	Ravens Meadow Bus Station (8.00-23.00) Abbey Foregate (Daytime) *(Town Council)* Hills Lane (8.00-17.00) *(Town Council)* Quarry Bottom (8.00-17.30) *(Town Council)* Quarry Top (8.00-17.30) *(Town Council)* Sydney Avenue (8.00-16.30) *(Town Council)* Shrewsbury Station, Platform 4 *(Arriva Wales)* 'Shrewsbury Hotel', Bridge Place *(JDW)* 'Yates's Bar', The Mardol *(Private)* Gala Bingo, Castle Gate *(Gala)*

Snailbeach		Village Hall *(Parish Council)*
Wem		High Street Car Park *(Town Council)*

Solihull

Balsall Common		'Ye Old Saracens Head', Balsall Street *(Marstons)*
Berkswell		'Bear Inn', Spencer Lane *(Private)*
Castle Bromwich		'The Farthings'', Green Lane *(Private)*
Chelmsley Wood		Chelmsley Wood Library (Library hrs)
	CP	Chelmsley Wood Shopping Centre *(Private)*
Dorridge		Dorridge Station *(London Midland)*
		'Drum & Monkey', Four Ashes Road *(Spirit)*
Marston Green		Marston Green Station *(London Midland)*
		'Marston Green Tavern', Station Road *(Private)*
NEC/Airport		Birmingham Int. Station, Concourse *(Virgin Trains)*
		'Little Owl', Bickenhill Parkway *(M&B)*
	CP	Birmingham Int. Airport, Airside *(Airport)*
Olton		Olton Station *(London Midland)*
Sheldon		Rileys Snooker, Hobs Moat Road *(Private)*
Shirley		'Colebrook Inn', Haslucks Green Road *(M&B)*
		'Plume of Feathers', Stratford Road *(Private)*
		'Sharmans Cross', Prospect Lane *(Private)*
		'The Drawbridge', Drawbridge Road *(Spirit)*
		'Woodmans Rise', Union Road *(Private)*
Solihull		Mell Square
		Solihull Arts Complex (Centre hrs)
		Solihull Central Library (Library hrs)
		Solihull Station *(London Midland)*
		Touchwood Centre (5) *(Private)*
		'Apres Bar', Poplar Road *(Private)*
		'Assembley Rooms', Poplar Road *(JDW)*
		'Coach House', Herbert Road *(Marstons)*
		'Druckers Café', Touchwood Centre *(Private)*
		'Greville Arms', Damson Lane *(M&B)*
		'Jimmy Spices', Station Road *(Private)*
		'Nandos', Mill Lane Arcade, Touchwood *(Nandos)*
		'Nog', Station Road *(Private)*
		'O'Neil's', Poplar Road *(M&B)*

'Saddlers Arms', Warwick Road *(Marstons)*
'Slug & Lettuce', Touchwood Centre *(Private)*
'Town House', Warwick Road *(Private)*
'White Swan', Station Road *(JDW)*

Widney Manor   Widney Manor Station *(London Midland)*

South Staffordshire

Codsall	CP	Codsall Leisure Centre *(Private)*
Essington M6		Hilton Park Services J10a/11 M6 *(Moto)*
Gailey		'Spread Eagle', Watling Street *(Marstons)*
Himley		'Himley House', Stourbridge Road *(Chef & Brewer)*
Kinver		'The Whittington', Whittington *(Marstons)*

Stafford

Brocton		'Chetwynd Arms' *(Marstons)*
Little Haywood		Jubilee Playing Fields *(Parish Council)*
Milford		Brocton Lane (M+F)
Stafford		Broad Street Car Park, by Shopmobility
		Civic Centre, Ground Floor (Office hrs)
		Doxey Road Lorry Park
		North Walls Car Park
		Rowley Park Sports Stadium (Park hrs)
		Stafford Castle Visitor Centre, Newport Road
		Stafford Crematorium (8.00-dusk)
		Stafford Market (M+F) (Market hrs)
		Victoria Park (Park hrs)
		Stafford Station, Platform 1 *(Virgin Trains)*
		'Butlers Bell', Gaolgate Street *(JDW)*
		'Picture House', Bridge Street *(JDW)*
		Gala Bingo, Silkmore Lane *(Gala)*
	CP	1 Staffordshire Place *(County Council)*
Stone		Crown Street Car Park
		Station Road (M+F)
		'Post of Stone', Granville Square *(JDW)*
Stone M6		Stafford North Services J15/15 M6 *(Moto)*

Staffordshire Moorlands

Alstonfield	Car Park *(National Park)*
Biddulph	Biddulph Grange Country Park Town Hall Wharf Road Car Park [Closed at present] Greenway Bank Country Park *(Staffs CC)* 'Bradley Green', High Street *(JDW)*
Blythe Bridge	Cheadle Road
Cheadle	'Wheatsheaf', High Street *(JDW)*
Cheddleton	Deep Hayes Country Park *(Staffs CC)*
Cotton	The Star Caravan & Camping Park *(Private)*
Ilam	Wetton Mill, Ilam Park *(National Trust)*
Leek	Bus Station, Smithfield Centre Blackshaw Moor Caravan Site *(Caravan Club)*
Mildale	Mildale Village
Oakamoor	Oakamoor Picnic Area *(Staffs CC)*
Rudyard	Lakeside (Visitor Centre hrs)
Upper Tean	New Road
Waterhouses	Car Park *(National Park)*
Wetley Rocks	Consall Nature Park *(Staffs CC)*

Stoke-on-Trent

Abbey Hulton	Abbey Hulton Local Centre, Abbots Road (Office hrs)
Blurton	Blurton Local Centre, Finstock Avenue (Office hrs) 'The Gables', Trentham Road *(Marstons)*
Chell Heath	Chell Heath Local Centre, Cornhill Road (Office hrs)
Etruria	Odeon Cinema, Festival Park *(Odeon)* Tenpin, Marina Way *(Private)*
Fenton	City Road 'KFC', King Street *(KFC)* Gala Bingo, Victoria Road *(Gala)*
Hanley	Crown Bank, Stafford Street Debenhams Store, Potteries Centre *(Debenhams)* 'Caffe Nero', Parliament Road *(Caffe Nero)* 'Reginald Mitchell', The Tontine *(JDW)*

'Revolution', Trinity Street *(Private)*
'Varsity', Percy Street *(Barracuda)*
'Walkabout', Trinity Street *(Private)*
Dudson Museum *(Private)*
Gala Bingo, Albion Square *(Gala)*
Grosvenor Casino, New Century Square *(Private)*
CP   Potteries Shopping Centre, by Shopmobility *(Private)*

Longton	Longton Local Centre, Commerce Street (Office hrs)
	Longton Market, Transport Lane (Market hrs)
Meir	Meir Local Centre, Uttoxeter Road (Office hrs)
	Weston Road Car Park
Norton	Norton Local Centre, St Nicholas Avenue (Office hrs)
Smallthorne	Community Drive
Stoke	Kingsway Car Park
	South Wolfe Street
	Stoke-on-Trent Station, Platform 1 *(Virgin Trains)*
	'The Wheatsheaf', Church Street *(JDW)*
	Michelin Athletics Club, Trent Vale *(Private)*
Tunstall	Butterfield Place (2)
Weston Coyney	Park Hall Country Park (2)

Stratford on Avon

Alcester	Bulls Head Yard, Car Park
	'Royal Oak', High Street *(Spirit)*
Bidford-on-Avon	High Street
	Big Meadow *(Parish Council)*
Earlswood	'Reservoir', The Common *(Private)*
Henley-in-Arden	Station Road
Shipston-on-Stour	Telegraph Street
Southam	Wood Street
Stratford-upon-Avon	Avonbank Gardens, Old Town
	Bridgefoot, Car Park
	Recreation Ground, Play Area
	Waterside (M+F)
	Windsor Square, Car Park
	Town Square Shopping Centre *(Private)*
	'Golden Bee', Sheep Street *(JDW)*

'Ripple Café', Swans Nest Lane *(Private)*
'Yates's Bar', Windsor Street *(Private)*
Visitor & Leisure Centre, Bridgeway *(Private)*

Studley	Alcester Road
Warmington	'Wobbly Wheel', Warwick Road *(Private)*

Tamworth

Tamworth	Aldergate (08.00-16.00) Castle Pleasure Grounds (08.00-18.00) Ankerside Shopping Centre *(Private)* Co-op Store, Colehill *(Private)* 'The Bolebridge', Bolebridge Street *(JDW)* 'Yates's Bar', Lower Gungate *(Private)*
Tamworth M42	Tamworth Services, J10 M42/A5 *(Moto)*

Telford & Wrekin

Brookside	Brookside Community Centre
Dawley	King Street *(Parish Council)*
Hadley	District Centre [to be redeveloped] *(Parish Council)*
Ironbridge	The Square The Wharfage **CP** Self Unlimited, Forbes Close *(Private)*
Madeley	High Street *(Parish Council)*
Newport	Stafford Street Car Park *(Town Council)*
Oakengates	Stafford Road *(Parish Council)*
Priorslee	Telford Campus, SA Building *(Wolverhampton Univ.)* Telford Campus, SN Building *(Wolverhampton Univ.)*
Sutton Hill	Sutton Hill Community Centre
Telford	Town Park *(Parish Council)* Telford Shopmobility, Red Oak Car Park *(Private)* Telford Centre Bus Station *(Private)* Telford Central Station *(London Midland Trains)* Telford Shopping Centre (3) *(Private)* Debenhams Store, Sherwood Square *(Debenhams)* 'Taverners', Malinsgate *(Marstons)* 'Thomas Botfield', Telford Shopping Centre *(JDW)*

| Wellington | The Parade *(Town Council)* |

Walsall

Aldridge	Aldridge Shopping Centre, Anchor Road
	Gala Bingo, Anchor Road *(Gala)*
Bloxwich	Asda Car Park, High Street
	High Street/Wolverhampton Road
Pelsall	Norton Road
	'Old House at Home', Norton Road *(Marstons)*
Rushall	Pelsall Lane
Walsall	St Pauls Bus Station *(Centro)*
	Walsall Station *(London Midland)*
	'Park Tavern', Broadway North *(Private)*
	'Revolution', Bridge Street *(Private)*
	'The Imperial', Darwell Street *(JDW)*
	'Varsity', Darwell Street/Leicester Street *(Barracuda)*
	'Yates's Bar', Leicester Street *(Private)*
	Walsall Campus, WC Building *(Wolverhampton Univ)*
	Gala Bingo, Jerome Retail Park *(Gala)*
Walsall Wood	'Taverners', 146 Walsall Road *(Marstons)*
Willenhall	Market Car Park
	'Milestone', 130 Essington Road *(Marstons)*
	'The Malthouse', New Road *(JDW)*

Warwick

Kenilworth	Abbey End (Daytime)
	Abbey Fields, Bridge Street (Daytime)
	Kenilworth Cemetery, Oaks Road (Cemetery hrs)
Leamington Spa	Brunswick Street (Daytime)
	Covent Garden MSCP, Russell Street (Daytime)
	Crown Way (Daytime)
	Jephson Gardens, The Parade (Daytime)
	Leamington Cemetery, Brunswick Street (Daytime)
	Regent Grove, Holly Grove (Daytime)
	Victoria Park, Archery Road (Daytime)
	Leamington Spa Station, Platform 2 *(Chiltern Trains)*
	'Benjamin Satchwell', The Parade *(JDW)*
	'Jug & Jester'. Bath Street *(JDW)*
	'Yates's Bar', Warwick Street *(Private)*

Warwick	Market Place (Daytime)
	Myton Fields (Summer & weekends) (Daytime)
	Pageant Gardens, Castle Street (Daytime)
	St Nicholas Park, Banbury Road (Daytime)
	Warwick Cemetery, Birmingham Road (Cemetery hrs)
	'Thomas Lloyd', Market Place *(JDW)*
	'Unicorn', 64 Hardwick Field Lane *(Marstons)*
	'Varsity', Gibbett Hill Road *(Barracuda)*
	Warwick Racecourse Caravan Club Site *(Caravan Club)*
CP	Shire Hall *(Warwickshire CC)*

Wolverhampton

Bilston	Market (7.00-21.00)
	Bus Station, Coach Lounge *(Centro)*
	'Sir Henry Newbold', High Street *(JDW)*
Compton	'Oddfellows', Bridgnorth Road *(Marstons)*
Merry Hill	'Merry Hill', Trysull Road *(Private)*
Perton	'Wrottesley Arms', Severn Drive *(Marstons)*
Tettenhall	Stockwell Road (7.00-21.00)
Wednesfield	High Street (7.00-21.00)
	'Nandos', Bently Bridge Leisure Park *(Nando)*
	'Royal Tiger', High Street *(JDW)*
	AMF Bowl Bentley Bridge *(AMF)*
Wolverhampton	Art Gallery, Lichfield Street (Gallery hrs)
	Ashmore Park, Griffiths Drive (7.00-18.00)
	Civic Centre, St Peters Square (Office hrs)
	Faulkland Street Coach Park (7.00-19.00)
	WCityStop, Mander Centre (Mon-Sat, 9.00-17.00)
	West Park (7.00-21.00)
	Wolverhampton Market, School Street (Market hrs)
	Bus Station, Pipers Row *(Centro)*
	Wolverhampton Station, Platform 1 *(Virgin Trains)*
	Mander Shopping Centre *(Private)*
	Wulfrun Shopping Centre (2) *(Private)*
	Beatties Store, Victoria Street *(Private)*
	'Babylon', North Street *(Private)*
	'Bantock House Café', Finchfield Road *(Private)*
	'Goose in the City', Lichfield Street *(M&B)*
	'Hogs Head', Stafford Street *(Private)*

'Holly Bush Inn', 494 Penn Road *(Marstons)*
'Moon Under Water', Lichfield Street *(JDW)*
'Nandos', 23 Queen Street *(Nandos)*
'Oceana', Bilston Street *(Private)*
'O'Neills', Lichfield Street *(M&B)*
'Revolution', Princess Street *(Private)*
'Rothwells', Lichfield Street *(Private)*
'Royal London', Wulfruna Street *(Private)*
'The Tube', Princes Street *(Private)*
'Varsity', Stafford Street *(Barracuda)*
'Walkabout', Queen Street *(Private)*
'Yates's Bar', Queens Square *(Private)*
City Campus, MA Building Reception *(Wolverhampton Univ)*
City Campus, MC Building by lifts *(Wolverhampton Univ)*
City Campus, MI Building *(Wolverhamton Univ)*
City Campus, ML Building Reception *(Wolverhampton Univ)*
Express Bowling, Birminham Road *(AMF)*
Gala Bingo, Bushbury Lane *(Gala)*
Molineux Stadium *(Wolves FC)*

Wombourne	'New Inn', Station Road *(Marstons)* 'Waggon & Horses', Bridgnorth Road *(Marstons)*

Worcester

Worcester	Barbourne Lane (8.40-18.00) Reindeer Court Shopping Centre *(Private)* 'Barn Owl', Warndon *(Marstons)* 'Blackpole Inn', Blackpole Road *(Marstons)* 'Courtyard Worcester', St Nicholas Street *(Marstons)* 'Horn & Trumpet', Angel Street *(Marstons)* 'Nandos', 55 Friar Street *(Nandos)* 'Postal Order', Foregate Street *(JDW)* 'Slug & Lettuce', The Cross *(Private)* 'The Crown', Crown Passage *(JDW)* Gala Bingo, Foregate Street *(Gala)*

Wychavon

Broadway	Activity Park, Keytes Lane (8.00-18.00) Church Close Car Park (8.00-18.00) Milestone Ground Car Park (8.00-18.00) Broadway Caravan Club Site *(Caravan Club)*

Droitwich	Lido Park (8.00-18.00) St Andrews Square (8.00-18.00) Droitwich Spa Station *(London Midland)*
Evesham	Abbey Park (8.00-18.00) Oat Street (8.00-18.00) Old Brewery Car Park (8.00-18.00) Viaduct Meadow (8.00-18.00) Waterside (8.00-18.00) Evesham Station *(Gt Western)* 'Old Swanne Inn', High Street *(JDW)*
Martin Hussingtree	'Swan', Droitwich Road *(Marstons)*
Pershore	Church Walk (8.00-18.00) High Street Car Park (8.00-18.00)
Wychbold	'Crown', Worcester Road *(Marstons)*

Wyre Forest

Bewdley	Car Park, off Load Street Dog Lane Car Park 'George Hotel', Load Street *(JDW)* 'Running Horse Inn', Longbank *(Chef & Brewer)*

Kidderminster	Brintons Park, Sutton Road
	Broadwaters Park, Stourbridge Road
	Market Street
	Rowland Hill Shopping Centre (7.00-17.30)
	Kidderminster Station *(London Midland)*
	Swan Shopping Centre *(Private)*
	'Land Oak', Birmingham Road *(Marstons)*
	'Penny Black', Bull Ring *(JDW)*
	'Viaduct Tavern', 619 Chester Road South *(Marstons)*
	'Watermill', Park Lane *(Marstons)*
CP	Connect, Blackwell Street *(Worcs CC)*
Stourport-on-Severn	Raven Street Car Park
	Severn Meadows Car Park, by Civic Centre
	Vale Road Car Park
	'Ye Olde Crown Inn', Bridge Street *(JDW)*

Allerdale

Allonby	Central Green by Play Area
	West Green
Aspatria	Queen Street Car Park
Buttermere	Village Car Park *(National Park)*
Cockermouth	Harris Park
	Main Street
Keswick	Bell Close Car Park
	Central Car Park
	Lakeside Car Park, behind Theatre
	Station Platform
Maryport	High Street
	Irish Street, The Harbour
	The Promenade
Rosthwaite	by Car Park *(National Park)*
Silloth	Skinburness, opp. Solway Village
	The Green
Wigton	Market Hall
Workington	Harrington Marina
	Town Centre
	'Henry Bessemer', New Oxford Street *(JDW)*

Barrow-in-Furness

Barrow-in-Furness	Barrow Park, Bowling Pavilion
	Fell Street, Car Park
	Roa Island
	Barrow-in-Furness Station *(Transpennine)*
	Debenhams Store, Portland Walk *(Debenhams)*
	'Furness Railway', Abbey Road *(JDW)*
	'Yates's Bar', Duke Street *(Private)*
Dalton-in-Furness	Tudor Square
Walney Island	Earnse Bay, West Shore Road

Blackburn with Darwen

Blackburn	CP	Market Way (9.00-17.00)

Witton Country Park, Preston Old Road
Blackburn Station *(Northern Rail)*
The Mall Blackburn (3) *(Private)*
Debenhams Store, Northgate *(Debenhams)*
'Boddington Arms', Myerscough Road *(Spirit)*
'Postal Order', Darwen Street *(JDW)*
BowlPlex, Peel Leisure Park *(BowlPlex)*
Gala Bingo, Ainsworth Street *(Gala)*

Darwen   Town Hall, Parliament Street

Roddlesworth   Ryal Fold Information Centre *(United Utilities)*

Blackpool

Blackpool, Central   Bethesda Square, Central Drive
Central Car Park, Central Drive/New Bonny Road
Central Library, Queen Street (Library hrs)
Customer First, Corporation Street (Office hrs)
Layton Square, Westcliffe Drive
Lonsdale Coach Park
Lytham Road/Station Road
Stanley Park, West Park Drive (Park hrs)
Talbot Road Bus Station, by car park
Victoria Street, Town Centre
Central Coach Station *(Private)*
Blackpool North Station *(Northern Rail)*
Festival Shopping Mall *(Private)*
'Auctioneer', 135 Lytham Road *(JDW)*
'Belle Vue', Whitegate Drive *(Private)*
'Brannigans', Market Street *(Private)*
'King Edward VII Hotel', Central Drive *(Spirit)*
'Layton Rakes', 17 Market Street *(JDW)*
'Litten Tree', Queen Street *(Private)*
'Nandos'. Church Street *(Nandos)*
'Outside Inn', Whitehills Industrial Park *(Spirit)*
'Swift Hound', Festival Park *(Private)*
'Walkabout', Queen Street *(Private)*
'Yates's Bar', 407-411 South Promenade *(Private)*
Blackpool Magistrates Court *(Courts Service)*
Blackpool Pleasure Beach (3) *(Private)*

CP Blackpool Tower, Level 5 *(Private)*
Central Pier (3) *(Private)*
North Pier *(Private)*
South Pier (2) *(Private)*
Tower Game Zone, Blackpool Tower *(Private)*
Winter Gardens, Floral Hall *(Private)*
CP Blackpool CIL, 259 Whitegate Drive *(Private)*
CP Debenhams Store, Houndhill Centre *(Debenhams)*

Blackpool, North	Bispham Tram Station, Queens Promenade Bispham Village Car Park Cocker Square/Promenade Gynn Square, Promenade Jubilee Cycleway, Queens Promenade Little Bispham, Queens Promenade/Princes Way Queens Promenade, opp. Uncle Toms Cabin 'Red Lion', Devonshire Square, Bispham *(Beefeater)* 'The Highlands', 206 Queens Promenade *(Private)* **CP** Thornton Building, Bispham Campus *(Blackpool & Fylde Col)*
Blackpool, South	Central Gateway Harrowside, Promenade South Highfield Road, by Library New South Promenade, Starr Gate Starr Gate Tram Loop **CP** Solaris Centre
Marton	'Clifton Arms', Preston New Road *(Spirit)* Blackpool South Caravan Site *(Caravan Club)*

Bolton

Bolton	Bus Station, Moor Lane Topp Way MSCP Jumbles Country Park *(United Utilities)* Crompton Place Car Park *(Private)* Moor Lane Bus Station *(TfGM)* Bolton Station, by Footbridge *(Northern Rail)* 'Nandos', Middlebrook Retail Park *(Nandos)* 'Spinning Mule', Nelson Square *(JDW)* 'Varsity', Churchgate *(Barracuda)* 'Yates's Bar', Bradshawgate *(Private)* **CP** Bolton One Leisure Centre, Moor Lanr *(Private)*

Farnworth	Moses Gate Country Park
	Farnworth Bus Station *(TfGM)*
Horwich	Horwich Parkway Station *(Northern Rail)*
Westhoughton	Market Street
	'Robert Shaw', Market Street *(JDW)*

Burnley

Burnley	Briarcliffe Road, by Hospital
	Burnley Bus Station (5.00-23.00)
	Cemetery Chapel, Rossendale Road (Cemetery hrs)
	Market Hall (Mon-Sat, daytime)
	Millennium Car Park, Brick Street (8.00-18.00)
	Queens Park
	Scott Park (Park hrs)
	Thompson Park, Ormrod Road (Park hrs)
	Townley Park, Rotunda (8.00-16.00, weekdays, shorter at weekends)
	Yorkshire Street
	Burnley Central Station, Waiting Room *(Northern Rail)*
	'Brun Lee', Manchester Road *(JDW)*
	'Walkabout', Hammerton Street *(Private)*
	UCLan Burnley Campus, Foyer *(UCLan)*
	Gala Bingo, Centenary Way *(Gala)*
Padiham	Church Street

Bury

Bury		Kay Gardens
		Bury Interchange *(TfGM)*
		Mill Gate Shopping Centre *(Private)*
		'Art Picture House', Haymarket Street *(JDW)*
		'Nandos', The Rock, Rochdale Road *(Nandos)*
		'Robert Peel', Market Place *(JDW)*
		'Yates's Bar', Market Street *(Private)*
		Burrs Country Park Caravan Park *(Caravan Club)*
	CP	The Met, Market Street *(Private)*
Prestwich		Longfield Precinct
Radcliffe		Market Hall
Ramsbottom		Market Chambers
Tottington		Market Street

Carlisle

Brampton	Milburn Court (Daytime)
	Talkin Tarn Country Park (Park hrs)
Carlisle	Bitts Park (Daytime)
	St Nicholas, Botchergate (Daytime)
	Town Dyke Orchard Car Park (Daytime)
	Bus Station, Lonsdale Street *(Private)*
	Carlisle Station, Platforms 1 & 4 *(Virgin Trains)*
	Covered Market *(Private)*
	The Lanes Shopping Centre *(Private)*
	Debenhams Store, The Lanes *(Debenhams)*
	'Bar Code', Botchergate *(Private)*
	'Bar Suede', The Crescent *(Private)*
	'Casa', Botchergate *(Private)*
	'Club XS', West Walls *(Private)*
	'Gosling Bridge Inn', Kingstown Road *(Spirit)*
	'Leonardo's', Lonsdale Street *(Private)*
	'Litten Tree', Botchergate *(Private)*
	'Mood', Botchergate *(Private)*
	'Nandos', Warwick Street *(Nandos)*
	'Teza', English Gate Plaza *(Private)*
	'The Griffin', Court Square *(Spirit)*
	'The Holme Bistro', Denton Street *(Private)*
	'Turf Tavern', Newmarket Road, The Sands *(Private)*
	'Walkabout', English Gate Plaza *(Private)*
	'William Rufus', Botchergate *(JDW)*
	'Woodrow Wilson', Botchergate *(JDW)*

Disability Rights UK

Visit our online shop
For products and books that
open doors to independent living.

www.disabilityrightsuk.org

'Yates's Bar', English Street *(Private)*

Gala Bingo, English Gate Plaza *(Gala)*

CP Shaddon Gateway, Shaddongate *(YMCA)*

Dalston	The Square (Daytime)
Longtown	Bank Street (Daytime)
Penton	Nicolforest Public Hall *(Trust)*
Southwaite M6	Southwaite Services, J41/42 M6 *(Moto)*
Stapleton	Stapleton Public Hall, external access

Cheshire East

Alderley Edge		West Street
		The Wizard Car Park *(National Trust)*
		'De Trafford', Congleton Road *(Spirit)*
Alsager		Crewe Road *(Town Council)*
Audlem		Cheshire Street Car Park *(Parish Council)*
Bollington		Pool Bank Car Park
		Recreation Ground, Adlington Road
Brereton		Brereton Heath Local Nature Reserve
Congleton		Bridestones Shopping Centre
		Congleton Park
		Market Street
		West Heath Shopping Centre (Weekldays, 9.00-16.30)
		'The Counting House', Swan Bank *(JDW)*
Crewe	CP	Lyceum Square, Heath Street
		Queens Park, Victoria Avenue (Park hrs)
		Crewe Station, Platforms 5 & 6-11 *(Virgin Trains)*
		'Gaffers Row', Victoria Street *(JDW)*
		'The Earl', Nantwich Road *(Spirit)*
Disley		Station Approach
Handforth		Church Road
		'Millers', Wilmslow Road *(Spirit)*
Knutsford		Northwich Road
		King Street Car Park *(Town Council)*
		Stanley Road, by Supermarket *(Town Council)*
Knutsford M6		Knutsford Services J18/19 M6 *(Moto)*

Langley		Trentabank Car Park *(National Park)*
Lower Peover		'Bells of Peover', The Cobbles *(Spirit)*
Macclesfield		Churchill Way (8.15-17.15)
		Park Green
		Riverside Park, off Beech Lane (8.45-16.55)
		Macclesfield Station *(Virgin Trains)*
		'Society Rooms', Park Green *(JDW)*
		Macclesfield Bowl, Lyme Green Business Park *(AMF)*
Mere		'Kilton Inn', Warrington Road, Hoo Green *(Spirit)*
Middlewich		France Hayhurst Pavillion (Park hrs)
		Southway, off Wheelock Street
		Town Bridge, Leadsmithy Street
Nantwich		Snowhill Car Park, Wall Lane
	CP	Nantwich Market, Monks Lane *(Town Council)*
		'Cronkinson's Farm', Pear Tree Field *(Marstons)*
Poynton		Fountain Place
		Nelson Pit Visitor Centre (Centre hrs)
		'Kingfisher', London Road South *(JDW)*
Prestbury		Bridge Green *(Parish Council)*
Rode Heath		'Broughton Arms', Sandbach Road *(Marstons)*
Sandbach		High Street, by Town Hall *(Town Council)*
Wilmslow		South Drive
		'Bollin Fee', Swan Street *(J D Wetherspoon)*
		'Revolution', 27 Alderley Road *(Private)*

Cheshire West & Chester

Alvanley		'White Lion Inn', Manley Road *(Spirit)*
Blacton		Chester Crematorium, by Office (Crematorium hrs)
Cheshire Oaks		'Nandos', Stanney Lane *(Nandos)*
Chester	**CP**	Frodsham Street, by Car Park
		Princess Street, under Market (8.00-18.00)
		The Groves, nr Suspension Bridge (8.00-20.00)
		Bus Station, Princess Street *(Private)*
		Little Roodee Car/Coach Park *(Private)*
		Chester Station, Concourse *(Arriva Wales)*
		Grosvenor Shopping Centre *(Private)*
		'Forest House', Love Street *(JDW)*

'Little Owl', Gawer Park *(Marstons)*
'Pitcher & Piano', The Exchange *(Marstons)*
'Pizza Hut', 83 Foregate Street *(Private)*
'Revolution', 106 Foregate Street *(Private)*
'Square Bottle', Foregate Street *(JDW)*
'Yates's Bar', Frodsham Street *(Private)*
West Cheshire Magistrates Court *(Courts Service)*
Northgate Arena *(Private)*
Tenpin, Greyhound Retail Park *(Private)*

Chrisleton	Chrisleton Leisure Centre
Cuddington	Norley Road (Daytime) *(Parish Council)*
Dunham Hill	'Wheatsheaf', Dunham Hill *(Private)*
Ellesmere Port	Council Offices, Civic Way (Office hrs) Market (Market hrs) Port Arcades Car Park (Daytime) 'Grace Arms', Stanney Lane *(Private)* 'Old Hall Farm', Kinsey Road *(Marstons)* 'Thomas Telford', Whitby Road *(JDW)* 'Wheatsheaf', Overpool Road *(JDW)* 'Woodland', Chester Road, Whitby *(Private)* EPIC Leisure Centre, McGarva Way *(Private)*
Frodsham	Moor Lane (8.00-18.00) Frodsham Leisure Centre *(Private)*
Little Stanney	Chester Fairoaks Caravan Site *(Caravan Club)*
Neston	Brook Street (8.30-17.00)

Become a member

Help us realise our vision and make your voice count.

www.disabilityrightsuk.org

Cheshire West and Chester Council support the Radar National Key Scheme

This involves the creation of a new "Changing Places" toilet at the Frodsham Street facilities which opened in April 2011.

To find out more about our facilities call the council on **0300 123 8123** or email us at: **enquiries@cheshirewestandchester.gov.uk**

www. cheshirewestandchester.gov.uk

Northwich	Applemarket Street (8.00-18.00)
	Leicester Street (Mon-Sat, 8.00-18.00)
	'Penny Black', Witton Street *(JDW)*
Parkgate	Moston Square, School Lane (8.00-16.00)
Tarporley	High Street (8.00-18.00)
Upton-by-Chester	Chester Zoo, The Ark Restaurant *(Private)*
CP	Chester Zoo, Jubilee Toilets *(Private)*
Winsford	Winsford Library, High Street (Library hrs)
	'Queens Arms', Dean Drive *(JDW)*

Chorley

Adlington	Babylon Lane
Chorley	Astley Park Coach House
	Market Place, Cleveland Street
	'Bobbin Mill', Buckshaw Village *(Marstons)*
	'Millers', Bolton Road *(Spirit)*
	'Sir Henry Tate', Chorley East Business Centre *(JDW)*
	Gala Bingo, Market Street *(Gala)*
Rivington	Great House Information Centre *(United Utilities)*
	Rivington Lane Car Park *(United Utilities)*
Whittle-le-Woods	'Malthouse Farm', Moss Lane *(Chef & Brewer)*

Copeland

| Bootle | Car Park, off A595 *(Parish Council)* |
| Cleator Moor | Market Place Car Park |

Proud of our past. Energised for our future.

Waste Management Services
Copeland Borough Council
Whitehaven Commercial Park, Moresby Parks,
Whitehaven, Cumbria, CA28 8YD
Tel: 0845 054 8600
www.copeland.gov.uk

Supporting Disability Rights UK's work
with and for disabled people

Make a donation

Support our work with a one-off
or regular donation.

www.disabilityrightsuk.org

Egremont	Chapel Street
Eskdale	Ireton Road Station *(R&E Rlwy)*
	The Green Station *(R&E Rlwy)*
Gosforth	Village Car Park *(Parish Council)*
Haverigg	Foreshore *(Town Council)*
Millom	Millom Park, St Georges Road
	Lancashire Road *(Town Council)*
Seascale	Foreshore Car Park
St Bees	Foreshore Car Park
Whitehaven	James Street
	Whitehaven Station *(Northern Rail)*
	'Bransty Arch', Bransty Row *(JDW)*

Eden

Alston	Town Hall
	Station Car Park *(S Tynedale Rlwy)*
Appleby	Broad Close Car Park, Chapel Street
	Tourist Information Centre, Moot Hall
Brough	Main Street
Dufton	Car Park
Garrigill	Village Hall *(Hall Committee)*
Glenridding	Jenkins Field Car Park
	Ullswater Information Centre *(National Park)*
Kirkby Stephen	Stoneshot Car Park, Market Square
Patterdale	White Lion Car Park
Penrith	Bluebell Lane, Little Dockray
	Castle Park
	Sandgate Bus Station/Car Park
	Penrith Station, Platform 1 *(Virgin Trains)*
Pooley Bridge	by Tourist Information Centre
Shap	by Memorial Hall & Car Park
Threlkeld	behind Village Hall
Troutbeck	Troutbeck Head Caravan Club Site *(Caravan Club)*

Fylde

Fairhaven Lake	Marine Park
	Stanner Bank
Freckleton	Freckleton Centre
Greenhalgh	'Fairfield Arms', Fleetwood Road *(Spirit)*
Kirkham	Church Street
	Kirkham & Wesham Station *(Northern Rail)*
	'Bell & Bottle', Blackpool Road *(Marstons)*
Lytham	East Beach
	Lowther Pavilion, West Beach
	Pleasant Street
	'Railway Hotel', Station Road *(JDW)*
St Anne's	Ashton Gardens
	Fairhaven Road
	Promenade Gardens, by Monument
	St Annes Road West, by Station
	'Trawl Boat Inn', Wood Street *(JDW)*

Halton

Daresbury	'Ring O'Bells', Chester Road *(Chef & Brewer)*
Runcorn	Runcorn Station, Platform 1 *(Virgin Trains)*
	'Ferry Boat', Church Street *(JDW)*
Widnes	'Premier', Albert Road *(JDW)*

Hyndburn

Accrington		Accrington Town Hall
	CP	Hyndburn Leisure Centre (Centre hrs)
		Peel Street Bus Station
		Accrington Arndale Centre *(Private)*
Clayton-le-Moors		Public Library

Knowsley

Halewood	CP	Halewood Centre One Stop Shop (Office hrs)
Huyton		Bus Station *(Merseytravel)*
		'Barkers Brewery', Archway Road *(JDW)*
	CP	Huyton Municipal Buildings
	CP	Knowsley Leisure & Culture Park

Kirkby	Kirkby Bus Station, Cherryfield Drive
	Kirkby Market
	'Gold Balance', New Town Gardens *(JDW)*
	Gala Bingo, Telegraph Way *(Gala)*
Prescot	'Grapes Hotel', St Helens Road *(Spirit)*
	'Watch Maker', 60/62 Eccleston Street *(JDW)*
CP	The Prescot Centre
Rainhill	'Manor Farm', Mill Lane *(Marstons)*

Lancaster

Bolton-le-Sands	Community Centre (Centre hrs)
Carnforth	Market Square
Carnforth M6	Burton-in-Kendal Services, J35 M6 *(Moto)*
Caton	Bull Beck Picnic Area
	Crook of Lune Car Park *(Lancashire CC)*
Glasson Dock	Condor Green Picnic Area *(Lancashire CC)*
Heysham	'Strawberry Gardens', Heysham Road *(Spirit)*
Lancaster	Bus Station
	Market Gate
	Market Hall
	Mitre House, China Street
	Nelson Street Car Park
	St Nicholas Arcades
	Williamson Park
	Lancaster Station, Platforms 3 & 4 *(Virgin Trains)*
	'Green Ayre', North Road *(JDW)*
	'Revolution', Penny Street *(Private)*
	'Sir Richard Owen', Spring Garden Street *(JDW)*
	'Varsity', George Street *(Barracuda)*
	'Yates Bar', Dalton Square *(Private)*
	A Block, Morecambe Road *(Lancaster & Morecambe College)*
	Gala Bingo, King Street *(Gala)*
Lancaster M6	Lancaster Services J32/33 M6 *(Moto)*
Middleton	Parish Hall *(Private)*
Morecambe	Morecambe Leisure Park (Summer)
	Stone Jetty

West End Gardens
'Eric Bartholomew', Euston Road *(JDW)*
Gala Bingo, Marine Road East *(Gala)*
CP Festival Market Hall, Central Drive

Silverdale Gaskell Hall *(Private)*

Liverpool

Allerton CP Calderstones Park (Park hrs)
'Allerton Hall', Clark Gardens *(Private)*
'Yates's Bar', Allerton Road *(Private)*

Broadgreen CP Broadgreen Univ. Hospital, Alexandra Wing *(Hospital)*

Childwall 'Childwall Fiveways', 179 Queens Drive *(JDW)*

Croxteth CP Croxteth Country Park, Café Courtyard (Park hrs)
Gala Bingo, Stonedale Retail Park *(Gala)*

Garston Garston Library, Bowden Road (Libary hrs)
CP South Liverpool NHS Treatment Centre *(NHS)*

Gateacre 'Bear & Staff', Gateacre Brow *(Chef & Brewer)*

Liverpool City Centre Central Library, William Brown Street (Library hrs)
CP Museum of Liverpool, Pierhead *(Merseyside Museums)*
CP World Museum, William Brown St *(Merseyside Museums)*
Coach Station, Norton Street *(National Express)*
Liverpool One Bus Station *(Merseytravel)*
Queen Square Bus Station *(Merseytravel)*
Liverpool Lime Street Station *(Network Rail)*
Albert Dock, The Colonnades *(Private)*
Clayton Square Shopping Centre *(Private)*
CP Liverpool One, Wall Street *(Private)*
St Johns Shopping Centre & Market *(Private)*
'All Bar One', Atlantic Block, Albert Dock *(Private)*
'Fall Well', St Johns Way *(JDW)*
'Fly in the Loaf', Hardman Street *(Private)*
'Lime Kiln', Fleet Street *(JDW)*
'Nandos', 6 Queen Square *(Nandos)*
'Nandos', Liverpool One *(Nandos)*
'Norwegian Blue', Bold Street *(Spirit)*
'Rat & Parrot', Queens Square *(Spirit)*
'Revolution', Atlantic Pavilion, Albert Dock *(Private)*
'Revolution', St Peters Square *(Private)*
'Richard John Blackler', Charlotte Row *(JDW)*

	'Slug & Lettuce', North John Street *(Private)*
	'The Picturedrome', 286 Kensington *(JDW)*
	'The Welkin', Whitechapel *(JDW)*
	'Thomas Frost', 177 Walton Road *(JDW)*
	'Wagamama', P10, Liverpool One *(Private)*
	'Walkabout', Fleet Street *(Private)*
	'Yates's Bar', Queens Square *(Private)*
	Haigh Building, Maryland Street *(LJM University)*
CP	Royal Liverpool Hospital *(Hospital)*
	Vauxhall Road Centre (3) *(Liverpool Community Col.)*
Norris Green	Lifestyles Ellersgate, Carr Lane (Centre hrs)
Speke	Pizza Hut, New Mersey Retail Park *(Private)*
	'The Argosy', John Lennon Airport *(JDW)*
Stoneycroft	'The Navigator', Queens Drive *(JDW)*
Toxteth	Lifestyles Toxteth, Upper Hall Road (Centre hrs)
Walton	Lifestyles Alsop, Queens Drive (Centre hrs)
	'The Raven', Walton Vale *(JDW)*
Wavertree	Wavertree Tech Park Station *(Northern Rail)*
	Gala Bingo, Wavertree Road *(Gala)*
	Liverpool Aquatics Centre, Wellington Road

Manchester

Belle Vue	Gala Bingo, Hyde Road *(Gala)*
Cheetham Hill	'Nandos', Manchester Fort *(Nandos)*
Chorlton-cum-Hardy	Bus Terminus, Barlow Moor Road
	'Sedge Lynn', Manchester Road *(JDW)*
Davyhulme	CP George Carnell Leisure Centre
Didsbury	'Milson Rhodes', School Lane *(JDW)*
	'Nandos', Parrs Wood Leisure *(Nandos)*
	'Slug & Lettuce', 651 Wilmslow Road *(Private)*
Eastlands	Etihad Stadium *(Mancherster City FC)*
Fallowfield	'Great Central', Wilmslow Road *(JDW)*
	'Nandos', 351 Wilmslow Road *(Nandos)*
	'Revolution', 311 Wilmslow Road *(Private)*
Harpurhey	Gala Bingo, North City Shopping Centre *(Gala)*
Heaton Park	Sainsbury's Store, Heaton Park Rd West *(Sainsbury)*

Manchester Airport	Bus Station *(TfGM)*
	Manchester Airport Station *(Transpennine)*

Manchester City Centre	Parker Street, Piccadilly Bus Station
	Stevenson Square
	Town Hall Extension, Mount Street (Daytime)
	Central Coach Station, Chorlton Street *(National Express)*
	Shudehill Interchange *(TfGM)*
	Deansgate Station *(Northern Rail)*
	Manchester Piccadilly Station *(Network Rail)*
	Manchester Victoria Station *(Northern Rail)*
CP	Arndale Centre *(Private)*
	Debenhams Store, Market Street *(Debenhams)*
	'All Bar One', Spinningfields *(Private)*
	'Manchester & County', Piccadilly *(JDW)*
	'Moon Under Water', Deansgate *(JDW)*
	'Nandos', Arndale Centre *(Nandos)*
	'Nandos', Hardman Street, Spinningfields *(Nandos)*
	'Nandos', The Print Works, Withy Grove *(Nandos)*
	'Nandos', The Quad, Oxford Road *(Nandos)*
	'Norwegian Blue', Printworks, Corporation Street *(Spirit)*
	'Old Orleans', The Printworks, Withy Grove *(Private)*
	'Pitcher & Piano', Deansgate Locks *(Marstons)*
	'Revolution', 7 Deansgate Locks *(Private)*
	'Revolution', 90 Oxford Road *(Private)*
	'Revolution', St Marys Gate, Parsonage Gdns *(Private)*
	'Sawyers Arms', Deansgate *(Spirit)*
	'Seven Stars', Dantzic Street *(JDW)*
	'Slug & Lettuce', 64 Deansgate *(Private)*
	'Slug & Lettuce', Heron House, Albert Square *(Private)*

'The Paramount', Oxford Street *(JDW)*
'Varsity', The Circus, Oxford Street *(Barracuda)*
'Walkabout', Quay Street *(Private)*
'Waterhouse', Princess Street *(JDW)*
'Yates's Bar', Portland Street *(Private)*
Barnes Wallis Building, Sackville St. *(Manchester Univ.)*
Crawford House, Booth St East *(Manchester Univ.)*
Humanities Building, Bridgeford Street *(Manchester Univ.)*
Roscoe Building, Brunswick Road *(Manchester Univ)*
Samuel Alexander Building, Oxford Rd *(Manchester Univ)*
Students' Union, Oxford Road *(Manchester Univ)*
Williamson Building, Oxford Road *(Manchester Univ)*

Rusholme	'Ford Maddox Brown', Wilmslow Park *(JDW)* 'Varsity', Wilmslow Park *(Barracuda)*
Wythenshawe	Civic Centre Wythenshawe Bus Station *(TfGM)* Gala Bingo, Rowlandsway *(Gala)*

Oldham

Chadderton	Shopping Precinct
Greenfield	Dovestones Reservoir Greenfield Station *(Northern Rail)* 'Kingfisher', Chew Valley Road *(Marstons)*
Oldham	Alexandra Park (Park hrs) Civic Centre Bus Station Tommyfield Market 'Shay Wake', Milnrow Road *(JDW)* 'Squire Knott', Yorkshire Street *(JDW)* 'Up Steps Inn', High Street *(JDW)* Oldham College, Rochdale Road (5) *(College)*
Royton	Shopping Precinct
Uppermill	Uppermill Park

Pendle

Barley	Picnic Area Car Park
Barnoldswick	Central Car Park, Fernlea Avenue Letcliffe Park, Manchester Road
Barrowford	Gisburn Road/Church Road

Brierfield	Town Centre, Colne Road
Colne	Bus Station, Craddock Road
	Market Hall, Market Street
	'Wallace Hartley', Church Street *(JDW)*
Cotton Tree	Ball Grove Picnic Area
Earby	Bus Station
	Colne Road, by Station Road
	Sough Park, Colne Road
Laneshawbridge	Keighley Road
Nelson	Market Hall, Leeds Road
	Market Street
Newchurch	opp. Lamb Inn
Salterforth	Kelbrook Lane/Earby Road
Wycoller	Wycoller Country Park *(Lancashire CC)*

Preston

Ashton	Haslam Park, Bowls Pavilion
Preston	Avenham MSCP (6.45-23.30)
	Avenham Park Pavilion
	Bus Station (M+F) (4.30-23.30)
	Guild Hall Concourse, 1st Floor (Hall hrs)
	Lune Street, nr Mobility Centre
	Market Hall (8.00-18.00)
	Moor Park, Bowls Pavilion (Events only)
	Preston Station (2) *(Virgin Trains)*
	St Georges Shopping Centre, Lwr Ground Floor *(Private)*
	'Centro Oriental Buffet', The Mall *(Private)*
	'Nandos', Deepdale Retail Park *(Nandos)*
	'Revolution', Mainsprit Weind *(Private)*
	'The Greyfriar', Friargate *(JDW)*
	'Wall Street', Fishergate *(Spirit)*
	'Yates's Bar', Church Street *(Private)*
	Students' Union, Fylde Road (2) *(UCLan)*
	Gala Bingo, Market Street *(Gala)*
	CP Deepdale Stadium *(Preston North End FC)*
	CP Preston Specialist Mobility Rehab Centre *(NHS)*
Ribbleton	Ribbleton Park, Blackpool Road

Ribble Valley

Beacon Fell	Bowland Visitor Centre (Centre hrs) *(Lancashire CC)*
Bolton-by-Bowland	Car Park
Chipping	Car Park
Clitheroe	Castle Field Grounds Church Walk Edisford, Riverside Market Waddington Road Cemetery Clitheroe Station *(Northern Rail)*
Downham	Car Park
Dunsop Bridge	Car Park
Hurst Green	St Pauls Club
Ribchester	Car Park
Sabden	Car Park
Slaidburn	Car Park
Whalley	King Street Springwood Picnic Site *(Lancashire CC)*

Rochdale

Heywood	Bamford Road 'Edwin Waugh', Market Street *(JDW)*
Heywood M62	Birch Services J18/19 M62 *(Moto)*
Hollingworth Lake	Lake Bank (Daytime) Pavilion Café (Café hrs) Visitor Centre (Centre hrs) 'Millers', Hollingworth Lake *(Spirit)*
Littleborough	The Square
Middleton	Bus Station *(TfGM)* 'Harboard Harboard', Long Street *(JDW)*
Ogden Reservoir	Ogden Car Park *(United Utilities)*
Rochdale	Bus Station Rochdale Exchange, Market Hall subway (Daytime) South Parade Wheatsheaf Centre (2) *(Private)*

'Regal Moon', The Butts *(JDW)*
'Yates's Bar', Yorkshire Street *(Private)*

Rossendale

Haslingden Grane	Clough Head Information Centre *(United Utilities)*
Rawtenstall	The Market, Newchurch Road
	'Old Cobblers Inn', New Hall Hey Road *(Spirit)*

Salford

Eccles	Eccles Gateway Centre, Barton Lane (Centre hrs)
	Eccles Shopping Precinct (Trading hrs)
	Eccles Metrolink/Bus Interchange *(TfGM)*
	'Albert Edward', Church Street *(Private)*
	'Blue Bell', Monton Green *(Private)*
	'Eccles Cross', Regent Street *(JDW)*
	'White Horse', Gilda Brook Road *(Private)*
	Eccles Rugby Club, Gorton Street *(Private)*
Irlam	Tesco Store, Fairhills Industrial Estate *(Tesco)*
	'Railway Inn', Liverpool Road *(Private)*
Salford	Pendleton Gateway Centre, Broadwalk (Centre hrs)

NATIONAL KEY SCHEME GUIDE 2013

Salford Museum & Art Gallery (Museum hrs)
Salford Central Station *(Northern Rail)*
Salford Crescent Station *(Northern Rail)*
Salford Shopping City *(Private)*
Mothercare, West One Retail Park *(Private)*
Sainsbury's Store, Regent Road *(Sainsburys)*
'Quay House Beefeater', The Quays *(Private)*
Salford City Reds Stadium *(Private)*

Swinton	Victoria Park, Pavilion (Pavilion hrs) Swinton Shopping Precinct *(Private)* 'New Ellesmere', East Lancs Road *(Spirit)* 'Swinton Free House', Chorley Road *(Private)*
Walkden	Ellesmere Shopping Centre *(Private)* Tesco Store, Ellesmere Shopping Centre *(Tesco)* 'Bulls Head', 12 High Street *(JDW)*
Worsley	'Barton Arms', Stable Fold *(Private)* 'Moorings', Quayside Close, Boothstown *(Private)*

Sefton

Ainsdale	'The Railway', 668 Liverpool Road *(Spirit)*
Blundellsands	Burbo Bank
Bootle	Bootle Bus Station *(Merseytravel)* 'Merton Inn', Merton Road *(JDW)* 'Wild Rose', Triad Centre *(JDW)* 'Yates's Bar', Triad Centre *(Private)*
Churchtown	Preston New Road
Crosby	Moor Lane
Formby	Freshfield Car Park *(National Trust)*
Maghull	Leighton Avenue 'Coach & Horses', Liverpool Road North *(Private)* 'Frank Hornby', 38 Eastway *(JDW)*
Southport	Eastbank Street (9.00-21.00) Hill Street (9.00-17.00) Park Crescent, Hesketh Bank Promenade Central (9.00-21.00) Ocean Plaza, Marine Drive *(Private)* 'Nandos', 7 Ocean Plaza *(Nandos)* 'Sir Henry Seagrave', Lord Street *(JDW)*

'Willow Grove', Lord Street *(JDW)*
'Yates Bar', Lord Street *(Private)*
'Clouds', Tony Leigh Building *(Southport College)*
New Pleasureland Southport (5) *(Private)*
Esplanade Caravan Club Site *(Caravan Club)*
CP Southport Community Service Station

Waterloo	Waterloo Interchange, South Road (7.30-20.00) 'Queens Picture House', South Road *(JDW)*

South Lakeland

Ambleside	Rydal Road Car Park Waterhead Information Centre Car Park Mechanics Institute (Daytime) *(Parish Council)* Rothay Park (March-November) *(Parish Council)*
Cark-in-Cartmell	Village *(Parish Council)*
Coniston	Tilberthwaite Road Car Park Park Coppice Caravan Club Site *(Caravan Club)*
Dent	Car Park *(Parish Council)*
Grange-over-Sands	Church Hill/Hampsfell Road *(Town Council)* Grange-over-Sands Station *(Transpennine)* Meathop Fell Caravan Club Site *(Caravan Club)*
Grasmere	Moss Parrock, Village Centre
Hawkshead	Car Park, Main Street
Kendal	'Miles Thompson', Allhallows Lane *(JDW)*
Kirby Lonsdale	Jingling Lane *(Town Council)*
Lake Coniston	Bown Howe, south of Torver *(National Park)* Monk Coniston, north end of Lake *(National Park)*
Milnthorpe	The Square
Oxenholme	Oxenholme Station, Platform 1 *(Virgin Trains)*
Sedbergh	Market Place, Joss Lane *(Parish Council)*
Sedgwick	Low Park Wood Caravan Club Site *(Caravan Club)*
Ulverston	Gill Car Park Market Hall (Daytime, not Wed or Sat) Brogden Street *(Town Council)*
Windermere	Bowness Bay, Glebe Road Baddeley Clock *(Town Council)*

Braithwaite Fold Car Park *(Town Council)*
Broad Street Car Park *(Town Council)*
Ferry Nab Car Park *(Town Council)*
Rayrigg Road Car Park *(Town Council)*
Windermere Station *(Transpennine)*
Braithwaite Fold Caravan Club Site *(Caravan Club)*
White Cross Bay Leisure Park *(Private)*

South Ribble

Bamber Bridge		Withy Grove, by Supermarket (Daytime)
		'Millers', Lostock Lane *(Spirit)*
Leyland	CP	Roccoco Lounge & Bakery, Chapel Brow *(Private)*
Lostock Hall		Hope Terrace, behind shops (Daytime)

St Helens

Bold Heath	'Griffin Inn', Warrington Road *(Private)*
Garswood	Garswood Station *(Northern Rail)*
Rainford	'Bottle & Glass Inn', St Helens Road *(Chef & Brewer)*
St Helens	Bus Station, Bickerstaffe Street *(Merseytravel)*
	St Marys Arcade *(Private)*
	'Carr Mill', East Lancashire Road *(Spirit)*
	'Glass House', Market Street *(JDW)*
	'Royal Oak', East Lancashire Road, Eccleston *(Spirit)*
	'Sefton Arms', Baldwin Street *(Spirit)*

Stockport

Bramhall	Bramhall Station *(Northern Rail)*
	'Napa Lounge Bar', Bramhall Lane South *(Private)*
Bredbury	Bredbury Library (Library hrs)
Cheadle	'Cheadle Royal', Royal Crescent *(Private)*
	'The Weavers', Gatley Road *(Private)*
	'Turquoise', 65 High Street *(Private)*
Cheadle Hulme	'John Millington', 67 Station Road *(Private)*
	'King's Hall', Station Road *(JDW)*
Compsall	Etheron Country Park, Café *(Private)*
Edgeley	Alexandra Park, Edgeley Road (Park hrs)
	Edgely Library (Library hrs)

Great Moor		Great Moor Library (Library hrs)
Hazel Grove		Hazel Grove Library (Library hrs)
		Torkington Park
		'Fiveways Hotel', Macclesfield Road *(Spirit)*
		'KFC', 258 London Road *(KFC)*
		'Phoenix', London Road *(Greene King)*
Heald Green		Heald Green Library (Library hrs)
		'Griffin', Wilmslow Road *(Private)*
Heaton Moor		The Heatons Library (Library hrs)
		Thornfield Park, Balmoral (Park hrs)
		'Elizabethan', Heaton Moor Road *(Private)*
		'Moortop', Heaton Moor Road *(Private)*
High Lane		High Lane Library (Library hrs)
Marple		Derby Street
		Marple Library (Library hrs)
		'Marple Tavern', 120 Cross Lane *(Private)*
Offorton		Dialstone Centre, Lisburn Lane (Centre hrs)
Reddish		Reddish Library (Library hrs)
		'Carousel', Reddish Road *(Spirit)*
Romiley		Forum Car Park, Compsall Road
Stockport		Bus Station, Daw Bank
	CP	Fred Perry House, Edward Street (Office hrs)
		Produce Market, Market Place (Market hrs)
		Stockport Market Hall (Market hrs)
		Vernon Park, Turncroft Lane (Park hrs)
		Stockport Station. Platform 1/2 *(Virgin Trains)*
		Merseyway Shopping Centre (2) *(Private)*
		Debenhams Store, Princes Street *(Debenhams)*
		Westgate Store, Chestergate *(Private)*
		'Calverts Court', St Petergate *(JDW)*
		'Chestergate Tavern', Mersey Square *(Private)*
		'George & Dragon', Manchester Road *(Spirit)*
		'Old Rectory', 48 Churchgate *(Private)*
		'Pizza Hut', Wellington Road *(Private)*
		'Toby Carvery', Wellington Road *(Private)*
		Stockport College, Town Centre Campus *(Stockport College)*
		Grand Central Pools *(Private)*

Tameside

Ashton-under-Lyne	Market Hall, Market Square (Market hrs)
	Ashton Bus Station *(TfGM)*
	Ashton-under-Lyne Station *(Northern Rail)*
	'Ash Tree', Wellington Road *(JDW)*
	'Nandos', Ashton Leisure Park, Fold Way *(Nandos)*
	Elysium Centre,Beaufort Road *(Tameside College)*
	Gala Bingo, Wellington Road *(Gala)*
Denton	Albert Street, by Market
	Festival Hall (Hall hrs)
Droylesden	Market Street/Greenside Lane
Hyde	Clarendon Square Shopping Centre (Shopping hrs)
	Town Hall, Greenfield Street (Hall hrs)
	Hyde Bus Station *(TfGM)*
	'Cotton Bale', Market Place *(JDW)*
Mossley	Market Ground, Stamford Street
Mottram	'Mottram Wood', Stockport Road *(Spirit)*
Stalybridge	Civic Hall, Trinity Street
	'Society Rooms', Grosvenor Street *(JDW)*

Doing Transport Differently

This guide includes information and travellers' tales to help and inspire people with lived experience of disability or health conditions to use public transport.

Available to order from our online shop
www.disabilityrightsuk.org

Trafford

Altrincham		Halecroft Park (Park hrs)
		John Leigh Park (Park hrs)
		Regent Road Car Park
		'Caffe Nero', 9 Shaws Road *(Caffe Nero)*
		'Cresta Court Hotel', Church Street *(Private)*
		'The Unicorn', Ashley Road *(JDW)*
Bowden		'Griffin', Stamford Road *(Chef & Brewer)*
Dunham Massey		'Axe & Cleaver', School Lane *(Spirit)*
Hale		Cecil Road, Car Park
Sale		Hereford Street (9.15-17.30)
		Woodheys Park (Park hrs)
		Worthington Park (Park hrs)
		'Cape', Waterside Plaza *(Barracuda)*
		'Deckers', Sale Water Park *(Private)*
		'J P Joule', Northenden Road *(JDW)*
		'Sale Hotel', Marsland Road *(Spirit)*
		'Slug & Lettuce', 11/13 School Road *(Private)*
Stretford		Longford Park (Park hrs)
		'Bishop Blaize', 708 Chester Road *(JDW)*
		'KFC', Castlemore Retail Park *(KFC)*
		'Robin Hood', Barton Road *(Private)*
Trafford Centre	**CP**	Trafford Centre (5) *(Private)*
		Barton Square *(Private)*
		Debenhams Store, Regents Crescent *(Debenhams)*
		'Exchange Bar & Grill', The Orient *(Greene King)*
		'Mardi Gras', The Trafford Centre *(JDW)*
		'Nandos', The Orient *(Nandos)*
		'Rice Flamebar', The Orient *(Private)*
		'Tampopo', The Orient *(Private)*
		'TGI Fridays', The Orient *(Private)*
		Namco Station, The Orient *(Private)*
Trafford Park		Third Avenue (9.00-17.00)
		'Castle in the Air', Chill Factore Centre *(JDW)*
Urmston		Moorfield Walk (Mon-Sat, 9.15-17.30)
		'Chadwick', Flixton Road *(Barracuda)*
		'Tim Bobbin', Flixton Road *(JDW)*

Warrington

Birchwood	Birchwood Station *(Transpennine)*
Grappenhall	'Springbrook', Stockport Road *(Marstons)*
Great Sankey	'Trigger Pond', Lindley Green Avenue *(Marstons)*
Higher Walton	Walton Hall Estate, Walton Lea Road (M+F)
	'Walton Arms', Old Chester Road *(Spirit)*
	CP Walton Hall Gardens, Park Entrance
Latchford	Latchford Village
Lymm	Church Green
	Pepper Street
Lymm M6	Lymm Services, J20 M6 *(Moto)*
Stockton Heath	The Forge Car Park
	'Nandos', 109 London Road *(Nandos)*
Stretton	'Cat & Lion', Tarporley Road *(Spirit)*
	'Hollow Tree', Tarporley Road *(Spirit)*
Warburton	'Saracens Head', Paddock Lane *(Private)*

Warrington	CP	Warrington Bus Station (8.30-23.00 Mon-Sat)
		Warrington Market (9.00-17.30 Mon-Sat)
		Golden Square MSCP *(Private)*
		Warrington Bank Quay Station, Platform 2 *(Virgin Trains)*
		Golden Square Centre *(Private)*
		Lyme Street *(Private)*
		'Friar Penketh', Barbould Street *(JDW)*
		'Looking Glass', Buttermarket Street *(JDW)*
		'Nandos', Old Market Square *(Nandos)*
		'Yates's Bar', Buttermarket Street *(Private)*
		Gala Bingo, Cockhedge Centre *(Gala)*
	CP	Centre of Independent Living, Beaufort St *(Private)*
Winwick		'Swan', Golborne Road *(Chef & Brewer)*

West Lancashire

Burscough		School Lane, Car Park
Mawdesley	CP	Rock & River Activity Centre *(Private)*
Ormskirk	CP	Bus/Rail Interchange
		Church Walks
		Moor Street
		Moorgate, opp. Market
		Park Road, in Park
		Shopmobility Office, Park Road *(Private)*
Parbold		Parbold Station *(Northern Rail)*
Skelmersdale		Concourse Shopping Centre (2) *(Private)*
Tarleton		Church Road, Car Park

Wigan

Ashton-in-Makerfield		Princess Road (8.00-15.30)
		'Bay Horse', Warrington Road *(Spirit)*
		'Sir Thomas Gerard', Gerard Street *(JDW)*
Atherton		'Talbot', Gibfield Park *(Marstons)*
Goose Green		'Venture', Billinge Road *(Spirit)*
Leigh		Bus Station, King Street (8.00-17.00)
		'Thomas Burke', Leigh Road *(JDW)*
	CP	Leigh Sports Village, Sale Way *(Private)*
Standish		'Charnley Arms', Almond Brook Road *(Spirit)*

Wigan	Bus Station. Hallgate (8.45-16.30)
	Town Hall (8.45-16.30)
	Wigan North Western Station, Subway *(Virgin Trains)*
	Wigan Wallgate Station *(Northern Rail)*
	Grand Arcade Shopping Centre *(Private)*
	The Galleries, Hindley Walk *(Private)*
	'Brocket Arms', Mesnes Road *(JDW)*
	'Moon Under Water', Market Place *(JDW)*
	'Revolution', 49 King Street *(Private)*
	'Walkabout', King Street *(Private)*
	Gala Bingo, Robin Park *(Gala)*
	Robin Park Sports Complex *(Private)*
CP	Wigan Life Centre

Wirral

Bebington	Bebington Civic Centre (Office hrs)
	Bebington One Stop Shop (Office hrs)
	Higher Bebington Library (Library hrs)

Birkenhead	Cheshire Lines Building (Office hrs)
	Conway One Stop Shop (Office hrs)
	Shopmobility Centre (Centre hrs)
	Bus Station, Claughton Road *(Merseytravel)*
	'Brass Balance', Argyle Street *(JDW)*
	'John Laird', Europa Centre *(JDW)*
	'Yates's Bar', Exmouth Street *(Private)*
	Main Building, Conway Park Campus *(Wirral Met Col)*
	Main Building, Twelve Quays Campus *(Wirral Met Col)*

| Bromborough | Bromborough Civic Centre (Centre hrs) |
| | Gala Bingo, Wirral Leisureland *(Gala)* |

Eastham	Eastham Country Park
	Eastham One Stop Shop (Office hrs)
	West Building, Carlett Park Campus *(Wirral Met Col)*

| Greasby | Greasby Library (Library hrs) |

| Heswall | Heswall Library & One Stop Shop (Office hrs) |

Hoylake	Hoylake Station
	Meols Parade Gardens, by bowling green
	'Hoylake Lights', Market Street *(JDW)*

| Irby | Irby Library (Library hrs) |

| Meols | Bennetts Lane, Meols Parade |

Moreton		Leasowe Common
		Moreton Cross, Garden Lane
		'Grange', Hoylake Road *(Spirit)*
		'Mockbeggar Hall', Hoylake Road *(JDW)*
New Brighton		Harrison Drive
		New Brighton One Stop Shop (Office hrs)
	CP	Marine Point *(Private)*
New Ferry		Woodhead Street Car Park
		'John Masefield' *(JDW)*
Prenton		Prenton Library (Library hrs)
	CP	Prenton Park Stadium *(Tranmere Rovers FC)*
Rock Ferry		Rock Ferry One Stop Shop (Office hrs)
Thornton Haugh		Thornton Common Road
Thurstaston		Wirral Country Park Visitor Centre (Centre hrs)
		Wirral Country Park Caravan Club Site *(Caravan Club)*
Upton		Upton Library (Library hrs)
Wallasey		Cherrytree Centre
		Liskeard One Stop Shop (Office hrs)
		Seacombe Library (Library hrs)
		Shopmobility Centre (Centre hrs)
		Wallasey Central Library (Library hrs)
		Wallasey Town Hall (Office hrs)
		'Claireville', Wallasey Road *(JDW)*
West Kirby		Dee Lane, West Kirby Lakes
		Grange Road, by Station
		West Kirby Concourse (Centre hrs)
		'Dee Hotel', Grange Road *(JDW)*
Woodchurch		Landican Cemetery (Cemetery hrs)
		Woodchurch Library (Library hrs)

Wyre

Cleveleys	Bus Station, Rough Lea Road
	North Drive
	Rough Lea Road, Car Park
Fleetwood	Beach Road, by Cemetery
	Bold Street
	Marine Hall Car Park

	Memorial Park
	Preston Street
	Rossall Viewing Tower, Rossall Promenade
	'Thomas Drummond', London Street *(JDW)*
Garstang	High Street, Car Park
	Park Hill Road Car Park
CP	Cherestanc Square, by Tourist Information *(Private)*
Great Eccleston	The Weind, off High Street
Knott End	Barton Square
	The Ferry
Pilling	School Lane
Poulton-le-Fylde	Teanlowe Centre, Queensway
	Carleton Crematorium (Crematorium hrs) *(Blackpool Council)*
CP	United Reformed Church, Tithebarn Street *(Church)*
	Poulton-le-Fylde Station *(Northern Rail)*
Scorton	Gubberford Road
Thornton	Shoppping Precinct, Victoria Road East
	Wyre Estuary Country Park

YORKSHIRE

Barnsley

Barnsley		Cheapside
		Alhambra Shopping Centre *(Private)*
		Metropolitan Shopping Centre *(Private)*
		'Escapade', Wellington Street (2) *(Private)*
		'Heart of Barnsley', Peel Street *(Marstons)*
		'Joseph Brammah', Market Hill *(JDW)*
		'Silkstone Inn', Market Street *(JDW)*
		'Walkabout', Church Street *(Private)*
		'White Bear', Church Street *(Private)*
		'Yates's Bar', Shambles Street *(Private)*
		Parkway Cinema, Eldon Street *(Private)*
	CP	Barnsley Town Hall
Cudworth		'Fayre & Square', Darfield Road *(Private)*
Monk Bretton		'Norman Inn', Burton Road *(Private)*
Wombwell		'The Horseshoe', High Street *(JDW)*

Bradford

Bingley		Market, Chapel Lane
		'Midland Hotel', Main Street *(Private)*
		'Myrtle Grove', Main Street *(JDW)*
Bradford	CP	Bradford Central Library (Library hrs)
		City Hall (M+F)
	CP	City Park, Hall Ings (Park hrs)
		Lister Park (Park hrs)
		Bradford Interchange, Bus Station *(WYMetro)*
		Bradford Forster Square Station *(Northern Rail)*
		Centenary Square *(Private)*
		Kirkgate Shopping Centre *(Private)*
		Oastler Shopping Centre *(Private)*
		'City Vaults', Hustlergate *(Marstons)*
		'Goose on Bridge Street', Bridge Street *(M&B)*
		'Markez Restaurant', Centenary Square *(Private)*
		'Nandos', The Leisure Exchange, Vicar Lane *(Nandos)*
		'Revolution', Glydegate Square *(Private)*
		'Sir Titus Salt', Windsor Baths *(JDW)*

'Turis Green', Centenary Square *(JDW)*
'Unicorn', Ivegate *(Private)*
'Yates's Bar', Queensgate *(Private)*
Bradford College, Great Horton Street *(Bradford College)*
Gala Bingo, Tong Street *(Gala)*
Ladbrokes Bookmaker, Lillycroft Road *(Ladbrokes)*
CP Carlisle Business Centre *(Private)*
CP Mind the Gap Studios, Patent Street *(Private)*
CP University of Bradford, Richmond Building *(University)*

Burley-in-Wharfdale		Station Road
East Bowling	CP	Bowling Pool, Flockton Road (Pool hrs)
Eccleshill		'Manor House', Leeds Road *(Private)*
	CP	Eccleshill Leisure Centre, Harrogate Road
Esholt		Station Road Car Park
Guiseley		Guiseley Station *(Northern Rail)*
Harden		St Ives Estate Car Park
Haworth		Bronte Parsonage Car Park (M+F)
		Central Park, Rawdon Road (M+F)
		Penistone Hill Country Park (M+F) (Summer)

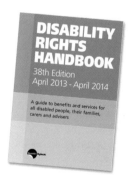

Disability Rights Handbook

Comprehensive information and guidance on benefits and services for all disabled people, their families, carers and advisers.

Available to order from our online shop
www.disabilityrightsuk.org

Peer Support Service
Run by and for disabled people

Carlisle Business Centre,
Unit 69, 60 Carlisle Road
Bradford, BD8 8BD

Ansaphone and fax
☎ **01274 494121**

Across the Bradford District

E: admin@contactpeersupport.org.uk
W: www.contactpeersupport.org.uk

Idle	'Hitching Post', Leeds Road *(Marstons)*
Ilkley	Central Car Park, Brook Street
	Riverside, Bridge House Lane (M+F)
	White Wells
CP	Ilkley Pool & Lido
Keighley	Cavendish Street
	Cliffe Castle Depot, Spring Gardens Lane
	Keighley Market
	Bus Station, Airedale Centre *(WYMetro)*
	'Livery Rooms', North Street *(JDW)*
	Gala Bingo, Alice Street *(Gala)*
	Keighley Bowl, Alston Retail Park *(AMF)*
CP	Keighley Leisure Centre
Menston	'Hare & Hounds', Bradford Road *(Private)*
Odsal	Odsal Stadium *(Bradford Bulls)*
Saltaire	Caroline Street (M+F)
Shipley	Market Square
	'Sir Norman Rae', Market Square *(JDW)*
Silsden	Bridge Street Car Park
Thornbury	'The Farmers', Bradford Road *(Private)*
Thornton CP	Thornton Recreation Centre (Centre hrs)
Wibsey	'Ancient Foresters', High Street *(Private)*
Wilsden	'Prune Park Bar' *(Private)*

Calderdale

Brighouse	Brighouse Library (Library hrs)
	Rastrick Library (Library hrs)
	Thornton Square (6.00-18.00)
	'Richard Ostler', Bethel Street *(JDW)*
	Holiday Inn Health Club, Clifton Village *(Private)*
Elland	Market Square (Market hrs)
	Town Hall Square (6.00-18.00)
Halifax	Albion Street (Mon-Sat, daytime)
	Borough Market (Market hrs)
	George Square (6.00-18.00)
	Manor Heath Park (8.00-15.00)
	North Bridge Leisure Centre (Centre hrs)

	Ogden Water Country Park
	Piece Hall (2) (10.00-17.30)
	Savile Park, Skircoat
	Halifax Bus Station *(WYMetro)*
	Halifax Station, Platform 2 *(Northern Rail)*
	'Barum Top Inn', Rawston Street *(JDW)*
	'Caffe Nero', Southgate *(Caffe Nero)*
	'Goose at the Arcade', Commercial Street *(Private)*
	'Millers', Salterhebble Hill *(Spirit)*
	'Percy Shaw', Broad Street Plaza *(JDW)*
	'Salvation', Bull Green *(Barracuda)*
	Calderdale College Reception, Francis Street *(College)*
	The Shay Stadium, South Stand *(Private)*
Hebden Bridge	Calder Holmes Park (Summer) (Park hrs)
	Hardcastle Craggs [Ambulant only] (Summer)
	Market Square (Market hrs)
	New Road (6.00-18.00)
	Valley Road (6.00-18.00)
	Hebden Bridge Station *(Northern Rail)*
Heptonstall	Towngate Car Park (6.00-18.00)
Luddenden	Luddenden Lane (6.00-18.00)
Mytholmroyd	Bridge End (6.00-18.00)
Ripponden	Brig Royd
Shibden	Shibden Hall (10-16.30)
	Shibden Park, Playground (Park hrs)
Sowerby Bridge	Wharf Street Car Park (6.00-18.00)
Todmorden	Brook Street (6.00-18.00)
	Centre Vale Park, South Lodge (Daylight hrs)
	Market Hall (Market hrs)

Craven

Bolton Abbey	Strid Wood Caravan Club Site *(Caravan Club)*
Buckden	Car Park *(National Park)*
Clapham	Car Park, Church Lane *(National Park)*
Gargrave	High Street/South Street (Dawn-dusk) *(Parish Council)*
Grassington	Car Park, Hebden Road *(National Park)*
Horton-in-Ribblesdale	Car Park *(National Park)*

Ingleton	Community Centre Car Park *(Parish Council)*
Kettlewell	Car Park *(National Park)*
Malham	Car Park *(National Park)*
Settle	Whitefriars Car Park
Skipton	Bus Station
CP	Council Offices, Belle Vue Square (Office hrs)
	High Street Car Park (8.00-18.00)
	Skipton Station *(Northern Rail)*
	'Devonshire', Devonshire Mews *(JDW)*
CP	Craven College, Aireville Campus *(College)*
CP	South Craven Day Service *(Private)*
Stainforth	Car Park *(National Park)*
Threshfield	Wharfdale Caravan Club Site *(Caravan Club)*

Doncaster

Adwick	Adwick Station *(Northern Rail)*
Balby	'Maple Tree', Woodfield Plantation *(Marstons)*
Doncaster	Council House, College Road (Mon-Fri, 8.30-17.00)
	Market Place, High Fishergate (7.00-17.00)
	Southern Bus Station
	Doncaster Station, Platform 8/3A *(East Coast)*
	'Che Bar', Silver Street *(Private)*
	'Gatehouse', Priory Walk *(JDW)*
	'Old Angel', Cleveland Street *(JDW)*
	'Red Lion', Market Place *(JDW)*
	'Sportsman', off Leger Way *(Marstons)*
	'Walkabout', Priory Walk *(Private)*
CP	Flying Scotsman Centre, St Sepulchre Gate *(Private)*
CP	Frenchgate Shopping Centre, off Food Court *(Private)*
Hatfield M18	Doncaster North Services *(Moto)*
High Melton	University Centre *(Doncaster College)*
Mexborough	Market Street, opp Fish Market
	'Old Market Hall', Market Square *(JDW)*
Thorne	The Green, Finkle Street
Tickhill	The Library

East Riding of Yorkshire

Beverley		Dyer Lane (Daytime)
		Lord Roberts Road
		Sow Hill Bus Station (Daytime)
		Station Square
		'Kings Head', Market Place *(Marstons)*
		'Victoria', Victoria Road *(Marstons)*
	CP	Beverley Leisure Complex, Flemingate
Bridlington		Beaconsfield Promenade (Summer)
		Belvedere Parade, Boat Compound (Summer)
		Coach Park, Hildenthorpe Road
		Limekiln Lane
		Princess Mary Promenade (Summer)
		Queen Street
		Royal Princess Parade
	CP	South Cliff Gardens
		South Marine Drive (Summer) (Daytime)
		Bridlington Station *(Northern Rail)*
		The Promenades *(Private)*
		'Prior John', Promenade *(JDW)*

Get Motoring

A practical guide for disabled motorists to help find and finance a car. New 2012 edition.

Available to order from our online shop
www.disabilityrightsuk.org

		Gala Bingo, Promenade *(Gala)*
Brough		'Ferry Inn', Station Road *(Marstons)*
Cottingham		Market Green
Driffield		North Street *(Town Council)*
		Cross Hill *(Town Council)*
		'Benjamin Fawcett', Middle Street North *(JDW)*
	CP	Driffield Leisure Centre, Bridlington Road
Flamborough		Lighthouse
Goole		Escourt Street
		'City & County', Market Square *(JDW)*
	CP	Goole Leisure Centre, North Street *(Private)*
Hedon		Watmoughs Arcade
Hessle		Cliff Road, Hessle Mill
		The Square (Daytime)
		Humber Bridge Car Park *(Humber Bridge Board)*
Hornsea		Boat Compound (Summer)
		Cinema Street
		Marine Drive
Howden		St Helens Square
Kilnsea		Seaside Road Car Park
Mappleton		Cliff Road Car Park
Market Weighton		Londesborough Road
Melton		'Sandpiper', Melton Park *(Marstons)*
North Ferriby		'Duke of Cumberland', High Street *(Marstons)*
Pocklington		Railway Street
	CP	Francis Scaife Sports Centre
Routh		'Nags Head', Hornsea Road *(Marstons)*
Sewerby		Sewerby Cricket Club, by Pavilion (Daytime)
		Sewerby Park (Summer)
Stamford Bridge		The Square
Welton		'Green Dragon', Cowgate *(Marstons)*
Withernsea		Central Promenade
		Piggy Lane

Hambleton

Chopgate		Nat. Park Car Park *(National Park)*
Kildale		Nat. Park Car Park *(National Park)*
Northallerton	CP	Hambleton Forum (Centre hrs)
		'Durham Ox', 157 High Street *(Marstons)*
	CP	Chopsticks Workshop & Resource Centre *(Private)*
	CP	Northdale Horticulture, Yafforth Road *(Private)*
Sutton Bank		Visitor Centre *(National Park)*
Thirsk	CP	Thirsk Leisure Centre (Centre hrs)
		Thirsk Station *(Transpennine)*
		'Three Tuns', Market Place *(JDW)*

Harrogate

Beckwithshaw	'Smiths Arms', Church Row *(Spirit)*
Boroughbridge	Back Lane Car Park
Harrogate	Crescent Gardens, Crescent Road
	Devonshire Place, Skipton Road
	Jubilee MSCP
	Library Gardens, Victoria Avenue

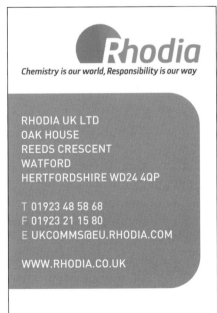

	Oatlands Recreation Ground, Hookstone Road
	Stray Ponds, York Place
	Tower Street MSCP
	Valley Gardens
	Victoria MSCP
	Harrogate Station *(Northern Rail)*
	Victoria Shopping Centre *(Private)*
	'Winter Gardens', Royal Baths *(JDW)*
CP	Harrogate Library, 1st floor *(County Council)*

Knaresborough	Bond End, High Street
	Bus Station
	Castle Yard
	Conyngham Hall Car Park
	York Place Car Park
	Knaresborough Caravan Site *(Caravan Club)*
CP	Gracious Street Methodist Church Centre *(Private)*
CP	Henshaw's Arts & Crafts Centre *(Private)*
CP	Knaresborough Swimming Pool *(Private)*

| **Masham** | Dixon Keld, nr. Police Station |

| **Pateley Bridge** | Recreation Ground |
| | Southlands Car Park |

| **Ripley** | Car Park |

Ripon	Bus Station
	Minster Road
	Spa Gardens
	Wakemans House, High Skelgate

| **Starbeck** | High Street |

| **Stickinghall** | 'Scotts Arms', Main Street *(Private)* |

Kingston-upon-Hull

Hull	Albert Avenue Pools (Centre hrs)
	Costello Athletics Stadium (Stadium hrs)
	Guildhall Square
	Holderness Road, by East Park
	Hull Arena (Arena hrs)
	Hull Central Library (Library hrs)
	West Park (Park hrs)
	Woodford Leisure Centre (Centre hrs)

Hull Station *(Transpennine)*
North Point Shopping Centre *(Private)*
Princes Quay Shopping Centre *(Private)*
Prospect Shopping Centre *(Private)*
CP St Stephen's Shopping Centre *(Private)*
Trinity Market, North Church Street *(Private)*
Debenhams Store, Prospect Street *(Debenhams)*
'Admiral of the Humber', Anlaby Road *(JDW)*
'Apollo', 1082 Holderness Road *(Marstons)*
'Biarritz', George Street *(Marstons)*
'Bridges', Sutton Road *(Private)*
'Goodfellowship', Cottingham Road *(Marstons)*
'Hallgate Tavern', Hallgate *(Marstons)*
'Highway', Willerby Road *(Marstons)*
'Hull Cheese', Paragon Street *(Private)*
'Linnet & Lark', Princess Avenue *(Marstons)*
'Lyrics', Whitefriargate *(Private)*
'Mainbrace', Beverley Road *(Private)*
'Nandos', St Stephens Centre *(Nandos)*
'Oystercatcher', Kingswood Leisure Park *(Private)*
'Parkers', Anlaby Road *(Private)*
'Priory Inn', Priory Road *(Marstons)*
'Revolution', Lowgate *(Private)*
'Sutton Fields', Oslo Road *(M&B)*
'Three John Scotts', Alfred Gelder Street *(JDW)*
'White Horse', Carr Lane *(Private)*
'William Wilberforce', Trinity House Lane *(JDW)*
'Zachariah Pearson', 386 Beverley Road *(JDW)*

Visit our online shop
For products and books that
open doors to independent living.

www.disabilityrightsuk.org

Ellifoot Lane, Burstwick, Near Hull
East Yorkshire, HU12 9EF.

Email: enquiries@brianfawcett-joinery.com
Telephone: 01964 670818
Fax: 01964 671138

www.brianfawcett-joinery.com

Applied Science Building 3 *(Univ of Hull)*
CP Block A, Queens Gardens *(Hull College)*
Chemistry Building *(Univ of Hull)*
Chesters Building, Queens Gardens *(Hull College)*
Graduate School *(Univ of Hull)*
Gulbenkian Centre *(Univ of Hull)*
Larkin Building *(Univ of Hull)*
Sport & Fitness Centre *(Univ of Hull)*
University House *(Univ of Hull)*
Ven Building *(Univ of Hull)*
Gala Bingo, Oslo Road *(Gala)*
Mecca Bingo, Anlaby Road *(Mecca)*
Odeon Cinema, Kingston Retail Park *(Odeon)*
CP Goodwin Centre, Guildhall Road
CP Wilson Centre, Alfred Gelder Street

Kirklees

Batley	Batley Town Hall (Office Hours)
	Market Square
	Wilton Park (Park hrs)
	'Union Rooms', Hick Lane *(JDW)*
Birstall	Oakwell Hall Information Centre
	Town Centre
	'Nandos', Gelderd Road *(Nandos)*
	CP Fieldhead Co-location Centre
Cleckheaton	Cleckheaton Town Hall (Office hrs)
	Market Arcade
	'Obediah Brooke', Bradford Road *(JDW)*
Dalton	Rawthorne & Dalton Library, Ridgeway (Library hrs)
Dewsbury	**CP** Crows Nest Park (Park hrs)
	Dewsbury Library (Library hrs)
	Dewsbury Museum (Museum hrs)
	Dewsbury Town Hall (Office hrs)
	Longcauseway, Market Place
	Social Services Information Point
	Dewsbury Bus Station *(WYMetro)*
	'The Principal', Northgate, Kingsway Arcade *(Barracuda)*
	'Time Piece', Northgate *(JDW)*
	'West Riding', by Station *(M&B)*

Fartown		Birkby & Fartown Library (Library hrs)
Heckmondwike		Heckmondwike Market
		Oldfield Lane
Holme		Village Centre
Holmfirth		Bus Station, Towngate
Honley		Moorbottom
Huddersfield		Albion Street. Civic Centre Car Park
		Central Library (Library hrs)
		Civic Centre 1 (Office hrs)
		Greenhead Park (Park hrs)
		Huddersfield Covered Market
		Queensgate Market, Princess Alexandra Walk
	CP	Town Hall, Ramsden Street (Office hrs)
		Bus Station, Albion Street *(WYMetro)*
		Huddersfield Station *(Transpennine)*
		Beatties Store, Kingsgate Centre *(Private)*
		'Caffe Nero', King Street *(Caffe Nero)*
		'Cherry Tree', Pearl Assurance House *(JDW)*
		'Court House', Queen Street *(Private)*
		'Lord Wilson', King Street *(JDW)*
		'Nandos', John William Street *(Nandos)*
		'The Warehouse', Zetland Street *(Private)*
		'Varsity', 24 Zetland Street *(Barracuda)*
		'Yates's Bar', King Street *(Private)*
		The Media Centre *(Private)*
Marsden		Peel Street
Marsh		Westbourne Road
Milnsbridge		Morley Lane
Mirfield		Knowle Park
		Station Road
		'Ship Inn', Steanant Lane *(Greene King)*
New Mill		Holmfirth Road
Outlane		'Wagon & Horses', New Hay Lane *(Private)*
Ravensknowle		Tolson Museum (Museum hrs)
Shepley	CP	Cliffe House Field Study Centre (2) *(Private)*
Slaithwaite		Carr Lane

Leeds

Aberford	CP	Lotherton Hall, Stable Courtyard (Hall hrs)
Armley		Theaker Lane
	CP	Armley Leisure Centre *(Private)*
Beeston		Cottingley Hall Crematorium (Crematorium hrs)
		'Broadway', Dewsbury Road *(Marstons)*
	CP	John Charles Centre for Sport
Boston Spa		Village Hall, High Street (Hall hrs) *(Parish Council)*
Bramhope		Golden Acre Park (Park hrs)
		Old Lane Car Park
Bramley		Town Street
Chapel Allerton	CP	Reginald Centre, 263 Chapeltown Road (Centre hrs)
		Scott Hall Sports Centre, Scott Hall Road (Centre hrs)
		'Three Hulats', Harrogate Road *(JDW)*
	CP	Tech North, Harrogate Road *(Private)*
Crossgates		Crossgates Library (Library hrs)
		Crossgates Shopping Centre *(Private)*
Garforth		Barleyhill Road
Gildersome		Gildersome Library (Library hrs)
Gledhow		Fernville Leisure Centre, Oakwood Lane (Centre hrs)
Headingley		Ash Road/North Lane
		Carnegie Stadium, South Stand *(Leeds Rugby)*
		Headingley Stadium *(Yorkshire CCC)*
	CP	Headingley HEART *(Private)*
Holt Park		Holt Park Community Library (Library hrs)
Horsforth		Horsforth Library (Library hrs)
		Horsforth Station *(Northern Rail)*
Leeds City Centre		County Arcade, Vicar Lane
		Kirkgate Market, Vicar Lane
		St John's Centre, Albion Street/Merrion Street
		Coach Station, Dyer Street *(National Express)*
		Leeds City Bus Station *(WYMetro)*
		Leeds Station (2) *(Network Rail)*
		Headrow Shopping Centre *(Private)*
		The Corn Exchange, Call Lane *(Private)*
		The Light, The Headrow (2) *(Private)*

Debenhams Store, Briggate *(Debenhams)*
'All Bar One', Millennium Square *(Private)*
'Beckett's Bank', Park Row *(JDW)*
'Bourbon', Cookridge Street *(Private)*
'Browns', The Headrow *(M&B)*
'Cuthbert Brodrick', Millennium Square *(JDW)*
'Edwards', Merrion Street *(M&B)*
'Hogs Head', Great George Street *(Private)*
'J D Wetherspoon', Leeds Station *(JDW)*
'Japanic', Clay Pit Lane *(Private)*
'Jongleurs', The Cube *(Private)*
'Majestyk', City Square *(Private)*
'McDonalds', Briggate *(McDonalds)*
'McDonalds', St John's Shopping Centre *(McDonalds)*
'Nandos', 152 Briggate *(Nandos)*
'Nandos', Cardigan Fields *(Nandos)*
'Nandos', The Light *(Nandos)*
'Nation of Shopkeepers', Cookridge Street *(Private)*
'Packhorse', Briggate *(Private)*
'Prohibition', Greek Street *(Private)*
'Qube', Portland Crescent *(Private)*
'Queens Court', Lower Briggate *(Private)*
'Quid Pro Quo', Greek Street *(Private)*
'Revolution', Cookridge Street *(Private)*
'Slug & Lettuce', Park Row *(Private)*
'Squares', Boar Lane *(Private)*
'Stick or Twist', The Podium *(JDW)*
'Tampopo', South Parade *(Private)*
'The Courtyard', Cookridge Street *(Private)*
'The Wellington', Wellington Square *(Private)*
'Tiger Tiger', 117 Albion Street *(Private)*
'Varsity', 24 Woodhouse Lane *(Barracuda)*
'Walkabout', Cookridge Street *(Private)*
'Waterhole', Great George Street *(Private)*
'Yates's Bar', Boar Lane *(Private)*
'Yates's Bar', Woodhouse Lane *(Private)*
Elland Road Stadium *(Leeds Utd FC)*
CP West Yorkshire Playhouse *(Private)*
CP Central Library, Gallery Café

Moor Allerton	'Penny Fun', Shopping Centre *(Private)*
Morley	Morley Town Hall (Office hrs)

		Wesley Street/Queen Street
	CP	Morley Leisure Centre, Queens Way
Osmondthorpe		Osmondthorpe Library/One Stop Shop (Library hrs)
Otley	CP	Chevin Forest Park, by Study Centre
		Nelson Street, Visitor Centre & Library
Pudsey		Market Place
		'Crossed Shuttle', Manor House Street *(JDW)*
Rothwell		Marsh Street, Car Park
Roundhay		Tropical World (Park hrs)
Wetherby		The Shambles
Wetherby A1(M)		Wetherby Services J46 *(Moto)*
White Rose		Debenhams Store, White Rose Centre *(Debenhams)*

Richmondshire

Askrigg		Village Hall
Aysgarth Falls		Car Park *(National Park)*
Bainbridge		Village
Colburn	CP	Community Health & Recreation Centre
Gunnerside		Village
Hawes		Market Place
		Car Park *(National Park)*
		Brown Moor Caravan Site *(Caravan Club)*
Hipswell		Hildyard Row/White Shops
Keld		Village
Leyburn		Railway Street
		Kelberdale *(Town Council)*
		Lower Wesleydale Caravan Club Site *(Caravan Club)*
Middleham		Village
Muker		Village
Reeth		Village
Richmond		Nuns Close Car Park
		Ronaldshay Park
		Round House
		The Falls

Victoria Road *(Trust)*
'Ralph Fitz Randal', Queens Road *(JDW)*
Hargill House Caravan Site *(Caravan Club)*

Rotherham

Aston-cum-Aughton	Aston-cum-Aughton Leisure Centre *(DC Leisure)*
Bramley	'Woodman', Woodlaithes Road *(Marstons)*
East Dene	Mowbray Gardens Library (Library hrs)
Greasbrough	Greasbrough Library (Library hrs)
Maltby	Joint Customer Care Centre (Centre hrs)
	'Queens Hotel', Tickhill Road *(JDW)*
	Maltby Leisure Centre *(DC Leisure)*
Rotherham	All Saints Square (Daytime)
	Centenary Market Hall Entrance (Mon-Sat, daytime)
	Clifton Park Museum, Clifton Lane (Museum hrs)
CP	Clifton Park Wet Play Area (Park hrs)
	'Corn Law Rhymer', High Street (Trading hrs) *(JDW)*
	St Ann's Leisure Centre (Centre hrs)
	Rotherham Central Station *(Northern Trains)*
	'Blue Bell Inn', Manvers Way *(Marstons)*
	'Blue Coat', The Crofts *(JDW)*
	'Rhinoceros', Bridgegate *(JDW)*
	'Tabbard', Herringthorpe Valley Road *(Marstons)*
Thrybergh	Country Park, Anglers' Lodge
Wath upon Dearne	'Church House', Montgomery Square *(JDW)*

Ryedale

Danby	The Moors Centre *(National Park)*
Farndale	Low Mill
Grosmont	Grosmont Station [Restricted space] *(NYMR)*
Helmsley	Borogate
	Cleveland Way Car Park
Hutton-le-Hole	Car Park *(National Park)*
Kirkbymoorside	Town Farm Car Park
Malton	Market Place
	Wentworth Street
CP	Cauwood Day Centre, Old Maltron Road *(Private)*

Norton-on-Derwent	Church Street
Pickering	Eastgate
	The Ropery Car Park
	Pickering Station *(NYMR)*
Rosedale	Rosedale Abbey
Thornton-le-Dale	Lakeside Car Park

Scarborough

Filey	Evron Centre, John Street (Centre hrs)
	Filey Foreshore (Easter-October)
	Royal Parade (7.30-20.00)
	Station Avenue Car Park (7.30-20.00)
	The Ravine, Cobble Landing
Glaisdale	Station Yard Car Park
Goathland	Car Park *(National Park)*
	Goathland Station *(NYMR)*
Grosmont	Village, west end
Ravenscar	Raven Hall Road, Car Park *(National Park)*
Robin Hood's Bay	Station Car Park (Easter-October *&* winter weekends)
Scaling Dam	Car Park *(National Park)*
Scarborough	Burniston Road Car Park
	North Bay, Superloo
	Peasholme Park
	Royal Albert Drive, North Bay
	South Cliff Gardens (Easter-October)
	Sports Centre (Centre hrs)
	St Helens Square
	St Nicholas, Foreshore (Easter-October)
	West Pier
	Scarborough Station, Platform 3 *(Transpennine)*
	Brunswick Shopping Centre *(Private)*
	Debenhams Store, Brunswick Pavilion *(Debenhams)*
	'Lord Rosebery', Westborough *(JDW)*
	'West Riding', Castle Road *(Private)*
	'Yates's Bar', St Nicholas Street *(Private)*
	Scarborough Campus, Filey Rd *(Univ of Hull)*

NATIONAL KEY SCHEME GUIDE 2013

Staithes	Staithes Bank Bottom
	Staithes Top Car Park
West Ayton	West Ayton Caravan Club Site *(Caravan Club)*
Whitby	Abbey Headland, Car Park
	Kyber Pass, The Battery
	New Quay, New Quay Road
	North Promenade, The Beach (Easter-October)
	West Cliff Beach
	Whitby Leisure Centre (Centre hrs)
	Whitby Marina, Car Park

Selby

Barlow Common	Nature Reserve Visitor Centre
Hambleton	'Owl Hotel', Main Street *(Marstons)*
Selby	Abbey Leisure Centre (Centre hrs)
	Back Micklegate Car Park
	Park Street, by Selby Park
	Morrisons Store, Market Cross *(Morrisons)*
	Tesco Store, Portholme Road *(Tesco)*
Sherburn-in-Elmet	Low Street
Tadcaster	Britannia Car Park

Sheffield

| Beighton | 'Belfry', Eckington Road *(Spirit)* |
| Broomhill | 'Francis Newton', Clarkehouse Road *(JDW)* |

For more information on Public Facilities and access at many attractions, why not telephone for more details before you travel?

Please telephone for all enquiries:

....

 SELBY DISTRICT COUNCIL *Moving forward with purpose* **01757 705101**

 Disability Rights UK

Become a member

Help us realise our vision and make your voice count.

www.disabilityrightsuk.org

Chapeltown		Park Gates, Cowley Lane
Crystal Peaks		Crystal Peaks Shopping Centre *(Private)*
Foxhouse		Public House Car Park, Hathersage Road
Gower Street		Ellesmere Road Shops
Hillsborough		'Rawson Spring', Langsett Road *(JDW)*
Meadowhall		Meadowhall Station *(Northern Rail)* Debenhams Store, Park Lane *(Debenhams)* 'Nandos', The Oasis *(Nandos)*
Norton		Main Road/Meadowhead
Parsons Close	CP	Asda Store, Chaucer Road *(Asda)*
Rivelin		Manchester Road/Rivilin Valley Road
Sheffield City Centre		Angel Street Moorfoot (Mon-Sat, 7.00-18.15) Transport Interchange, Pond Street *(National Express)* Sheffield Station, Concourse & Platform 5 *(East Midlands Trains)* Castle Market *(Private)* Orchard Square *(Private)* Debenhams Store, The Moor *(Debenhams)* 'All Bar One', St Pauls Parade *(Private)* 'Bankers Draft', Market Place *(JDW)* 'Benjamin Huntsman', Cambridge Street *(JDW)* 'Nandos', Royal Plaza, West Street *(Nandos)* 'Revolution', The Plaza, Fitzwilliam Street *(Private)* 'Sheffield Waterworks Company', Division Street *(JDW)*

'Swim Inn', Glossop Road *(JDW)*
'Varsity', 173 West Street *(Barracuda)*
'Varsity', 261 Ecclesall Road *(Barracuda)*
'Walkabout', Carver Street *(Private)*
'Yates's Bar', Carver Street *(Private)*
CP Royal Hallamshire Hospital, Floor B *(Health Authority)*
Bramall Lane Stadiun *(Sheffield Utd FC)*
CP Ponds Forge Int. Sports Centre
CP 33 Love Street Resource Centre
CP Crucible Theatre, Norfolk Street *(Private)*
CP Sheffield Hallam University, Arundel Building *(University)*
CP Sheffield Town Hall, Surrey Street

Stocksbridge	Market Street
Tinsley	**CP** Tinsley Green Children's Centre
Valley Centertainment	'Nandos', Broughton Lane *(Nandos)*
Woodseats	**CP** Abbey Lane 'Woodseats Palace', 692 Chesterfield Road *(JDW)*

Wakefield

Ackworth	'Beverley Arms', Doncaster Road *(Marstons)*
Castleford	Castleford Bus Station *(WYMetro)* Carlton Lanes Shopping Centre *(Private)* 'Carltons', Carlton Street *(Private)* 'Glass Blower', Bank Street *(JDW)* 'Nandos', 9 Xscape, Colorada Way *(Nandos)* 'Shout', Station Road *(Private)* 'Winter Seam', Colorado Way *(JDW)* Bowlplex, Xscape *(Bowlplex)*
Darrington	'The Darrington', Great North Road *(Spirit)*
Durkar	'Swan & Cygnet', Denby Dale Road *(Marstons)*
Hemsworth	Vale Head Sports Pavilion (Centre hrs)
Horbury	Horbury Library, Westfield Road (Library hrs)
Knottingley M62	Ferrybridge Services, M62/A1 J30 *(Moto)*
Ossett	Ossett Town Hall (Office hrs)
Pontefract	Pontefract Town Hall (Office hrs) Pontefract Bus Station *(WYMetro)* 'Red Lion', Market Place *(Private)*

Wakefield		The Springs
		Wakefield Reference Library (Library hrs)
		Wakefield Town Hall (Office hrs)
	CP	The Ridings Centre, Lower Mall *(Private)*
		'Caffe Nero', Kirkgate *(Caffe Nero)*
		'Gate', Northgate *(Marstons)*
		'Lupset Hotel', Horbury Road *(Private)*
		'Nandos', 11 Westgate Retail Park *(Nandos)*
		'Quest', Westgate *(Private)*
		'Six Chimneys', Kirkgate *(JDW)*
		'Slug & Lettuce', Almsgate *(Private)*
	CP	Ridings Centre Car Park, by Shopmobility *(Private)*
West Bretton M1		Woolley Edge Services, M1 J38/39 *(Moto)*
Wintersett	CP	Discovery Centre, Anglers Country Park (Centre hrs)

York

Acomb		Front Street (8.00-20.00)
		'Marcia Grey', Front Street *(Private)*
		'Quaker Wood', Acomb Wood Drive *(Private)*
	CP	Acomb Discovery, Front Street
	CP	Energise, Cornsland Road *(Private)*
Clifton		Homestead Park *(Rowntree Trust)*
Dringhouses		Askham Bar Park & Ride
		York Racecourse *(Private)*
Fulford		York Designer Outlet *(McArthurGlen)*
Grimston		Grimston Bar Park & Ride
Haxby		Town Centre (8.00-20.00)
Monks Cross		Huntington Stadium *(York City Knights)*
Rawcliffe		Rawcliffe Bar Park & Ride
York		Coppergate (8.00-20.00)
		Nunnery Lane (8.00-20.00)
	CP	Silver Street (Daytime)
		St George's Field, Car Park (April-September) (8.00-20.00)
		St Leonards Place, Exhibition Square (8.00-20.00)
		St Sampsons Square (8.00-20.00)
		Tanner Row (8.00-20.00)
		Union Terrace, Car Park (8.00-20.00)
		York Station, Platforms 2 & 8 *(East Coast)*

'All Bar One', New Street *(Private)*
'Cross Keys', Deangate *(Private)*
'Graduate', 6/12 Lendal *(Barracuda)*
'Loch Fyne Restaurant', Walmgate *(Private)*
'Nandos', High Ousegate *(Nandos)*
'Pitcher & Piano', Coney Street *(Marstons)*
'Postern Gate', 90 Piccadilly *(JDW)*
'Punchbowl', Blossom Street *(JDW)*
'Royal York Hotel', Station Road *(Private)*
'Slug & Lettuce', Low Ousegate *(Private)*
'Windmill', Blossom Street *(Private)*
'Yates's Bar', Church L:ane, Low Ousegate *(Private)*
City Screen, Coney Street *(Private)*
Mecca Bingo, Fishergate *(Mecca)*
Beechwood Grange Caravan Club Site *(Caravan Club)*
Rowntree Park Caravan Club Site *(Caravan Club)*
CP   Long Close Lane, Walmgate
CP   York Explore Library

NORTH EAST ENGLAND

Darlington

Darlington	Horsemarket, by Shopmobility
	Darlington Station, Platform 4 *(East Coast)*
	Cornmill Shopping Centre *(Private)*
	'Tanners Hall', Skinnergate *(JDW)*
	'The Brinkburn', Lady Kathrine Grove *(Private)*
	'The Mowden', Staindrop Road *(M&B)*
	'White Heifer That Travelled', John Fowler Way *(Marstons)*
	'William Stead', Crown Street *(JDW)*
	'Yates's Bar', Skinnergate *(Private)*
	Gala Bingo, Skinnergate *(Gala)*

Durham

Allensford	Allensford Caravan/Picnic Park, off A68
Barnard Castle	Morrison's Car Park
Bishop Auckland	Bus Station
	'Stanley Jefferson', Market Place *(JDW)*
Chester-le-Street	Riverside Park, by kiosk
	Chester-le-Street Station *(Northern Rail)*
	'Wicket Gate', Front Street *(JDW)*
Crimdon	Crimdon Park
Crook	South Street (7.00-17.00)
	'Horseshoe Inn', Church Street *(JDW)*
Durham	Durham Station *(East Coast)*
	The Gates Shopping Centre *(Private)*
	'Bishops Mill', Walkergate *(JDW)*
	'Nandos', 5 Walkergate *(Nandos)*
	'Varsity', Saddlers Street *(Private)*
	'Water House', North Road *(JDW)*
	'Yates's Bar', North Road *(Private)*
	Grange Caravan Club Site *(Caravan Club)*
CP	Freeman's Quay Leisure Centre *(Private)*
CP	Science Block, Durham University *(University)*
Middleton-in-Teesdale	Chapel Row
Newton Aycliffe	Newton Aycliffe Leisure Centre (Centre hrs)

Peterlee	Peterlee Leisure Centre (Centre hrs) 'Five Quarter', Hailsham Place *(JDW)*
Seaham	Seaham Hall Car Park Seaham Leisure Centre (Centre hrs) South Street Vane Tempest Car Park 'Crows Nest', East Shore Village *(Marstons)*
Staindrop	Duke Street (8.00-17.00)
Stanhope	Durham Dales Visitor Centre (9.00-17.00)
Stanley	Stanley Bus Station
Wearhead	by Bridge
Willington	High Street Lido
Wolsington	Angate Street (7.00-17.00)

Gateshead

Birtley		Harraton Terrace
Blaydon		The Precinct
	CP	Blaydon Leisure & Primary Care Centre (2)

Gateshead		Gateshead Shopping Centre *(Private)*
		'Baja Beach Club', Pipewellgate *(Spirit)*
	CP	Chowdene Children's Centre, Waverley Road
	CP	Gateshead Central Library
	CP	Gateshead Civic Centre
	CP	Gateshead Leisure Centre
	CP	Sage Gateshead *(Private)*
	CP	Teams Children's Centre
	CP	Tyne View Children's Centre, Redheugh Building
	CP	Tyne View Children's Centre, Tyne Building
Lamesley		'Ravensworth Arms', Greenford Lane *(Spirit)*
Leam Lane	CP	Gateshead@Leam Lane, Cotermede
Lowfell		Lowerys Lane
	CP	Dryden Professional Development Centre
MetroCentre	CP	MetroCentre *(Private)*
		Debenhams Store, Redpath Way *(Debenhams)*
		'Nandos', Garden Walk *(Nandos)*
		'Nandos', Russell Way *(Nandos)*
		'Wetherspoons', Russell Way *(JDW)*
		Gala Bingo, Metro Retail Park *(Gala)*
Whickham		'Woodmans Arms', Whickham Park *(Spirit)*

Hartlepool

Hartlepool		Central Library, York Road (Library hrs)
		Coronation Drive Car Park (9.00-17.00, later in summer)
		Rossmere Park (9.00-17.00, later in summer)
		Town Hall Theatre, Foyer (Theatre hrs)
		Ward Jackson Park (9.00-17.00, later in summer)
		Hartlepool Station *(Northern Rail)*
		'Greenside', Stockton Road *(Marstons)*
		'Jacksons Wharf', The Highlight *(Marstons)*
		'King John's Tavern', South Road *(JDW)*
		'Ward Jackson', Church Square *(JDW)*
		'Yates's Bar', Victoria Road *(Private)*
	CP	Marina Way, Jackson Dock *(Private)*
Old Hartlepool		Hartlepool Maritime Experience (Museum hrs)
Seaton Carew		Clock Tower, Esplanade (M+F)

| The Headland | Moor Terrace (9.00-17.00, later in summer) |
| | Town Square, Middlegate (9.00-17.00, later in summer) |

Middlesbrough

Middlesbrough	Middlesbrough Station *(Transpennine)*
	Hillstreet Shopping Centre *(Private)*
	The Cleveland Centre *(Private)*
	Debenhams Store, Newport Road *(Debenhams)*
	'Isaac Wilson', Wilson Street *(JDW)*
	'Nandos', Middlesbrough Leisure Park *(Nandos)*
	'The Resolution', Newport Crescent *(JDW)*
	'The Shakespeare', Linthorpe Road *(Private)*
	'The Wellington', Albert Road *(Private)*
	'Walkabout', Corporation Road *(Private)*
	'Yates's Bar', Newport Road *(Private)*
CP	Bus Station *(Private)*
CP	James Cook University Hospital *(Hospital)*
CP	Neptune Leisure Centre, Ormesby Road *(Private)*

| North Ormesby | 'The Buccaneer', Kings Road *(Private)* |

Newcastle upon Tyne

| Benwell | West End Customer Service Centre (Centre hrs) |
| | 'Fox & Hounds', West Road *(Spirit)* |

Byker	East End Customer Service Centre, Shields Rd (Centre hrs)
	East End Library, Hadrian Square (Library hrs)
	East End Pool, Foyer (Pool hrs)
	Shields Road/Edwin Street

| Elswick | CP | Elswick Pool, Beech Grove Road *(Private)* |

| Fenham | West Road Crematorium (Crematorium hrs) |

Gosforth	Gosforth Library, Regent Farm Road (Library hrs)
	'Adrianos', Gosforth High Street *(Private)*
	'Job Bulman', St Nicholas Avenue *(JDW)*
	'Scalini's', Great North Road *(Private)*
CP	Gosforth Swimming Pool *(Private)*

| Jesmond | Paddy Freeman's Park, Freeman Road |
| CP | Skills for Life, Tankerville Place *(Private)* |

| Kenton | Kingston Park Stadium, East Stand *(Newcastle Falcons)* |

| Newburn | Newburn Country Park (Park Building hrs) |

Newcastle City Centre

Barrack Road, by St James's Park (8.00-15.00)
Bigg Market
Chillingham Road/Tosson Terrace
Dean Street MSCP
Eldon Garden MSCP (8.00-22.00)
Exhibition Park, by Café (Café hrs)
Grainger Market, Grainger Street (Trading hrs)
Grainger Town MSCP
Haymarket, Bus Station
Leazes Park, Lodge (Park hrs)
Percy Street/Morden Street
Sidgate, Eldon Square (Trading hrs)
Watergate, Quayside
Wesley Square, Quayside

CP Discovery Museum, Blandford Square *(Museum)*
Coach Station, St James Boulevard *(National Express)*
Newcastle Station, Platform 4 *(East Coast)*
The Gate, Newgate Street *(Private)*
Fenwicks Store, Northumberland Street (3) *(Private)*
'Bar 38', Exchange Building, Lombard Street *(Spirit)*
'Baron & Baroness', Times Square *(Private)*
'Centurion', Central Station *(Private)*
'Eye on the Tyne', Broad Chare *(Greene King)*
'Fluid Bar', 17-25 Gallowgate *(Private)*
'Hide Café Bar', The Gate *(Private)*
'Keel Row', The Gate, Newgate Street *(JDW)*
'Mile Castle', Westgate Road/Grainger Street *(JDW)*
'Mood', The Gate *(Private)*
'Nandos', Eldon Square *(Nandos)*
'Nandos', The Gate, Newgate Street *(Nandos)*
'Quayside Bar', The Close, Quayside *(JDW)*
'Raw Hide', Newgate Street *(Private)*
'Revolution', Collingwood Street *(Private)*
'Rusty's', Times Square *(Private)*
'Slug & Lettuce', Exchange Buildings *(Private)*
'The Yard', Scotswood Road *(Private)*
'Union Rooms', Westgate Road *(JDW)*
'Waterline Bar', East Quayside *(Private)*
'Yates's Bar', Grainger Street *(Private)*
Metro Radio Arena, Arena Way *(Private)*
The Gate Centre *(Private)*

Tyneside Cinema, 10 Pilgrim Street *(Private)*
CP City Library, Charles Avison Building
CP Eldon Square Shopping Centre *(Private)*

West Denton	Denton Park Centre (Shopping hrs)
	Outer West Customer Service Centre (Centre hrs)
	CP Outer West Pool
Woolsington	'Millers', Callerton Lane Ends *(Spirit)*
	CP Newcastle Airport *(Airport)*

North Tyneside

Four Lane Ends	Metro Interchange
Howdon	**CP** Howdon Library, Churchill Street (Library hrs)
Marden	'Fox Hunters', Prestongate *(Spirit)*
Monkseaton	Souter Park North
North Shields	Duke Street
	Fish Quay
	Saville Street
	Suez Street
Tynemouth	Front Street
	Long Sands North (May-September)
	Tynemouth Park
Wallsend	Forum Shopping Centre
	Metro Bus Station
	Gala Bingo, Middle Engine Lane *(Gala)*
	CP Hadrian Leisure Centre, St Peters Road *(Private)*

Space donated by a friend

In support of
Disability Rights UK

Whitley Bay	Central Lower Promenade (May-September)
	Dukes Walk, Northern Promenade
	Metro Station
	Park Road, by Library
	South Parade
	'Fire Station', York Road *(JDW)*
CP	Waves, The Links *(Private)*
	Old Hartley Caravan Club Site *(Caravan Club)*

Northumberland

Allendale	Dawson Place, off Market Square
Alnmouth	Alnmouth Station *(Northern Rail)*
Alnwick	The Shambles, Market Place
	'Penny Black', Fenkle Street *(Private)*
Amble	Tourist Information Centre
Ashington	off Woodhorn Road (Daytime)
	Station Road
	'Block & Tackle', Blackthorne Way *(Marstons)*
	'Fox Cover', Freeman Way *(Private)*
	'Rohan Kanhai', Woodhorn Road *(JDW)*
	Gala Bingo, Milburn Road *(Gala)*
Bamburgh	Bamburgh Links Car Park
	Church Street
Beadnell	Car Park, Dunes Court (April-October)
Bedlington	Bower Grange, Station Road (Daytime)
	Town Centre, Library
	'Red Lion', Front Street West *(JDW)*
Bellingham	High Street
Berwick-upon-Tweed	Castlegate Car Park
	Eastern Lane
	Magdelene Fields
	Woolmarket
	Berwick-on-Tweed Station, Waiting Room *(East Coast)*
	'Leaping Salmon', Golden Square *(JDW)*
Blanchland	The Square
Blyth	Keel Row Shopping Centre
	Market Place

Blyth Valley Links	Fort House, Links Road
	Ranch Car Park
Boulmer	Coastguard Cottage
Corbridge	Princes Street
Cramlington	Gala Bingo, Forum Way *(Gala)*
Craster	Tourist Information Centre
East Ord	Ord House Country Park *(Private)*
Haltwhistle	Westgate
Haydon Bridge	John Martin Street
Heatherslaw Mill	Car Park (M+F) (Summer) (Daytime) *(Parish Council)*
Hexham	St Mary's Wynd
	Tyne Green
	Wentworth Car Park
	The Sele *(Town Council)*
	Hexham Station *(Northern Rail)*
	'Caffe Nero', Fore Street *(Caffe Nero)*
	'The Forum', Market Place *(JDW)*
Holy Island	Green Lane Car Park
Housesteads	Housesteads Visitor Centre *(National Trust)*
Morpeth	Bus Station *(Town Council)*
	Carlisle Park *(Town Council)*
	'Black Bull', Bridge Street *(Spirit)*
Newbiggin by the Sea	Promenade, by The Cobble (Daytime)
Norham	off West Street
Otterburn	Main Street
Ponteland	Thornhill Road Car Park (Daytime) *(Town Council)*
Powburn	River Breamish Caravan Club Site *(Caravan Club)*
Prudhoe	Neale Street
	West Road
Riding Mill	'Wellington Hotel', Main Road *(Chef & Brewer)*
Seahouses	Seahouses Car Park, Seafield Road
Seaton Delaval	The Avenue
Seaton Sluice	Fountain Head Bank Car Park (Daytime)
	West Terrace Car Park

Spittal		Promenade Car Park
		Seaview Caravan Club Site *(Caravan Club)*
Widdrington		'Widdrington Inn', Widdrington Village *(Private)*
Wooler		Bus Station, High Street
Wylam		Main Road

Redcar & Cleveland

Guisborough		Fountain Street Car Park
		Northgate/Patten Lane Car Park
Marske		Redcar Road, off High Street
Redcar		Locke Park
		Moore Street, off High Street
		The Stray, opp. Green Lane (April-September)
		Zetland Park, The Stray
		'Plimsoll Line', High Street East *(JDW)*
		'Royal Standard', West Dyke Road *(Private)*
Saltburn	CP	Cat Nab
		Pier (April-September)
		Saltburn Station
Upsall		'Cross Keys', Middlesbrough Road *(Chef & Brewer)*

South Tyneside

Hebburn		'Cock Crow Inn', Mill Lane *(Marstons)*
		'The Longship', Ushaw Road *(Private)*
South Shields		Coast Road, Marsden
		Promenade, Amusement Park (Summer)
		Queen Street, by Metro Station
		Sea Road
		'New Crown Hotel', Mowbray Road *(Marstons)*
		'Wouldhave', Mile End Road *(JDW)*
		'Yates's Bar', Mile End Road *(Private)*

Stockton-on-Tees

Billingham		Billingham Beck Valley Country Park
		Cowpen Bewley Woodland Park
		Town Square

Eaglescliff	Preston Park Country Park
	Preston Park Museum (Museum hrs)
	'Eagle Inn', Durham Lane *(Marstons)*
Ingleby Barwick	'Myton House Farm', Ingleby Way *(Marstons)*
Norton	High Street
Stockton	High Street
	Ropner Park, Hartburn
	Wellington Square Shopping Mall
	Debenhams Store, High Street *(Debenhams)*
	'Thomas Sheraton', Bridge Road *(JDW)*
Tees Barrage	White Water Caravan Club Site *(Caravan Club)*
Thornaby	Thornaby Station *(Transpennine)*
Yarm	High Street

Sunderland

Hetton	Easington Lane, High Street
	Town Hall Car Park, Front Street
Seaburn	Seaburn Centre (Daytime)
	South Bents (Summer)
Sunderland	Harbour View, Roker Seafront
	Lower Promenade, Roker
	Park Lane Interchange
	Park Parade, Roker (Daytime)
	Southwick Green
	Central Stores, Fawcett Street *(Private)*
	Debenhams Store, The Bridges *(Debenhams)*

Visit our online shop

For products and books that
open doors to independent living.

www.disabilityrightsuk.org

C W Partitions and Floors Ltd

Is pleased to support
Disability Rights UK

'Bar Me', Low Row *(Private)*
'Cooper Rose', Albion Place *(JDW)*
'Lampton Worm', Victoria Building *(JDW)*
'Nandos', 118 High Street West *(Nandos)*
'Old Orleans', Timber Beach Road *(Private)*
'Revolution', Victoria Building, Low Roe *(Private)*
'Varsity', Galen Buildings, Green Terrace *(Barracuda)*
'William Jameson', Fawcett Street *(JDW)*
'Yates's Bar', Burdon Road *(Private)*
Gala Bingo, Pallion New Road *(Gala)*
Stadium of Light *(Sunderland FC)*
CP Barnes Park
CP Sunderland Customer Service Centre, Fawcett St

Washington

Concord Centre, Bus Station
'Sir William de Wessyngton', Victoria Road *(JDW)*
Gala Bingo, The Galleries *(Gala)*

East Lothian

Athelstaneford		Main Street (Summer) (9.00-21.00)
Dirleton		Yellow Craig Caravan Club Site *(Caravan Club)*
Dunbar		Bayswell Road (9.00-20.00 summer, 10.00-17.00 winter)
		Bellhaven Bay Picnic Site
		John Muir Country Park (9.00-18.00, later in summer)
		Shore Road (9.00-18.00, later in summer)
		Skateraw (Summer) (9.00-21.00)
		Whitesands (Summer)
East Linton		East Linton Park (9.00-18.00, later in summer)
Gullane		Bents (Summer)
		Goose Green (9.00-18.00, later in summer)
Haddington		Neilson Park Road (9.00-18.00, later in summer)
Longniddry		Bents 1 (Summer) (9.00-20.30 *&* daytime winter weekends)
		Bents 2 (Summer) (9.00-20.30 *&* daytime winter weekends)
		Bents 3 (Summer) (9.00-20.30 *&* daytime winter weekends)
Musselburgh	CP	Fisherrow Harbour (9.00-18.00, later in summer)
		Shorthope Street (9.00-18.00, later in summer)
		'David Macbeth Moir', Bridge Street *(JDW)*
North Berwick		Quality Street (9.00-18.00, later in summer)
Port Seaton		Links Road (9.00-20.00 summer, 10.00-17.00 winter)
Prestonpans		Ayres Wynd (9.00-18.00, later in summer)
Tranent		Lindores Drive (9.00-18.00, later in summer)

Edinburgh

Colinton		Colinton Road/Bridge Road (10.00-18.00)
Corstorphine		St John's Road (10.00-18.00)
Drumbrae South		'Rainbow Inn', Craigmount View *(Spirit)*
	CP	Drumbrae Leisure Centre, Drumbrae Terrace *(Private)*
Edinburgh City Centre		Ardmillan Terrace, Gorgie Road

Bruntsfield Place
Cannonmills
Castle Terrace Car Park (8.00-20.00)
Cathedral Lane (10.00-20.00)
Hamilton Place (10.00-18.00)
Haymarket, Morrison Street (M+F) (8.00-20.00)
Hope Park (10.00-18.00)
Hunter Square (10.00-20.00)
Mound, by Art Gallery
Nicolson Square (10.00-22.00)
Ross Band Stand, W. Princes Street Gdns (Summer)
   (10.00-20.00)
St James Place (8.00-18.00)
West End, West Princes Street Gdns (8.00-22.00)
West Tollcross (10.00-20.00)
Edinburgh Bus Station, Elder Street *(Private)*
Edinburgh Waverley Station *(Network Rail)*
'Au Bar', Shandwick Place *(Private)*
'Bar 38', George Street *(Spirit)*
'Black Bull', Grassmarket *(Spirit)*
'Browns', George Street *(M&B)*
'Edwards', South Charlotte Street *(M&B)*

'Grape', Capital Building, St Andrews Square *(Spirit)*
'Hamiltons', Hamilton Place *(Private)*
'Jongleurs', Omni Centre *(Private)*
'McCowans Brew House', Fountain Park *(Private)*
'Milnes Bar', Hanover Street *(Spirit)*
'Nandos', 71-73 Lothian Road *(Nando)*
'Nandos', Dundee Road, Fountain Park *(Nandos)*
'Playfair', Omni Centre *(JDW)*
'Revolution', 30 Chambers Street *(Private)*
'Slug & Lettuce', Omni Centre *(Private)*
'Standing Order', George Street *(JDW)*
'Walkabout', Omni Centre *(Private)*
St Christophers Backpackers, Market St *(Private)*
CP Capability Scotland, 11 Ellersley Road *(Private)*
CP Scottish Parliament, Garden Lobby *(SP)*

Granton
Granton Square (10.00-18.00)
CP Granton Campus, 350 West Granton Road (2) *(Edinburgh College)*
Gala Bingo, West Granton Road *(Gala)*

Leith
Taylor Gardens (10.00-18.00)
'Foot of the Walk', Constitution Street *(JDW)*

WM Cadenhead
172 Canongate
Edinburgh

Tel: 0131 556 5864

'Quality, Purity, Choice'

Edinburgh's best established
whisky shop

Meadowbank	'KFC' Meadowbank (KFC)
	Gala Bingo, Moray Park (Gala)
Morningside	Canaan Lane (10.00-18.00)
Newcraighall	'Cuddie Brae', Newcraighall Roundabout (Spirit)
Portobello	Bath Street (10.00-20.00)
	Joppa Promenade
	Pipe Lane (10.00-20.00)
Silverknowles	Edinburgh Caravan Club Site (Caravan Club)
South Queensferry	High Street
	Dalmeny Station (ScotRail)
Wester Hailes	Westside Plaza Shopping Centre (Private)
	Gala Bingo, Westside Plaza (Gala)

Falkirk

Blackness	The Square (9.00-17.00)
Bo'ness	Kinneil Park, by Nursery
	Register Street Car Park
Bonnybridge	High Street Car Park, near ScotMid
Camelon	The Hedges, Main Street
Falkirk	Callender Park
	Glebe Street (9.00-18.00)
	Public Library, Hope Street (Library hrs)
	Falkirk Grahamston Station (ScotRail)
	Falkirk High Station (ScotRail)

Surprise yourself!

Burns Storytelling, Alloway, Ayrshire

......not all of our stories are in books

NATIONAL KEY SCHEME GUIDE 2013

	Callender Square Shopping Centre Car Park *(Private)* 'Carron Works', Bank Street *(JDW)* Gala Bingo, Kerse Lane *(Gala)*
Grangemouth	'Earl of Zetland', Bo'ness Road *(JDW)*
Larbert	Larbert Station *(ScotRail)* 'Outside Inn', Glenbervie Business Park *(Spirit)*
Polmont	Polmont Station, Booking Hall *(ScotRail)*

Midlothian

Dalkeith	'Blacksmiths Forge', Newmills Road *(JDW)*
Loanhead	IKEA Store, Straiton Road *(IKEA)*

Scottish Borders

Broughton	King George VI Park
Chirnside	Cross Hill
Cockburnspath	Main Street
Coldingham Sands	Beach Front (Summer)
Coldstream	Courthouse
Duns	Brierybaulk
Earlston	Main Street
Eyemouth	Harbour Road, Car Park High Street Car Park
Galashiels	Bank Street Bus Station High Street Car Park 'Hunters Hall', High Street *(JDW)*
Greenlaw	The Square
Hawick	Common Haugh Car Park, Victoria Road Howegate, Drumlanrig Square Volunteer Park
Innerleithen	Hall Street
Jedburgh	Lothian Car Park (7.30-18.00) Tourist Information Centre
Kelso	Woodmarket/Horsemarket
Lauder	Market Place

Melrose	Abbey Street
	Gibson Park Caravan Club Site *(Caravan Club)*
Morebattle	Main Street
Newcastleton	Langholm Street, by Fire Station
Newton St Boswells	Main Street
Peebles	Eastgate Car Park
	Kingsmeadows Car Park
	School Brae, off High Street
Selkirk	Market Square Car Park
St Boswells	Main Street
St Mary's Loch	by Café
Town Yetholme	off High Street

West Lothian

Bathgate	Bathgate Station *(ScotRail)*
	'James Young', Hopetoun Street *(JDW)*
Linlithgow	Linlithgow Station *(ScotRail)*
Livingston	Livingston Designer Outlet *(McArthurGlen)*
	'Almond Bank', Almondvale Boulevard *(JDW)*
	'The NewYearField', Livingston Designer Outlet *(JDW)*

Dumfries & Galloway

Annan	Downies Wynd
Ardwell	Picnic Site (April-October)
Carsethorn	Shore Road
Castle Douglas	Market Hill Car Park
Creetown	The Hollow
Dalbeatie	Water Street Car Park
Drummore	Harbour Road
	Mull of Galloway
Dumfries	Muchies Street
	Whitesands
	Dumfries Station, Concourse *(ScotRail)*
	'Robert the Bruce', Buccleuch Street *(JDW)*
	Gala Bingo, Shakespeare Street *(Gala)*
CP	DGOne Leisure Centre
Garlieston	by Public Hall
Gatehouse of Fleet	High Street Car Park
Glenairlie Bridge	Picnic Site, A76
Glencaple	Shore Road
Glenluce	Public Hall, Main Street (Summer)
Glentrool	Stroan Bridge (Summer)
Kippford	Village Hall Car Park
Kirkconnel	Main Street (M+F) (Daytime)
Kirkcudbright	Harbour Square
Langholm	Kiln Green Car Park
Lochmaben	Castle Street
Lockerbie	Station Square
	Lockerbie Station *(ScotRail)*
Moffat	Station Park
Moniave	Ayr Road (M+F) (Daytime)

New Abbey	Car Park
Newton Stewart	Riverside Car Park, Riverside Road
	Garlieston Caravan Club Site *(Caravan Club)*
Palnure	Kirroughtree Visitor Centre *(Forestry Commission)*
Penpont	Marrburn Road Car Park (M+F) (Daytime)
Port Logan	New England Bay Caravan Club Site *(Caravan Club)*
Port William	Village Square
Portpatrick	Harbour
Sandhead	Main Street
Sanquhar	South Lochan (M+F) (Daytime)
Southerness	Car Park, Shore Road
Stairhaven	Car Park (Summer)
Stranraer	Agnew Park Pavilion (Daytime)
	Hanover Square Car Park
	Stair Park (Summer)
	Stranraer Station, Car Park *(ScotRail)*
Thornhill	St Cuthberts Walk (M+F) (Daytime)
Wanlockhead	Lead Mining Museum
Whithorn	Bruce Street (Daytime)
Wigtown	High Vennel

East Ayrshire

Cumnock	Cumnock Town Hall (Booking hrs)
	Glaisnock Shopping Centre
Kilmarnock	Burns Mall
	Dick Institute Library & Gallery (Library hrs)
	Foregate Square
	Kilmarnock Station, Concourse *(ScotRail)*
	'Wheatsheaf Inn', Portland Gate *(JDW)*
	Gala Bingo, Portland Street (2) *(Gala)*
Mauchline	Loudoun Street

East Dunbartonshire

Bishopbriggs	'Eagle Lodge', Hilton Road *(Spirit)*
Clachan of Campsie	Recreational Area

Kirkintilloch	Southbank Road
	'Kirky Puffer', Townhead *(JDW)*
Lenzie	Lenzie Station *(ScotRail)*
Milngavie	Milngavie Station *(ScotRail)*
	'Cross Keys', Station Road *(Private)*
Westerton	Westerton Station *(ScotRail)*

East Renfrewshire

Barrhead	Main Street
	Barrhead Station *(ScotRail)*
CP	Barrhead Health & Care Centre, 213 Main Street *(Private)*
CP	Barrhead Centre
Busby	'White Cart', East Kilbride Road *(Spirit)*
Clarkston	Clarkston Station *(ScotRail)*
Eaglesham	Eaglesham Pavilion, Gilmour Street
Neilston	Neilston Station *(ScotRail)*
Newton Mearns	The Avenue Shopping Centre *(Private)*

Glasgow

Anniesland	Anniesland Station *(ScotRail)*
Darnley	Gala Bingo, Woodneuk Road *(Gala)*
Drumchapel	Drumchapel Shopping Centre
	Sainsbury's Store, Allerdyce Drive *(Sainsbury)*
Garrowhill	'Barrachnie Inn', 192 Glasgow Road *(Spirit)*
Glasgow City Centre	Collins Street
	St Vincent Street, St Vincent Place
	Stevenson Street
	West Campbell Street
	Buchanan Bus Station (2) *(SPT)*
	Glasgow Central Station (2) *(Network Rail)*
	Glasgow Charing Cross Station *(ScotRail)*
	Glasgow Queen Street Station (2) *(ScotRail)*
	Buchanan Galleries *(Private)*
	Princes Square, Buchanan Street *(Private)*
	St Enoch Shopping Centre *(Private)*
	Debenhams Store, Argyle Street *(Debenhams)*
	'All Bar One', St Vincent Street *(M&B)*

'Bar Censsa', West George Street *(Spirit)*
'Buffalo Joes', Hope Street *(Private)*
'Camperdown Place', West George Street *(JDW)*
'Central Bar', Central Station *(Private)*
'Counting House', St Vincent Place *(JDW)*
'Crystal Palace', Jamaica Street *(JDW)*
'Edward Wylie', Bothwell Street *(JDW)*
'Edwards', West George Street *(M&B)*
'Esquire House', 1487 Great Western Road *(JDW)*
'Frankenstein 1818', West George Street *(Private)*
'Hengler's Circus', Sauchihall Street *(JDW)*
'Jongleurs', Renfrew Street *(Private)*
'Lakoto', 110 West George Street *(Private)*
'Mojama', Sauchiehall Street *(Private)*
'Nandos', St Enoch Centre *(Nando)*
'Nandos', The Quay, West Paisley Road *(Nandos)*
'O'Neills', Albion Street *(M&B)*
'Revolution', 67 Renfield Street *(Private)*
'Sir John Moore', Argyle Street *(JDW)*
'Sir John Stirling Maxwell', Kilmarnock Road *(JDW)*
'Society Room', West George Street *(JDW)*
'The Arches', Argyle Street *(Private)*

'The Sauciehaugh', 410 Sauchihall Street *(Private)*
'Walkabout', Renfield Street *(Private)*
'Yates's Bar', Sauchiehall Street *(Private)*
'Yates's Bar', West George Street *(Private)*
Glasgow Caledonian University (7) *(GCU)*
Glasgow Bowl, Springfield Quay *(AMF)*
O2 Academy, 121 Edlinton Street *(Private)*

Glasgow Fort	'Nandos', Glasgow Fort Shopping Park *(Nandos)*
Hyndland	Hyndland Station *(ScotRail)*
Mount Florida	Hampden Car Park/Bus Interchange, Aitkenhead Rd
	Mount Florida Station *(ScotRail)*
	Langside College, Business School *(Langside College)*
	Langside College, LITE House *(Langside College)*
Parkhead	Forge Shopping Centre, Gallowgate *(Private)*
Partick	Exhibition Centre Station *(ScotRail)*
	Partick Station *(ScotRail)*
	Queen Margaret Union *(Glasgow University)*
	Scottish Exhibition & Conference Centre *(Private)*
Pollock	'Nandos', Silverburn Shopping Centre *(Nandos)*
CP	Cardonald College, Moor Park Drive *(College)*
Possil Park	Gala Bingo, Hawthorn Street *(Gala)*
Shettleston	Shettleston Station *(ScotRail)*

Inverclyde

Gourock	Albert Road
	Shore Street
	Gourock Station *(ScotRail)*
Greenock	Campbell Street
	Hunters Place
	Kilblain Street
	Greenock Central Station *(ScotRail)*
	'James Watt', Cathcart Street *(JDW)*
Inverkip	Greenock Road
Port Glasgow	Coronation Park
	Port Glasgow Station *(ScotRail)*
Wemyss Bay	Wemyss Bay Station *(ScotRail)*

North Ayrshire

Ardrossan	North Crescent Road (9.00-17.00)
Fairlie	Main Road
Irvine	East Road
	Low Green Road
	Shorehead (April-September) (9.00-18.00)
	Irvine Station *(ScotRail)*
	Gala Bingo, Townhead *(Gala)*
Isle of Arran	Blackwaterfoot, Harbour
	Brodick, Low Green
	Lamlash, Shore Road
	Whiting Bay, Shore Road
Kilwinning	Abbey Green
	Kilwinning Station *(ScotRail)*
Largs	Pierhead (Daytime)
	Largs Station *(ScotRail)*
Saltcoats	Melbourne Gardens (April-Sept) (9.30-20.00)
	The Braes (9.30-20.00, later in summer)
	'The Salt Cot', Hamilton Street *(JDW)*
Stevenston	Alexander Place/New Street
	Stevenston Shore (Summer) (12.00-18.00)

North Lanarkshire

Airdrie		Town Centre
		Airdrie Station *(ScotRail)*
		'Robert Hamilton', Bank Street *(JDW)*
	CP	Airdrie Locality Support Services, Hall Graig Street.
Bellshill		Bellshill Station *(ScotRail)*
		'Avondale Bar/Lily Restaurant' *(Private)*
	CP	Bellshill Locality Support Services, Main Street
	CP	Sir Matt Busby Sports Complex
Coatbridge		Main Street
		'The Vulcan', Main Street *(JDW)*
	CP	Summerlee Museum of Industrial Life
Croy		Croy Station, Ticket Office *(ScotRail)*
Cumbernauld		Cumbernauld Station *(ScotRail)*
		Tay Walk *(Private)*

	Teviot Walk *(Private)*
	'Carrick Stone', 52 Teviot Walk *(JDW)*
	Cumbernauld College, Main Building *(College)*
	Cumbernauld College, New Building *(College)*
	Cumbernauld College, Technical Block *(College)*
CP	Cumbernauld Locality Support Service
CP	Tryst Sports Centre
Moodiesburn	CP Pivot Community Education Centre
Motherwell	Brandon Parade East
	Brandon Parade South
	Motherwell Station *(ScotRail)*
	'Brandon Works', Merry Street *(JDW)*
CP	Isa Community Centre, Muirhouse Road *(Private)*
CP	Motherwell Locality Support Service
Muirhead	'Muirhead Hotel' *(Private)*
Shotts	CP Shotts Community Centre
Uddingstone	CP Viewpark Community Centre
Wishaw	Kenilworth Avenue
	'Wishaw Malt', Kirk Road *(JDW)*
CP	Wishaw Library

Renfrewshire

Bishopton	Bishopton Station *(ScotRail)*
Braehead	'Lord of the Isles', Xscape *(JDW)*
	'Nandos', Xscape *(Nandos)*
	Bowlplex, Xscape *(Bowlplex)*
CP	Braehead Shopping Centre *(Private)*
Johnston	Johnston Station *(ScotRail)*
Paisley	Paisley Gilmour Street Station *(ScotRail)*
	'Last Post', County Square *(JDW)*
	Gala Bingo, Phoenix Retail Park *(Gala)*
Renfrew	Inchinnan Road

South Ayrshire

Ayr	Arthur Street
	Blackburn Car Park, Seafront (Easter-October)
	Pavilion. Esplanade (M+F)

	Ayr Station, Concourse *(ScotRail)*
	'West Kirk', Sandgate *(JDW)*
	Craigie Gardens Caravan Club Site *(Caravan Club)*
Ballantrae	Forelands
Girvan	Ainslie Car Park
	The Harbour
	Girvan Station *(ScotRail)*
Prestwick	Links Road
	Prestwick Town Station *(ScotRail)*
	'Prestwick Pioneer', 87 Main Street *(JDW)*
Prestwick Airport	Prestwick Airport Station *(ScotRail)*
Troon	Church Street
	St Meddans Street Car Park
	Troon Station *(ScotRail)*

South Lanarkshire

Biggar	Main Street
Cambuslang	Newton Station *(ScotRail)*
Carluke	Carnwath Road
	CP Carluke Lifestyles, Carnwarth Road *(Private)*
Carnwath	Main Street
Carstairs	Carstairs Station *(ScotRail)*
Crossford	Lanark Road (Daytime)
East Kilbride	Greenhills Square
	Maxwell Drive
	Plaza Centre (9.00-18.00)
	St Leonards Shopping Centre (8.00-19.00)
	'Peel Park', Eaglesham Road *(Spirit)*
	CP Murray Owen Centre, Liddell Grove
Forth	Main Street (Daytime)
Hamilton	Hamilton West Station *(ScotRail)*
	CP South Lanarkshire Lifestyles, Fairhill
Lanark	Horsemarket (Daytime)
	'Clydesdale Inn', Bloomgate *(JDW)*
	CP South Lanarkshire Lifestyles, Thomas Taylor Ave.
Larkhall	King Street

Law	Station Road
Leadhills	Main Street
Rutherglen	King Street
	'An Ruadh Ghlean' 44 Main Road *(JDW)*
	CP South Lanarkshire Lifestyles, Glenside Drive
Stonehouse	King Street
Strathaven	Green Street
Uddingston	Uddingston Station *(ScotRail)*

West Dunbartonshire

Alexandria	Leven Vale Pool (Pool hrs)
	Main Road/Overtoun Road
Balloch	Balloch Station *(ScotRail)*
Clydebank	Clydebank Station *(ScotRail)*
	Singer Station *(ScotRail)*
	Clyde Shopping Centre, Kilbowie Road *(Private)*
	In Shops, Sylnania Road South *(Private)*
	'KFC', Livingstone Street, Clyde Retail Park *(KFC)*
	Gala Bingo, Graham Avenue *(Gala)*
	CP The Playdrome, Abbotsford Road (5)
Dumbarton	Riverside Lane (2)
	Dumbarton Central Station *(ScotRail)*
	CP Dumbarton Disability Resource Centre

EASTERN SCOTLAND

Aberdeen

Aberdeen	Beach Esplanade, Central (Mon-Sat, 9.30-17.30)
	Beach Esplanade, Footdee (9.30-17.30)
	Central Library, Rosemount Viaduct (Library hrs)
	Chapel Street (8.00-18.30)
	Duthie Park, Riverside Drive
	Seaton Park, Don Street, by Play Park
	Spa Street, behind Library (8.00-18.00)
	Victoria Park, Watson St/Westburn Rd
	Aberdeen Station, Concourse *(ScotRail)*
	Debenhams Store, Trinity Centre *(Debenhams)*
	'Archibald Simpson', 5 Castle Street *(JDW)*
	'Beluga', Union Street *(Private)*
	'J G Ross Coffee Shop', King Street *(Private)*
	'Justice Mill', Union Street *(JDW)*
	'Nandos', Union Square *(Nandos)*
	'Revolution', 25 Belmont Street *(Private)*
	'Slains Castle', Belmont Street *(Private)*
	'Yates's Bar', Langstane Place *(Private)*
CP	Aberdeen Royal Infirmary *(Hospital)*
	Gala Bingo, King Street *(Gala)*
	Linx Ice Centre *(Private)*
CP	Kincorth Sports Centre, Corthan Crescent
CP	Marischial College, Broad Street *(College)*
CP	Union Square, nr. Bus Station *(Private)*
CP	Woodend Hospital, South Block *(Hospital)*
Cults	North Deeside Road, by Library
Mastrick	Sheddocksley Sports Centre (Centre hrs)
Peterculter	North Deeside Road, by restaurant

Aberdeenshire

Aberchirder	Market Street
Aboyne	Ballater Road
Alford	Car Park
Auchenblae	MacKenzie Avenue/Hill View Road

Auchnagatt	Martin Terrace *(Community Council)*
Ballater	The Square
Balmedie	The Haughs (Summer) (Daytime)
Banchory	Bellfield Car Park
	Bridge of Feugh
	Silverbank Caravan Site *(Caravan Club)*
Banff	Duff House Grounds
	Marina
	St Mary's Car Park
	The Harbour *(Community Council)*
Bellabeg	Strathdon
Bennachie	Rowan Tree Car Park (April-October)
Boddam	Harbour Street
Braemar	Balnellan Road
	The Invercauld Caravan Site *(Caravan Club)*
Cornhill	Mid Street
Crathie	Tourist Office Car Park (April-October)
Crimond	Logie Drive
Ellon	Market Street
Fordyce	East Church Street
Fraserburgh	Castle Street
	Interpretative Centre
	Fraserburgh Bus Station, Hanover Street *(Private)*

Aberdeenshire

COUNCIL

For more information on public facilities and access to many attractions, why not telephone for more details before you travel.

Please telephone for all enquiries:

08456 08 1207

Fyvie	Cuminestown Road
Gardenstown	The Harbour
Gourdon	Boath Park
Hatton	Station Road
Huntly	Castle Street
	Market Muir
	Huntly Station *(ScotRail)*
Inverallochy	Allochy Road
Inverurie	Station Road/Burn Lane
	Inverurie Station *(ScotRail)*
Johnshaven	Fore Street
Maud	Station Road
Mintlaw	Aden Country Park, Bottom Car Park (Summer)
	Aden Country Park, Coach House (Park hrs)
	Aden Country Park, Top Car Park (Summer)
	The Square
New Byth	Playing Fields
New Pitsligo	High Street/Market Place
Oldmeldrum	Urquhart Road
Peterhead	Drummers Corner/Tolbooth
	'Cross Keys', Back Street *(JDW)*
	Gala Bingo, Marischal Street *(Gala)*
Port Elphinstone	Port Road
Portsoy	Shore Street
Potarch	Potarch Green
Rosehearty	Union Street
Stonehaven	Beach (Summer)
	Harbour
	Margaret Street
	Stonehaven Station *(ScotRail)*
Strichen	Bridge Street
Stuartfield	Knock Field (April-October)
Tarves	Pleasure Park, Tolquhon Avenue
Turriff	High Street

| Westhill | Shopping Centre |
| | 'Shepherds Rest', Arnhall Business Park *(Private)* |

Angus

Arbroath	Hamilton Green
	Harbour Visitor Centre
	Market Place
	Ness-Victoria Park
	Tennis Courts (April-October)
	Arbroath Station *(ScotRail)*
	'Corn Exchange', Market Place *(JDW)*
	Gala Bingo, High Street *(Gala)*
CP	Lochlands Adult Resource Centre

| Auchmithie | Fountain Square |

| Brechin | Church Street |

| Carnoustie | Carnoustie House Park (Events only) |
| | Ferrier Street |

| Edzell | The Muir |

| Forfar | Buttermarket |
| CP | Lilybank Resource Centre |

| Kirriemuir | CP | Websters Sports Centre *(Private)* |

| Monifieth | Riverview Drive, Play Area (April-September) |

Montrose	Town Buildings
	Trail Pavilion
	Montrose Station *(ScotRail)*
	Gala Bingo, Hume Street *(Gala)*
CP	Rose Hill Resource Centre, Forties Road

Dundee

Broughty Ferry	CP	Beach, Windmill Gardens (9.00-18.00)
	Queen Street Car Park
	'Bell Tree', Panmurefield Road *(Spirit)*
	'Bruarch', 326 Brook Street *(Private)*

| Camperdown | CP | Camperdown Country Park Crows Nest *(Private)* |

Dundee	Central Library, Wellgate (Library hrs)
	Dundee Law Car Park, Law Road
	Hilltown, Main Street

Seagate Bus Station (Shopping hrs)
Dundee Station *(ScotRail)*
Debenhams Store, Overgate *(Debenhams)*
'Counting House', Reform Street *(JDW)*
'KFC', Kingsway West *(KFC)*
'KFC', Tom Jackson Drive *(KFC)*
'Old Bank Bar', 67 Reform Street *(Private)*
'Outside Inn', Camperdown Leisure Park *(Spirit)*
'The Capitol', Seagate *(JDW)*
'Yates's Bar', Seagate *(Private)*
Gala Bingo, The Stack Leisure Park *(Gala)*
Grosvenor Casino, 142 West Marketgait *(Private)*
CP Dalhousie Building, University of Dundee *(University.)*
CP Gardyne Campus *(College)*
CP HRD Ltd, Logie Avenue *(Private)*
CP Kemback Adult Resource Centre
CP Ninewells Hospital & Medical School *(Hospital)*
CP Pamis, Springfield House *(University)*
CP White Top Centre, Westfield Ave.

Lockee Aimer Square Car Park (Shopping hrs)

Fife

Aberdour Aberdour Station *(ScotRail)*

Burntisland Links Place (8.45-18.45, later in summer & weekends)

Cowdenbeath Cowdenbeath Station *(ScotRail)*
CP Brunton House, High Street

Cupar Bonnygate Car Park (9.00-15.30)
Cupar Station *(ScotRail)*

Dunfermline Dunfermline Town Station *(ScotRail)*
'Guildhall & Linen Exchange', 79 High Street *(JDW)*
'Nandos', Whimbrel Place, Fife Leisure Park *(Nandos)*
Bowlplex, Fife Leisure Park *(Bowlplex)*
CP Carnegie Leisure Centre *(Private)*
CP Duloch Leisure Centre *(Private)*
CP Lynebank Wheelchair Clinic *(Hospital)*

Glenrothes Church Street Bus Station (Station hrs)
Glamis Centre
Kingdom Shopping Centre (2)

286

	'Golden Acorn', North Street *(JDW)*
CP	Fife Inst. of Physical & Recreational Education *(College)*
Inverkeithing	Inverkeithing Station *(ScotRail)*
	'Burgh Arms', High Street *(Private)*
Kinghorn	Kinghorn Station *(ScotRail)*
Kirkcaldy	Esplanade (8.15-18.45)
	Kirkcaldy Station *(ScotRail)*
	William Hill Bookmakers, Dunearn Drive *(Wm Hill)*
	'Robert Nairn', Kirk Wynd *(JDW)*
Leuchars	Leuchars Station *(ScotRail)*
Leven	Pleasureland, Promenade (9.45-15.45, later in summer)
CP	Levenmouth Swimming Pool
Lochgelly CP	Bowhill Swimming Pool *(Private)*
CP	Lochore Meadows, Activity Centre *(Private)*
Markinch	Markinch Station *(ScotRail)*
	Balbirnie Park Caravan Site *(Caravan Club)*
Newport-on-Tay	Blyth Hall
Pittenweem	The Harbour (9.00-17.00, later in summer)
St Andrews	Bruce Embankment (9.15-16.45)
St Monans	Hope Place (9.00-15.30)
Tayport	The Harbour (9.15-15.30)

Perth & Kinross

Auchterarder	Crown Wynd Car Park
Blair Atholl	Village Hall Car Park
Blairgowrie	Wellmeadow
Comrie	Dalginross
Coupar Angus	Largan Park
Crieff	James Square
	MacRosty Park
Dunkeld	North Car Park
Kinross	Kirkgate Park
Perth	A K Bell Library, York Place (Library hrs)
	Bus Station, Leonard Street

Marshall Place (9.00-18.00)
Ropemakers Close (9.00-18.00)
Perth Station, Entrance Hall *(ScotRail)*
St Johns Shopping Centre *(Private)*
'Capital Asset', Tay Street *(JDW)*
CP Bells Sports Centre, Hay Street *(Private)*
CP Perth College, Braham Building *(College)*

Pitlochry	West Lane (9.00-18.00)
	Pitlochry Station *(ScotRail)*
St Fillans	Main Street
Turfhills M90	Kinross Services *(Moto)*

Stirling

Callander	Station Road
Crianlarich	Glenfalloch Road
Dunblane	Dunblane Station, Platform 1 *(ScotRail)*
Killin	Maragowan Caravan Site *(Caravan Club)*
Stirling	Bus Station *(Private)*

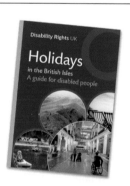

Stirling Station, Platform 2 *(ScotRail)*
Debenhams Store, Thistle Centre *(Debenhams)*
'Nandos', Forthside *(Nandos)*
Stirling Bowl, Forth Street *(AMF)*
CP Riverbank Resource Centre, Forthview

HIGHLANDS & ISLANDS

Argyll & Bute

Ardishaig	Car Park (8.00-17.00, later in summer)
Campbelltown	Bolgam Street, off Main Street (8.00-17.00)
	CP Aqualibrium, Kinloch Road *(Private)*
Dunoon	Glenmorag, West Bay (8.00-20.00)
	Moir Street (8.00-22.00)
Glenbarr	Killegruerr Caravan Site
Helensburgh	Kidston Park, The Pier
	Helensburgh Central Station *(ScotRail)*
Innellan	Shore Road, Sandy Beach (Summer)
Inveraray	The Pier (8.00-20.30)
Isle of Bute	Ettrick Bay (April-September) (10.00-19.00)
	Port Bannatyne
	Rothsey Pier
Isle of Gigha	Location details not available (Summer)
Isle of Islay	Port Ellen, Charlotte Street
	Portnahaven
Isle of Mull	Craignure
	Fionnphort
Kilcreggan	The Pier (9.00-16.00, later in summer)
Kilmun	The Pier

Loch Lomond	Firkin Point *(Loch Lomond National Park)*
Lochgilphead	Lochnell Street (7.00-17.00, later in summer)
Luss	Car Park (8.00-16.00, later in summer)
Oban	Oban Staion *(ScotRail)*
Rhu	Main Road (9.00-16.00, later in summer)
Sandbank	Main Road (8.00-20.00)
Tarbert	Harbour Street (7.00-18.00, later in summer)
Taynuilt	School Road

Highland

Achiltibuie	North of Village
Achnasheen	Achnasheen Station *(ScotRail)*
Applecross	Shore Street
Ardgay	Village (Summer)
Arisaig	by Village Shop
Aviemore	Main Street Aviemore Station *(ScotRail)*
Beauly	High Street (M+F)
Bettyhill	Car Park, A836
Bonar Bridge	Picnic Site
Brora	Dalcham Caravan Club Site *(Caravan Club)*
Carrbridge	Car Park
Clachtoll	Beach
Corran	by Ferry
Cromarty	Allan Square
Culloden	Culloden Moor Caravan Club Site *(Caravan Club)*
Daviot Wood	A9 Northbound, by Information Centre
Dingwall	Tulloch Street Dingwall Station *(ScotRail)*
Dores	Dores Inn
Drumbeg	Car Park
Drumnadrochit	Tourist Information Centre Car Park

Dunbeath	Harbour
Dunnet Bay	Beach
Fort Augustus	A83, by Information Centre
Fort William	Viewforth Car Park
	Fort William Station (*ScotRail*)
Gairloch	Community Centre (M+F)
	Harbour Road
Glencoe	Car Park, opp. Hotel
Golspie	Car Park off Main Street
	CP Sutherland Swimming Complex
Grantown	Burnfield
	High Street (April-October)
Invergordon	King Street
Invermoriston	Glenmoriston Millennium Hall
Inverness	Castle Wynd
	Mealmarket Close
	Inverness Station (*ScotRail*)

NATIONAL KEY SCHEME GUIDE 2013

	'Kings Highway', Church Street *(JDW)*
	'The Fluke', Culcablock Road *(Spirit)*
CP	Inverness College, Longman Road *(College)*

Isle of Skye	Ardvasar, Village Hall
	Broadford, opp. Visitor Car Park
	Carbost, opp. Distillery
	Dunvegan, Visitor Car Park
	Kilmuir, by Thatched Museum
	Portree, Camanachd Square
	Portree, The Green
	Uig, Visitor Car Park
CP	Portree, Fingle Centre

| **John O'Groats** | Car Park |

| **Keiss** | Main Street |

| **Kingussie** | Kingussie Station *(ScotRail)* |

| **Kinlochewe** | Slioch Terrace |
| | Kinlochewe Caravan Club Site *(Caravan Club)* |

| **Kinlochleven** | nr. Ice Factor |

| **Kyle of Lochalsh** | Car Park |
| | Kyle of Lochalsh Station *(ScotRail)* |

| **Lairg** | Main Street |

| **Lochcarron** | by Village Hall |

| **Lochinver** | Main Street |

| **Mallaig** | East Bay Car Park |
| | Mallaig Station *(ScotRail)* |

| **Muir of Ord** | Seaforth Road |

Nairn	Court House Lane
	East Beach, Car Park
	Harbour Street
	Mill Road
	The Links, West Beach
	Nairn Station *(ScotRail)*

| **North Kessock** | A9 Northbound Picnic Area |
| | A9 Southbound Picnic Area (2) |

| **Onich** | Bunree Caravan Site *(Caravan Club)* |

| **Portmahomack** | Main Street |

Rogie Falls		Car Park, A835
Rosemarkie		Mill Road
Shiel Bridge		Morvich Caravan Club Site *(Caravan Club)*
Silver Bridge		Car Park, A835
Smoo		Smoo Cave
Strathpeffer		The Square
Tain		Rose Garden, off High Street (2)
	CP	Royal Academy Community Complex (Centre hrs)
Tarbet, Sutherland		Tarbet Pier
Thurso		Harbour
		Tanyard, Riverside Road
		Thurso Station *(ScotRail)*
	CP	North Highland College
	CP	Thor House
Ullapool		West Argyle Street (M+F)
Wick		Whitechapel Road
		Wick Station *(ScotRail)*
		'Alexander Blain', Market Place *(JDW)*

Moray

Aberlour		Alice Littler Park
Buckie		Fish Market
		Newlands Lane Car Park (8.00-17.00)
	CP	Burnie Day Centre, Highfield Road
Burghhead		Harbour (8.00-17.00)
Craigellachie		Victoria Road *(Community Council)*
Cullen		Cullen Harbour (April-October) (8.00-20.00)
		The Square
Dufftown		Albert Place Car Park
Elgin		Cooper Park (April-October) (8.00-20.00)
		Elgin Library (Library hrs)
		Elgin Station *(ScotRail)*
		Tesco Store, Lossie Green *(Tesco)*

	'Muckle Cross', High Street *(JDW)*
CP	Cedarwood Day Service
Findhorn	The Beach, Middle Block (M+F)
	The Beach, West Block
Findochty	Edindoune Shore
Forres	Grant Park (April-October) (8.00-17.00)
	The Leys (8.00-17.00)
	Forres Station *(ScotRail)*
Garmouth	Playing Field (April-October)
Hopeman	Harbour
Keith	Regent Square (M+F)
	Reidhaven Square (M+F)
	Keith Station *(ScotRail)*
Lossiemouth	Esplanade, Seatown Road
	Station Park
Portknockie	Harbour (April-October) (8.00-20.00)
Rothes	New Street (M+F)
Tomintoul	Back Lane

Orkney Islands

Deerness	Community Hall *(Community Council)*
Evie	Aikerness
	Tingwall Pier, Waiting Room

ORKNEY
ISLANDS COUNCIL

We are pleased to support
Disability Rights UK

Council Offices, School Place,
Kirkwall, Orkney, KW15 1NY.
Telephone 01856 873535

Gabh ballrachd de Disability Rights UK

Lìonra de dhaoine aig a bheil ùidhean co-ionann agus airson fios air saoghal nan daoine ciorramach.

www.disabilityrights.org

Finstown		Maitland Place
Kirkwall	CP	Kirkwall Travel Centre (Centre hrs)
		Peedie Sea Boat Store, Pickaquoy Road
		Scapa Beach
		Shapinsay Ferry Terminal
		Shore Street
Orphir		Waulkmill
Sanday		Kettletoft Pier, Waiting Room
Sandwick		Bay of Skaill
South Ronaldsay		4th Barrier
		Sands O'Wright
Stromness		Ferry Road
		Warbeth Beach
Stronsay		Whitehall Pier

Shetland Islands

Lerwick	CP	Harbour House
		The Viking Bus Station
Scalloway		Burn Beach Car Park (8.00-21.00)
Voe		Voe Toilets
Walls		Hall Car Park

Western Isles

Stornaway	Percival Square, opp. Tourist Information Centre

NORTH WALES

Conwy

Abergele	Water Street
Betwys-y-Coed	Pont-y-Pair Car Park
	Station Road Car Park
Capel Curig	Snowdon View, behind café
Cerrigydrudion	Tan Llan, off A55
Colwyn Bay	Eiras Park Coach Park (Easter-September)
	Ivy Street Car Park
	Promenade, Central (Easter-September)
	Promenade, The Dingle
	Colwyn Bay Station *(Arriva Wales)*
	'Picture House', Princes Drive *(JDW)*
Conwy	Morfa Bach Car Park (Easter-September)
	The Quay
	Castle Visitor Centre *(Cadw)*
Deganwy	Level Crossing, Marine Crescent
Dolwyddelan	A470, nr.Post Office
Kinmel Bay	The Square, Foryd Road
Llanddulas	Beach Car Park (April-September)
Llandudno	George Street
	Great Orme Visitor Centre (April-September)
	Happy Valley, Happy Valley Road (Easter-September)
	Heulfre Gardens
	North Shore, nr. Paddling Pool
	West Parade, West Shore
	Llandudno Station *(Arriva Wales)*
	Dale Park Café, West Shore *(Private)*
	'The Paladium', Gloddaeth Street *(JDW)*
Llandudno Junction	Osbourne Road Car Park
	Llandudno Junction Station *(Arriva Wales)*
CP	Welsh Assembly Government Office *(WA)*
Llanelian yn Rhos	by Recreation Field (April-September)
Llanfair Talhaern	School Lane, off A548

Llanfairfechan	Promenade Car Park
Llanrwst	Gwydir Park (Easter-September)
	Watling Street
Penmaenmawr	Fernbrook Road Car Park, off A55
	Promenade, by Paddling Pool
	Promenade, by Yacht Club
Pensarn	Promenade
Pentrefoelas	Monument, off A55, opp Café
Rhos-on-Sea	Rhos Promenade
Towyn	Sandbank Road
Trefriw	Singrig Gardens, Gower Road

Denbighshire

Corwen	Rug Chapel *(Cadw)*
Denbigh	Rosemary Lane
Llangollen	Market Street
Loggerheads	Country Park
Prestatyn	Barkby Beach
	Council Offices, Nant Hall Road (Office hrs)
	The Nova, Central Beach
Rhuddlan	Princes Road (Dawn-dusk)
Rhyl	Coronation Gardens (Park hrs)
	Events Arena
	Old Golf Road
	Town Hall
	West Parade, Childrens Village
	Rhyl Station *(Arriva Wales)*
	'The Sussex', Sussex Street *(JDW)*
Ruthin	Market Street
	'Castle Hotel', St Peters Square *(JDW)*
St Asaph	High Street, nr. Bridge (Daytime)
Trefnant	Trefnant Bowling Club *(Private)*

Flintshire

Caerwys	Drovers Lane
Cilcain	Village Community Centre
Connah's Quay	Fron Road
Holywell	Somerfield Car Park
	Tower Gardens Car Park
Mold	Bus Station
	Daniel Owen Centre (Mon-Sat, 8.00-18.00)
	New Street Car Park
	'Gold Cape', Wrexham Street *(JDW)*
Saltney	High Street
Shotton	Alexander Street

Gwynedd

Aberdaron	The Beach (April-October) (Daytime)
Aberdyfi	The Quay
Abersoch	Golf Road (April-October)
	The Harbour (Daytime)
Bala	Plassey Street
	The Green
Bangor	Glanrafon (Daytime)
	Tan y Fynwent (Daytime)
	Bangor Station *(Arriva Wales)*

Dewch i fod yn aelod o Disability Rights UK

Rhwydweithio gyda phobl o'r un anian a chadw i fyny â newyddion sector anabledd.

www.diabilityrights.org

Flintshire County Council

For more information on Public Conveniences within Flintshire please phone us on

01352 703 350

	'Black Bull Inn', High Street *(JDW)*
	'Varsity', 146 High Street *(Barracuda)*
Barmouth/Abermaw	Llys Cambrian, nr Station (Daytime)
	North Promenade (April-October) (Daytime)
	The Quay (Daytime)
Beddgelert	Village
	Ty Isaf *(National Trust)*
Blaenau Festiniog	Diffwys
	Coed-y-Llwyn Caravan Site *(Caravan Club)*
Caernarfon	by Empire (Daytime)
	Castle Hill (Daytime)
	Penllyn Car Park (Daytime)
	'Tafarn y Porth', Eastgate Street *(JDW)*
Criccieth	Car Park (Daytime)
	Marine (April-October) (Daytime)
	Morannedd Beach (April-October) (Daytime)
	Criccieth Castle *(Cadw)*
Dinas Dinlle	by The Marine (Daytime)
Dolgellau	Marian Mawr Car Park
Fairbourne/Friog	Penrhyn Drive South
Felinheli	Beach Road (Daytime)
Harlech	Bron y Graig Car Park
	by the Castle (April-October)
Llanberis	Ger y Llyn (Daytime)
	Maes Padarn (Daytime)
	Y Glyn (Daytime)
Llandanwg	The Beach
Llithfaen	Village
Machroes	by Beach (April-October) (Daytime)
Maentwrog	by Oakley Arms
Morfa Bychan	Beach entrance (April-October)
Mynytho	Chwarel Foel Gron (April-October)
Nefyn	Cefn Twr (Daytime)
Penrhyndeudraeth	Car Park (Daytime)

Porthmadog	Public Park (Daytime)
Pwllheli	Penlan (Daytime)
	South Beach (Daytime)
	The Square/Y Maes (Daytime)
	West End (April-October) (Daytime)
Trawsfynydd	Car Park
Trefor	Y Traeth/Beach (April-October) (Daytime)
Tudweiliog	Village (April-October)
Tywyn	by Cinema
	Recreation Ground

Isle of Anglesey

Aberffraw	Llys Llywelyn (Summer)
Amlwch	Lon Goch
Beaumaris	by Library
Benllech	Beach Car Park (Summer)
	The Square Car Park
Cemaes	High Street
Church Bay	Beach Car Park (Summer)
Holyhead	Breakwater Park (Summer)
	Newry Beach
	Porth Dafarch (Summer)
	Swift Square
	Holyhead Ferry Terminal *(Stena)*
Llanddona	Beach (Summer)
Llaneilian	Beach (Summer)
Llanfairpwll	Car Park, by Post Office
Llangefni	Lon y Felin
Menai Bridge	Bowling Green/Beach Road
	Library
	Pier
CP	Pili Palas Nature World *(Private)*
Newborough	Beach Road Car Park (Summer)
Penrhos	Nature Reserve Beach (Summer)
	Penrhos Caravan Club Site *(Caravan Club)*

Red Wharf Bay	Village (Summer)
Rhoscolyn	Beach Car Park (Summer)
Rhosneigr	Library Car Park
Traeth Bychan	Car Park (Summer)
Trearddur Bay	Beach Car Park (Summer)
Valley	Council Car Park

Wrexham

Cefn-Mawr	Ty-Mawr Country Park
Chirk	Colliery Road Car Park
	Lady Margaret's Park Caravan Club Site *(Caravan Club)*
Coedpoeth	Car Park, off A525
Erddig	Erddig Country Park *(National Trust)*
Froncysyllte	A5
Holt	Cross Street *(Community Council)*
Overton	School Lane Car Park *(Community Council)*
Rhosllanerchrugog	Market Street
Rossett	The Green, Chester Road *(Community Council)*
Trevor	Canal Basin Car Park
Wrexham	Henblas Street (F only)
	St Giles Link Road
	Waterworld Car Park (Mon-Sat 8.00-20.00)
	Wrexham General Station *(Arriva Wales)*
	'Elihu Yale', Regent Street *(JDW)*
	'Nandos', Eagles Meadow *(Nandos)*
	'North & South Wales Bank', High Street *(JDW)*
	'Plas Coch', Plas Coch Road *(Marstons)*
	'Yates's Bar', High Street *(Private)*

MID & WEST WALES

Carmarthenshire

Abergorlech	Village Centre (8.00-20.00)
Alltwalis	Village Centre (8.00-18.00, Weekdays)
Ammanford	Carregamman Car Park (6.00-20.00) Central Park (9.00-17.00, Weekdays) Co-op Car Park (9.00-17.00, Weekdays)
Brechfa	Village (8.00-20.00)
Burry Port	Railway Station (7.30-17.00, later in summer)
Carmarthen	John Street Car Park (6.00-20.00) St Peters Car Park (6.00-20.00) Carmarthen Bus Station *(Private)* Carmarthen Station, Platform 1 *(Arriva Wales)* 'Yr Hen Dderwen', King Street *(JDW)*
Carreg Cennen	Castle Car Park (8.00-20.00)
Cenarth	Village (Summer) (9.00-18.00)
Cross Hands	Carmarthen Road, nr. The Square (8.30-16.00)
Cynwyl Elfed	Village (7.30-17.30 Weekdays)
Ferryside	Beach Entrance (7.30-19.00, later in summer)
Glanamman	Cwmamman Square (9.00-14.00 Weekdays)
Gorslas	Car Park (7.30-20.00)
Kidwelly	Square (7.30-15.00, later weekends) Kidwelly Castle *(Cadw)*
Laugharne	by Castle (6.00-20.00)
Llanboidy	Village (8.00-17.30 Weekdays)
Llanddowror	Tenby Road (7.30-18.30 Weekdays)
Llandeilo	Central Car Park (6.00-20.00)
Llandovery	Castle Car Park (6.00-20.00, later in summer)
Llanelli	Bus Station, Island Place (6.00-20.00) Provision Market (Mon-Sat, 8.00-17.00) Town Hall Square (6.00-20.00) North Dock Beach *(Millennium Coastal Park)*

Llanelli Station *(Arriva Wales)*
'York Palace', Stepney Street *(JDW)*
Pembry Country Park *(Caravan Club)*

Llanpumsaint	Village (8.00-16.30 Weekdays)
Llansaint	Village Hall (8.00-18.00 Weekdays)
Llansteffan	Car Park, South (8.00-17.30, later in summer)
Llanybydder	by Cross Hands Hotel (7.00-19.00 Weekdays) Car Park (5.00-18.30 Weekdays)
Llyn Llech Owain	Country Park (Park hrs)
Meidrim	Village Centre (7.00-17.00 Weekdays, later in summer)
Meinciau	Community Hall (8.00-17.30 Weekdays)
Newcastle Emlyn	Mart Car Park (9.30-17.30)
Pencader	Village (7.30-17.30 Weekdays)
Pendine	Car Park (7.30-18.00, later in summer)
Pontweli	by Wilkes Head (8.00-18.00 Weekdays)
St Clears	Central Car Park (6.00-20.00)
Talley	nr. Abbey (8.00-20.00)
Tumble	Lower High Street (8.30-16.00)
Velindre	Parc Puw (7.30-17.30 Weekdays)
Whitland	West Street (8.00-18.00 Weekdays)

Ceredigion

Aberaeron	Masons Road North Beach (Daytime) Pen Cei
Aberporth	Glanmardy (April-October) Penrhodyn
Aberystwyth	Bath Street Castle Grounds (Daytime) Marine Terrace, The Shelter Park Avenue South Promenade, The Harbour Aberystwyth Station, Platform 1 *(Arriva Wales)* 'Varsity', Upper Portland Street *(Barracuda)* 'Yr Hen Orsaf', Alexandra Road *(JDW)*

	Glan-y-Mor Leisure Park *(Private)*
CP	Council Offices
CP	Welsh Assembly Government Buildings *(WA)*

Borth	North Beach, Pantyfedwen
	South Beach, by Coastguard
Cardigan	Bath House Car Park
	Greenfield Car Park
	Victoria Gardens
Cenarth	Town
Clarach Bay	Swn-y-Mor Leisure Park *(Private)*
Devils Bridge	behind Village Shop
Lampeter	Market Street Car Park
	Rookery Lane Car Park
	St Thomas Street
Llanarth	Shawsmead Caravan Site *(Caravan Club)*
Llandysul	Car Park (Daytime)
Llangrannog	Ger y Traeth/Beachside
Llanrhystud	Pengarreg Caravan Park *(Private)*
New Quay	Paragon Car Park
	Sandy Slip, Rhe Beach (Summer) (9.00-18.00)
	South John Street (Daytime)
Penbryn	Penbryn Beach (Easter-October)
Tregaron	Car Park
Tresaith	Ger y Traeth/ Beachside

CYNGOR SIR **CEREDIGION**
CEREDIGION COUNTY COUNCIL

Loo of the Year 2012
Overall Uk Trophy Winners

Canolfan Rheidol
Aberystwyth
Ceredigion
SY23 3UE

Tel: 01970 633900
e mail hpw@ceredigion.gov.uk
www.ceredigion.gov.uk/toilets

Powys

Gwasanaethau Adfywio
a'r Amgylchedd

www.powys.gov.uk

0845 607 6060

Pembrokeshire

Amroth	Amroth West
Bosherton	Car Park
Broad Haven	Marine Road National Park Car Park, Millmoor Way (April-October)
Burton	Jolly Sailor Car Park (April-October)
Carew	opp. The Castle
Cilgerran	Picnic Site
Cresswell Quay	The Quay
Crymych	Main Road, The Square
Dale	Coronation Hall
Dinas Cross	A487 by Playing Field
Felindre Farchog	A487 Lay-by
Fishguard	The Square (Daytime) West Street Car Park (Daytime) Fishguard Ferry Terminal *(Stena)*
Freshwater	Freshwater East Freshwater West Freshwater East Caravan Site *(Caravan Club)*
Goodwick	Parrog Car Park
Gwaun Valley	Location details not available
Haverfordwest	Castle Lake (Daytime) Leisure Centre (Daytime) Riverside MSCP (Daytime)
Johnston	Pope Hill
Kilgetty	Tourist Information Car Park
Letterston	The Square
Little Haven	Car Park
Manorbier	Beach
Marloes	Location details not available
Milford Haven	Gelliswick Manchester Square (Daytime)

	Market Square (Daytime)
	The Rath (Daytime)
Moylegrove	Location details not available
Narberth	Town Moor Car Park (Daytime)
Nevern	behind Old School
Newgale	by Duke of Edinburgh (April-October)
	Central Car Park
Newport	Long Street Car Park
Neyland	Brunel Quay Marina
Nolton Haven	Location details not available (Summer)
Pembroke	Commons (Daytime)
	Parade
Pembroke Dock	Front Street
	Hobbs Point (Daytime)
	Library (Daytime)
Penally	Location details not available
Penblewin	Car Park
Porthgain	Location details not available
Saundersfoot	Coppit Hall Car Park (April-October)
	Harbour Car Park
	Regency Car Park (April-October)
Solva	Lower Car Park
St Davids	Bryn Road, behind City Hall
	Porthclais
	Quickwell Hill Car Park
	The Grove Car Park (April-October) (Daytime)
	Whitesands Beach Car Park
	Lleithyr Meadow Caravan Site *(Caravan Club)*
St Dogmaels	High Street
	Poppit Sands
St Florence	Village Hall *(Hall Committee)*
St Ishmaels	Location details not available (April-October)
St Nicholas	Village Hall, near Church *(Hall Committee)*
Stackpole	Stackpole Quay *(National Trust)*

Stepaside	Heritage Park (April-October)
Templeton	Play Area (April-October)
Tenby	Buttsfield Car Park (Daytime) Castle Beach (Daytime) MSCP North Beach Salterns Car Park South Beach (April-October) (Daytime) Upper Frog Street
Trevine	Location details not available
Wisemans Bridge	Location details not available

Powys

Abergwesyn	Community Hall (Summer) *(Community Council)*
Brecon	Lion Yard Produce Market (Market days) Promenade, Upper Meadow (Summer) Theatr Brycheiniog (9.00-17.00) Brynich Caravan Site *(Caravan Club)*
Builth Wells	Groe Car Park The Strand *(Town Council)*
Caersws	Bridge Street
Carno	nr. Post Office
Clywedog	Y Dremfadeg, Main Dam *(Severn Trent)*
Crickhowell	Beaufort Street *(Private)*
Glasbury-on-Wye	off A438
Hay-on-Wye	Oxford Road Car Park
Knighton	Norton Arms Car Park Offa's Dyke Centre (Daytime)
Lake Vyrnwy	by Dam and Estate Office *(Severn Trent)*
Llanbrynmair	Car Park
Llandrindod Wells	Lakeside (9.00-17.00) Station Crescent Town Hall Grounds 'The Metropole', Temple Street *(Private)*

Llanfair Caereinon	Bridge Street
Llanfihangel-yng-Ngwynfa	Car Park *(Community Council)*
Llanfyllin	High Street, opp. Car Park
Llangorse Common	Car Park
Llangynog	Car Park
Llanidloes	Gro Car Park Town Hall (Office hrs) *(Town Council)*
Llanrheadr-ym-Mochnant	Village Waterfall
Llansantffraed	A40, west of Bwlch
Llansantfraid	A495 Main Road
Llanspyddid	A40, west of Brecon
Llanwrtyd Wells	nr. New Inn
Machynlleth	Maengwyn Street Car Park Machynlleth Station *(Arriva Wales)* **CP** Corris Craft Centre, Corris *(Private)*
Meifod	Car Park
Newtown	Back Lane Car Park Gravel Car Park
Presteigne	Hereford Street Car Park Wilson Terrace (Summer) *(Town Council)*
Rhayader	Dark Lane
Sennybridge	High Street
Storey Arms	A470, between Brecon & Merthyr
Talgarth	The Square
Tretower	Tretower Court & Castle *(Cadw)*
Welshpool	Berriew Street Car Park Church Street Car Park
Ystradgynlais	The Cross

SOUTH WALES

Blaenau Gwent

Abertillery	Tillery Street
	'The Pontlottyn', Somerset Street *(JDW)*
Blaina	Blaina Cemetery (Daytime)
	Cwm Celyn Road
Brynmawr	Brynmawr Cemetery (Daytime)
	Market Square
	'Willow Tree', Lakeside Retail Park *(Marstons)*
Cwm	Cwm Cemetery (Daytime)
Ebbw Vale	Ebbw Vale Cemetery (Daytime)
	Market Street
	'The Picture House', Market Street *(JDW)*
Tredegar	Cefn Golau Cemetery (Daytime)
	Dukestown Cemetery (Daytime)
	Gwent Shopping Centre *(Private)*
	'Olympia', Morgan Street *(JDW)*

Bridgend

Bridgend	Brackla Street, Cheapside
	Bridgend Bus Station
	Derwen Road (8.00-18.00)
	Bridgend Station, Platform 1 *(Arriva Wales)*
	'Dunraven Arms', Derwen Road *(Private)*
	'Lava Ignite', Derwen Street *(Private)*
	'O'Neills', Nolton Street *(M&B)*
	'Sax's', Derwen Street *(Private)*
	'Tair Plune', opp Bus Station *(Private)*
	'Tuskers Bar', Wyndham Street *(Private)*
	'West House', Cefn Glas *(Private)*
	'Wyndham Arms', Dunraven Place *(JDW)*
Maesteg	Maesteg Bus Station
Porthcawl	Griffin Park
	John Street
	Rest Bay Car Park
	'High Tide Inn', Mackworth Road *(Private)*

Caerphilly

Bargoed	Bus Terminus, behind High Street (8.00-18.00)
Blackwood	Bus Station 'Bumble Bee', Sirhowy Enterprise Way *(Marstons)* 'The Sirhowy', High Street *(JDW)*
Caerphilly	Bus/Railway Terminus (08.00-18.00) Lower Twyn, Tourist Information Office
Crosskeys	Sirhowy Valley Country Park
Deri	Parc Cwm Darren (2) (April-Oct)
Nelson	Bus Station (8.00-19.30)
Newbridge	High Street 'Otter', Bridge Street *(Marstons)*
Oakdale	Pen Y Fan Pond Country Park (April-Oct)
Risca	Tredegar Street
Ystrad Mynach	Bedlwyn Road, by Bus Terminus

Cardiff

Canton	Leckwith Road/Delta Street Sophia Gardens Car Park (9.00-16.00)

Bridgend County Borough Council
Passenger Transport
Co-ordination Unit

If visiting Bridgend by public transport, Bridgend Bus Station is staffed and able to provide assistance to travellers. All areas are accessible and toilets accept RADAR keys. If you require assistance please ring 01656 642591 to discuss your public transport requirements or for queries about the Welsh Government's Free Concessionary Travel Scheme. For timetable enquiries please contact Traveline Cymru 0871 200 22 33.

Should you require a little more help then why not make a booking with our Shopmobility team who can be contacted by telephone 01656 667992. Car owners with Blue Badges enjoy free parking at all Bridgend car parks.

If you intend to arrive by train, information on assistance can be obtained from Arriva Trains Wales, tel: 0845 6061 660 or
e-mail: customer.services@arrivatrainswales.co.uk

www.bridgend.gov.uk

Blaenau Gwent

For more information on public facilities and access at many attractions, why not telephone before you travel?

Please telephone for all enquiries:

01495 311 556

Thompsons Park, Romily Road (Park hrs)
Victoria Park, Cowbridge Road East (Park hrs)
Victoria Park, Paddling Pool (Park hrs)
Pontcanna Caravan Site

Cardiff City Centre	Frederick Street
	The Hayes
	Britannia Park *(Port Authority)*
	Havannah Street *(Port Authority)*
	Cardiff Central Station, East Subway *(Arriva Wales)*
	Cardiff Queen Street Station, Platform 1 *(Arriva Wales)*
	Capitol Shopping Centre *(Private)*
	Queens Arcade Shopping Centre *(Private)*
CP	St Davids Shopping Centre *(Private)*
	Debenhams Store, St Davids Way *(Debenhams)*
	'All Bar One', Greyfriars Road *(Private)*
	'Cayo Arms', Cathedral Road *(Marstons)*
	'Crockerton', Greyfriars Road *(JDW)*
	'Dewis', Mary Ann Street *(Private)*
	'Edwards', St Marys Street *(M&B)*
	'Great Western', St Marys Street *(JDW)*
	'Ivor Davis', 243 Cowbridge Road *(JDW)*
	'Jongleurs', Millennium Plaza *(Private)*
	'Moloko', Mill Lane *(Private)*
	'Nandos', 28 Bute Street, Mermaid Quay *(Nandos)*
	'Nandos', St Davids Centre *(Nandos)*
	'Nandos', The Old Brewery, St Marys Street *(Nandos)*
	'Old Orleans', Church Street *(Private)*
	'O'Neills', St Marys Street *(M&B)*
	'Philharmonic', St Marys Street *(Spirit)*
	'Prince of Wales', St Mary Street *(JDW)*
	'Que Pasa', Trinity Street *(Marstons)*
	'Revolution', Castle Street *(Private)*
	'Robins Bar', Cowbridge Road East *(Private)*
	'The Gatekeeper', Westgate Street *(JDW)*
	'The Halfway', Cathedral Road *(Private)*
	'Varsity', Greyfriars Road *(Barracuda)*
	'Walkabout', St Marys Street *(Private)*
	'Yates's Bar', Westgate Street *(Private)*
	Millennium Stadium *(Private)*
	St David's Hall (4)
	SWALEC Stadium *(Glamorgan Cricket)*
CP	National Assembly of Wales Building *(WA)*

Cathays		Whitchurch Road, by Library
	CP	National Museum Cardiff, Cathays Park *(NMW)*
Ely		Western Cemetery (Cemetery hrs)
Heath Park	CP	University Hospital Wales, Out patients *(Hospital)*
Lisvane		Cefn-on-Park, Cherry Orchard Road (Park hrs)
Llandaff		Llandaff Fields, Cathedral Road
Llanishin		Ty Glas Road
Plasnewydd		Albany Road
		Roath Park, Boatstage (Park hrs)
		Roath Park, Rose Gardens (Park hrs)
		'Central Bar', Windsor Place *(JDW)*
		'Ernest Willows', City Road *(JDW)*
		'Varsity', 199 Richmond Road *(Barracuda)*
St Fagans	CP	St Fagans National History Museum *(NMW)*
Whitchurch		Penlline Road

Merthyr Tydfil

Dowlais		Dowlais Shopping Centre (M+F) (9.00-17.00)
Llwn-On	CP	Garwnant Visitor Centre *(Forest Enterprise)*
Merthyr Tydfil		Bus Station (9.00-18.00)
		by Shopmobility, behind Police Station
		Cyfarthfa Park (Park hrs)
		St Tydfils Square *(Private)*
		'Nandos', Rhydycar Leisure Centre *(Nandos)*
		'Y Dic Penderyn', High Street *(JDW)*

Monmouthshire

Abergavenny	Brewery Yard, behind Market Hall
	Castle Street Car Park
	Market Hall (Market hrs)
	Old Bus Station Car Park
	Whitehorse Lane
	'The Coliseum', Lion Street *(JDW)*
	Pandy Caravan Club Site *(Caravan Club)*
Caldicot	Caldicot Castle Country Park

Chepstow	Bridge Street Car Park, by Castle
	Bank Street *(Town Council)*
	Riverside *(Town Council)*
Gilwern	Abergavenny Road *(Community Council)*
Grosmont	Village Square *(Community Council)*
Llanthony	Llanthony Abbey Picnic Site
	Llanthony Priory Car Park *(National Park)*
Mitchell Troy	Picnic Site, A449 Northbound
Monmouth	Cattle Market
	Waitrose Supermarket, Monnow Street *(Private)*
	'King's Head', Agincourt Square *(JDW)*
Tintern	Beaufort Cottage, The Abbey
Usk	Maryport Street Car Park

Neath Port Talbot

Aberdulais	Aberdulais Falls *(National Trust)*
Briton Ferry	Lodge Court
Dyffryn Cellwen	Main Road
Neath	Market
CP	Victoria Gardens
	Neath Station, Platform 1 *(Arriva Wales)*
	'David Protheroe', Windsor Street *(JDW)*
Pontardawe	Herbert Street Car Park
Port Talbot	Bus Station
	Princess Margaret Way, Sandfields
	Western Avenue, Sandfields
	Port Talbot Parkway Station *(Arriva Wales)*
	'Lord Caradoc', Station Road *(JDW)*
Resolven	Canal Car Park
Skewen	Queens Road

Newport

Bettws	Bettws Shopping Centre
Caerleon	Cricket Pavilion, The Broadway
	High Street

Maindee	Chepstow Road, opp Police Station
Newport	Bus Station, nr. Corn Street
	Caerlon Road, by The Victoria
	Cardiff Road, opp. Police Station
	Corporation Road, entrance to Park
	John Frost Square, by steps to Bus Station
	Newport Provision Market (Market hrs)
	Newport Station, Platform 2 *(Arriva Wales)*
	Kingsway Shopping Centre (3) *(Private)*
	'Godfrey Morgan', 158 Chepstow Road *(JDW)*
	'John Wallace Linton', The Cambrian Centre *(JDW)*
	'Revolution', Griffin Street *(Private)*
	'Tom Toya Lewis', Commercial Street *(JDW)*
	Tredegar House Caravan Club Site *(Caravan Club)*

Rhondda Cynon Taf

Aberdare	Duke Street, Bus Station
	Monk Street
	'Yr Iuean Ap Iago', High Street *(JDW)*
Cwmaman	Alexandra Terrace
Maerdy	Maerdy Park
Mountain Ash	Oxford Street
Nantgarw	'Nandos', Treforest Industrial Estate *(Nandos)*
Pentre	Bridgend Square, Ystrad Road
Pontyclun M4	Cardiff West Services J33 M4 *(Moto)*

Neath Port Talbot County Borough Council Directorate of Environment

Neath Port Talbot County Borough Council is committed to supporting the National Key Scheme Programme for access to all its toilets with Disabled Facilities

Become a member
Help us realise our vision and make your voice count.

www.disabilityrightsuk.org

Pontypridd	Bus Station, Morgan Street
	Sardis Road
	Pontypridd Station, Platform 1 *(Arriva Wales)*
	'Tumble Inn', Broadway *(JDW)*
Porth	Hannah Street
Talbot Green	Talbot Green Bus Depot, Talbot Road
Tonypandy	Dunraven Street
Treherbert	Bute Street
Treorchy	Station Road, nr. Park & Dare Theatre
Ynsybwl	Windsor Place

Swansea

Blackpill	Blackpill Lido, off Mumbles Road
Bracelet Bay	Car Park
Caswell Bay	off Caswell Road, Car Park
Clydach	Mond Square, High Street
Gorseinon	West Street, by Bus Station

Gowerton	Gowerton Caravan Club Site *(Caravan Club)*
Horton	Main Car Park
Llansamlet	'Dylan Thomas', Samlet Road *(Spirit)*
Morriston	Woodfield Street, nr. Church
Mumbles	Oystermouth Square
Oxwich	Oxwich Castle *(Cadw)*
Penllegaer	Swansea Services, M4 J27 *(Moto)*
Pontardulais	Water Street
Port Eynon	Foreshore Car Park
Rhossili	nr. Hotel

Swansea   Cear Street, Princess Way
CP Civic Centre, Oystermouth Road (Office hrs)
Guildhall, Guildhall Road South (Office hrs)
Liberty Stadium (Match Days)
Marina, South Dock Maritime Quarter
Marina, Trawler Road
CP Swansea Bus Station, Plymouth Street (Station hrs)
CP Swansea Station, Platform 4 *(Arriva Wales)*
Quadrant Shopping Centre, 1st Floor *(Private)*
Debenhams Store, The Quadrant *(Debenhams)*
'Bank Statement', Wind Street *(JDW)*
'Nandos', Wind Street *(Nandos)*
'Potters Wheel', The Kingsway *(JDW)*
'Revolution', 24 Wind Street *(Private)*
'The Square', Wind Street *(Spirit)*
'Varsity', Wind Street/Castle Square *(Barracuda)*
'Walkabout', Castle Square *(Private)*
'Yates's Bar', Caer Street *(Private)*
CP 360 Beach & Waterports Centre, Mumbles Road *(Private)*
CP LC Leisure Centre *(Private)*
CP National Waterfront Museum *(Private)*

Torfaen

Cwmbran	'John Fielding', Caradoc Road *(JDW)*
Pontypool	Indoor Market (Market hrs)
	'John Capel Hanbury', Osborne Road *(JDW)*

Vale of Glamorgan

Barry		Court Road/Holton Road MSCP
		Knap Car Terrace, Bron y Mor
		Park Crescent, Romilly Road/Park Crescent
		Porthkerry Country Park, by Café Car Park
		Romilly Park, Romilly Park Road (Park hrs)
		Thompson Street, by Home Bargains (Shopping hrs)
		Tynewydd Road, by Library (Daytime)
		Weston Square, Vere Street/Gladstone Road
		'Old College Inn', Barry Road *(Marstons)*
		'Sir Samuel Romilly', Romilly Buildings *(JDW)*
Barry Island		Car Park, Harbour Road/Clive Road
		Western Shelter, Promenade off Paget Road
Cowbridge	**CP**	Cowbridge Leisure Centre (Centre hrs)
		Town Hall Car Park, off High Street
Llantwit Major		Boverton Road, Poundfield Shopping Centre
		Cwm Colhugh, Llantwit Major Beach
		Town Hall Car Park, The Square
Ogmore by Sea		Car Park, off Main Road
Penarth		Albert Road/West Terrace
		Cosmeston Country Park, Lavernock Road
	CP	Penarth Leisure Centre, Andrew Road (Centre hrs)
		The Esplanade, Italian Gardens
		The Esplanade, Penarth Pier
		'Bears Head', Windsor Road *(JDW)*
Southerndown		Dunraven Beach, opp Beach Car Park

NORTHERN IRELAND

Antrim

Antrim	Castle Centre Car Park
	Antrim Bus Station *(Translink)*
	Antrim Station *(Translink)*
Crumlin Glen	Car Park, by bridge

Ards

Ballyhalbert	Harbour Car Park
Ballywalter	Springvale Road, by Tennis Courts
Cloughey	Warren Car Park, Main Road
Comber	Castle Street Car Park
	Islandhill Car Park, Ringhaddy Road
Donaghadee	The Commons, Millisle Road
	The Parade (8.00-18.00, later in summer)
Grey Abbey	Main Street
Killinchy	Whiterock Picnic Area, Ballydorn Road
Millisle	Ballywalter Road, Millisle Beach
Newtownards	Mill Street
	Bus Station *(Translink)*
	'Spirit Merchant', Regent Street *(JDW)*
Portaferry	Castle Park, by Exploris
	CP Strangford Bay Lodge, Ardkeed *(Private)*
Portavogie	Anchor Car Park, Springvale Road

Armagh

Armagh	Bus Station *(Translink)*
	CP Orchard Leisure Centre, Folly Lane
Markethill	The Square
Tandragee	Market Street

Ballymena

Ballymena	Ballymena Bus/Rail Station *(Translink)*
	'Spinning Mill', Broughshane Street *(JDW)*

CAFE Lamont *(Northern Regional College)*
Farm Lodge Building *(Northern Regional College)*
Trostan Avenue Building *(Northern Regional College)*

Banbridge

Banbridge	Corbet Lough, Aughnacloy Road
	Kenlis Street
	New Cemetery, Newry Road
	Solitude Park
	Southern Regional College *(College)*
Dromore	Dromore Park, Banbridge Road
	Market Square
Katesbridge	Katesbridge Picnic Area
Loughbrickland	Village Park, Poyntzpass Road
Rathfrland	Downpatrick Street Car Park
Scarva	Main Street
	Old Mill Road, Scarva Park
	Scarva Interpetive Centre

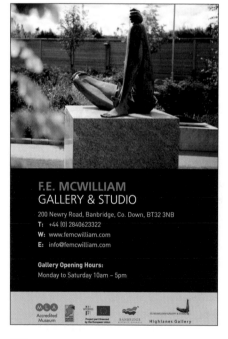

F.E. MCWILLIAM
GALLERY & STUDIO

200 Newry Road, Banbridge, Co. Down, BT32 3NB
T: +44 (0) 2840623322
W: www.femcwilliam.com
E: info@femcwilliam.com

Gallery Opening Hours:
Monday to Saturday 10am – 5pm

Accredited Museum · BANBRIDGE · Highlanes Gallery

Belfast

Belfast City Centre

Arthur Lane, Arthur Street (Daytime)
Bankmore Square, Dublin Road
Botanic Gardens (Park hrs)
Church Lane, Ann Street (Daytime)
Custom House Square
Lombard Street
St Georges Market (Market hrs)
Winetavern Street (Daytime)
Europa Bus Station *(Translink)*
Laganside Bus Station *(Translink)*
Belfast Botanic Station *(Translink)*
Belfast Central Station *(Translink)*
Great Victoria Street Station *(Translink)*
Debenhams Store, Castle Court *(Debenhams)*
'Bridge House', Bedford Street *(JDW)*
'Nandos', Bedford Street *(Nandos)*
'Nandos', Victoria Street *(Nandos)*

CP Parliament Building *(NIA)*

Doing IT Differently

Information to help everyone regardless of disability, take advantage of information technology (IT) and computers. Includes advice on how to choose and use a computer, and how to adapt it to suit your needs.

Available to order from our online shop
www.disabilityrightsuk.org

We have 14 public toilets across the City of Belfast, with disabled access available at 12 of these.

For more information call us on 0800 032 8100

www.belfastcity.gov.uk/waste

East Belfast	Connswater, Westminster Avenue (Mon-Sat, 9.00-18.00)
	CP George Best Belfast City Airport *(Private)*
North Belfast	Agnes Street, Shankhill Road (Mon-Sat, 9.00-18.00)
	Waterworks, Antrim Road
	Yorkgate Station *(Translink)*
South Belfast	Cranmore Park, Lisburn Road (Park hrs)
	Drumglass Park, Lisburn Road (Daytime)
	Gasworks, Ormeau Road
	Ormeau Embankment (Daytime)
	Roselawn Cemetery (Cemetery hrs)
	Sir Thomas & Lady Dixon Park (Park hrs)
	Stormont Estate (Park hrs)
West Belfast	**CP** Divis & Black Mountain Centre *(National Trust)*

Carrickfergus

Carrickfergus	Harbour Car Park, by Castle
	Carrickfergus Station *(Translink)*
	'Central Bar', High Street *(JDW)*
Whitehead	Whitehead Car Park
	Whitehead Station *(Translink)*

Coleraine

Castlerock	The Promenade
	Hezlett House *(National Trust)*
Coleraine	Long Commons
	Park Street
	Railway Road, Leisure Centre Car Park
	Strand Road
	Coleraine Bus/Rail Station *(Translink)*
	'Old Court House', Castlerock Road *(JDW)*
Downhill	Downhill Beach Car Park
Garvagh	Bridge Street
Kilrea	Garvagh Road
Portballintrae	Beach Road Car Park
	The Harbour
Portrush	Arcadia (May-September)
	Dunluce Avenue

	Kerr Street
	Strand Road, Riverside Park
	Whiterocks Car Park
Portstewart	Harbour Road
	Town Hall

Cookstown

| Cookstown | Burn Road |
| | Bus Station *(Translink)* |

Craigavon

Craigavon	CP	Brownlow Community Hub *(Private)*
Lurgan		Castle Lane
Portadown		William Street *(Portadown 2000)*
		Portadown Station *(Translink)*

Derry

| Derry | Victoria Car Park, Strand Road |
| | Derry City Bus Station *(Translink)* |

Delamont Country Park

- Award winning Caravan and Camping Club
- Full Events Programme
- Delamont Miniature Railway
- Outdoor Adventure Playground
- Strangford Stone
- Boat Trips on Strangford Lough *(Booking Essential)*
- Rambler Mobility Scooters available *(Booking Essential)*
- Canoe Trail
- Ice-cream Kiosk

Open daily 9am-dusk. All events weather permitting .

For further information contact
Tel/Fax 028 44828 333
www.delamontcountrypark.com
e-mail: delamont.park@downdc.gov.uk

DERRY CITY COUNCIL
Council Offices
98 Strand Road
Derry BT48 7NN

Telephone 028 7136 3569
Fax 028 7136 3569

DERRY CITY COUNCIL SUPPORT
THE PROVISION OF FACILITIES
FOR ALL ITS CITIZENS

Londonderry Station *(Translink)*
Debenhams Store, Foyleside *(Debenhams)*
Sainsbury's Store, Strand Road *(Sainsbury)*
'Ice Wharf', Strand Road *(JDW)*
'The Diamond', The Diamond *(JDW)*

Down

Ardglass	The Harbour
Ballyhornan	Village
Ballynahinch	Windmill Street
Castlewellan	Upper Square
Crossgar	Killyleagh Street
Downpatrick	Market Street
	Downpatrick Bus Station *(Translink)*
Dundrum	Dundrum Bay Picnic Area
Killyleagh	Delamont Country Park (Park hrs)
	High Street
Newcastle	Castle Park
	Central Promenade
	Donard Park
	Downs Road
	Islands Park
	South Promenade
	Bus Station *(Translink)*
Quoile	Car Park

Dungannon & South Tyrone

Augher	Clogher Road
Ballygawley	Church Street
Dungannon	Scotch Street
	Peatlands Park Visitor Centre *(NIEA)*
	Dungannon Bus Station *(Translink)*
Fivemiletown	Main Street
Moy	Charlemont Street

Fermanagh

Enniskillen	Bus Station *(Translink)*
	'Linen Hall', Townhall Square *(JDW)*

Larne

Larne	Larne Bus Station *(Translink)*
	Larne Station *(Translink)*

Limavady

Ballykelly	Glenhead Road
Benone	Beach
Dungiven	Main Street
Limavady	Catherine Street
	Main Street
	Bus Station *(Translink)*

Lisburn

Hillsborough	Ballynahinch Street
Lisburn	Lisburn Bus Station *(Translink)*
	Lisburn Station *(Translink)*
	'Tuesday Bell', Lisburn Square *(JDW)*
CP	Civic Centre, Lagan Valley Island

Make a donation
Support our work with a one-off
or regular donation.

www.disabilityrightsuk.org

Become a member
Help us realise our vision and
make your voice count.

www.disabilityrightsuk.org

Magherafelt

Draperstown	Derrynoid Road
Magherafelt	Magherafelt Bus Station *(Translink)*
	Magerafelt Campus *(Northern Regional College)*

Moyle

Armoy	Main Street
Ballintoy	Harbour
Ballycastle	Harbour Car Park
	Market Street
	Quay Road Pavilion
	Seafront Centre
Bushmills	Dundarave, Car Park
CP	Giants Causeway Visitor Centre
Cushendall	Legg Green
	Mill Street Car Park
	Waterford Slipway
Cushendun	Beach Car Park
Dunservick	Harbour
Rathlin Island	Church Bay
Waterfoot	Main Street

Newry & Mourne

Annalong	Marine Park (Daytime)
Bloodybridge	Amenity Area (Daytime)
Crossmaglen	Loughross Amenity Area (M+F) (April-October)
	The Square (8.00-18.00)
Hilltown	Rostrevor Road (8.00-18.00)
	Spelga Dam Amenity Area (M+F) (8.00-18.00)
Kilkeel	Cranfield Beach (M+F) (Summer) (8.00-18.00)
	Greencastle Street (M+F) (8.00-18.00)
	Lower Square (Daytime)
	Mourne Esplanade
Newry	Marcus Square (Daytime)
	Newry Market, Hill Street (8.00-18.00)
	Newry Sports Centre (Centre hrs)

	Newry Town Hall, Bank Parade Bus Station *(Translink)* Newry Station *(Translink)*
Rostrevor	The Square (M+F) (8.00-18.00)
Warrenpoint	The Park, Queen Street (M+F) (Daytime) The Square (M+F) (8.00-18.00)

Newtownabbey

Ballyclare	Main Street (7.30-dusk) Sixmilewater River Park (8.00-dusk) Ballyclare Bus Station *(Translink)*
Jordanstown	Loughshore Park, Shore Road (8.00-dusk)
Newtownabbey	Newtownabbey Bus Station *(Translink)*
Whiteabbey	Hazelbank Park, Shore Road (9.00-dusk)

North Down

Bangor	Abbey Street, opp. Bus Station Ballyholme Park, Ballyholme Esplanade Banks Lane, Groomsport Road

Doing Work Differently

Explores practical solutions to real questions related to work. This guide can help you overcome barriers and shows how small adjustments can make a big difference.

Available to order from our online shop
www.disabilityrightsuk.org

For information on obtaining RADAR keys for public convenience facilities please contact customer services on:

(028) 30313233

Newry & Mourne District Council
Haughey House, Rampart Road
Greenback Industrial Estate,
Newry, BT34 2QU
Tel: (028) 3031 3233 Fax: (028) 3031 3299
Minicom: (028) 3025 7859
www.newryandmourne.gov.uk
Email: techleisure@newryandmourne.gov.uk

	McKee Clock, Quay Street Pickie Fun Park, Marine Gardens Ward Park, Park Drive Bangor Bus/Rail Station *(Translink)*
Groomsport	Harbour Road
Helen's Bay	Crawfordsburn Country Park, Beach Car Park *(NIEA)* Crawfordsburn Country Park, Helen's Bay Car Park *(NIEA)*
Holywood	Hibernia Street Seapark Recreation Area, Seapark Road

Omagh

Omagh	Johnston Park/Kevlin Avenue

Strabane

Castlederg	William Street
Cranagh	Glenelly Road
Donemana	Berryhill Road
Newtownstewart	Main Street
Plumbridge	Fair Green
Sion Mills	Melmount Road
Strabane	Market Street Strabane Bus Station *(Translink)*

CHANNEL ISLANDS

Guernsey

Castel	Grande Rocque Beach
	Sausmarez Park
	Vazon Beach, by Café
St Martins	Icart Point Car Park
	Jerbourg Car Park
	Moulin Huet Bay Car Park
St Peter Port	Bus Terminus
	Castle Emplacement
	Crown Pier
	Market Buildings
	North Beach Car Park
	St Julians Avenue
	White Rock Ferry Terminal
St Peters	L'Erre Beach
St Sampsons	Delancy Park
	South Side
Vale	Bordeaux Beach
	Chouet Beach
	Northside, The Bridge

Jersey

Grouville	Gorey Common
	La Rocque (M+F)
St Brelades	Corbiere
	La Pulante
	Le Haule
	Red Houses
	St Aubins
	Underground, St Brelades Bay
	Woodford, St Brelades Bay
St Clements	La Mare (M+F)
	Millards Corner (M+F)
St Helier	First Tower
	Liberation Bus Station

	Minden Place, Car Park
	Patriotic Street, Car Park
	Sand Street Car Park
	Snow Hill Car Park [Under Review] (M+F)
	West Park
CP	Millennium Town Park
CP	Town Hall, Seale Street Offices
St John	Bonne Nuit
St Lawrence	Bel Royal
	Millbrook Promenade
	Millbrook, Coronation Park (Park hrs)
St Martin	Archirondel
	Gorey House
	St Catherines
St Ouens	Greve De Lecq
	Le Braye
	Les Laveurs
St Peters	Beaumont Gunsite
Trinity	Rozel

Doing Careers Differently

Packed with useful information, this guide includes stories from disabled people who have built satisfying careers, from part-time flexible work to a first-time management role and beyond.

Available to order from our online shop
www.disabilityrightsuk.org

ISLE OF MAN

Douglas	Drumgold Street Car Park
	Jubilee Clock, Loch Promenade
	Loch Promenade Gardens
	Nobles Park
	Shaw Brow Car Park
	York Road
	'Colours', Central Promenade *(Private)*
	'Fiesta Havana', Wellington Street *(Private)*
	'Slug & Lettuce', 7-17 Wellington Street *(Private)*
Laxey	The Harbour
Onchan	Onchan Pleasure Park
	Port Jack
Peel	Market Place
	Shore Road/Victoria Road
	Peel Camp Site
Ramsey	Bowring Road
	Coronation Park
	Market Place
	Mooragh Park, Lakeside Pavilion
	Ramsey Town Library (Library hrs)

INDEX OF ADVERTISERS

Disability Rights UK thanks all its advertisers for supporting the publication of our books for disabled people.

A

B

C

D

E

F

G

H

I

J

INDEX OF LOCALITIES

A

C

D

H

J

I

K

M

N

P

INDEX OF LOCALITIES

NATIONAL KEY SCHEME GUIDE 2013